MODERN SCIENCE AND THE NATURE OF LIFE

WILLIAM S. BECK is currently Assistant Professor of Medicine at the Harvard Medical School, a Tutor in the Biochemical Sciences at Harvard College, and Chief of the Hematology Unit and the Hematology Research Laboratory at Massachusetts General Hospital.

Born in 1923, Dr. Beck entered the University of Pennsylvania, later transferred to the University of Michigan where he took his B.S. in 1943 and his M.D. three years later. In 1950, he accepted an appointment as an instructor at the medical school of the University of California at Los Angeles. During this time, he was associated with the Atomic Energy Project as Chief of the Hematology and Medical Sections. In 1955, he took a leave of absence to study enzyme chemistry at New York University where he was concurrently engaged in teaching and research. *Modern Science and the Nature of Life* is the result of Dr. Beck's attempt "to educate my friends in science and to facilitate the exchange of ideas between people in different fields." He has been with the Harvard Medical School since 1957.

THE NATURAL HISTORY LIBRARY *makes available in paperback format books of enduring interest in the life and earth sciences. Published in co-operation with The American Museum of Natural History by Doubleday Anchor Books, this series introduces the student and the general reader to the study of man—his origins, his nature, and his environment—and to the whole natural world, from sub-microscopic life to the universe at large.*

MODERN SCIENCE AND THE NATURE OF LIFE

BY

WILLIAM S. BECK

PUBLISHED IN CO-OPERATION WITH
THE AMERICAN MUSEUM OF NATURAL HISTORY

THE NATURAL HISTORY LIBRARY
ANCHOR BOOKS
DOUBLEDAY & COMPANY, INC.
GARDEN CITY, NEW YORK

The Natural History Library Edition, 1961
by special arrangement with
Harcourt, Brace and Company

Printed in the United States of America

FOR
TOMMY AND PETER
AND HELENE

I do not know what I may appear to the world; but to myself I seem to have been only like a boy playing on the seashore, and diverting myself in now and then finding a smoother pebble or a prettier shell than ordinary, whilst the great ocean of truth lay all undiscovered before me.

—Isaac Newton

PREFACE

"The essence of crisis," according to Dr. Beck, "is a disproportionality between the amount of misery men suffer and the potentialities of their culture . . . a disparity between achievement and potentiality." The potentialities of our culture include, among other things, the full use of human knowledge to solve our problems and alleviate our sufferings. The knowledge and methods of science are often used poorly, or not at all.

Dr. Beck is concerned, greatly concerned, with the general lack of understanding, and occasional hostility, that many men have for science. This attitude is freely held by individuals who do not question that scientific knowledge and its use are, and will continue to be, the dominant forces that shape our lives.

The causes of this estrangement are numerous. Modern science arrived late on the scene. Like all latecomers, it was resisted—in this case by the established intellectual disciplines. It competed for students, readers, money, and a place in the school and university. Furthermore, it was brash, telling those who would listen that its methods were more likely to lead to "true" answers than the methods of the nonsciences. Science must have seemed ridiculous to those who doubted that it was even asking the right questions.

This estrangement, which became a problem a century ago and continues today, was self-reinforcing. To an ever-increasing extent, scientists talked to one another. The level of communication was that of the specialist. When the nonscientist attempted to listen in, he found the conversation largely unintelligible. This could hardly facilitate rapprochement.

It must be apparent to every thoughtful person—scientist and nonscientist—that science is an important aspect of culture. It *must* be understood. The nonscientist must make the effort to understand and the scientist must make the effort to communicate. The intellectual effort demanded of both is substantial. Science is not innately easy and, for many, its thought processes are not those regularly employed. For the scientist the task of telling his fellow citizens "what it is really about" is enormously difficult. But it is a rewarding task when, as in Dr. Beck's case, he succeeds. In a sense the scientist fulfills one responsibility of being man—for an essential characteristic of man, which sets him apart from all other animals, is his ability to transmit, by word and symbol, what has been created, learned, and believed.

Dr. Beck writes about science in general and biology in particular. The reader is taken on a brilliantly conducted tour of the historical development of the scientific attitude. (He will be relieved to find that the argument does not become mired in a welter of facts and technical jargon.) The bright chapters of biological thought are here: cell theory, Darwinian evolution, Pasteur and the continuity of life, Mendelian genetics, and the modern theory of the gene.

When the reader reaches the end of the book, he will understand why the scientist becomes increasingly hesitant as his achievement increases. From the seventeenth to the nineteenth century a scientist would say with conviction that A causes B. In the twentieth century, when he can split the atom and hit the moon, he admits only that, if A occurs, there is a predictable probability that B will occur. And the reader will also understand why one cannot cure cancer with a million dollars.

John A. Moore
Research Associate

March 1961
The American Museum of Natural History

FOREWORD

by Homer W. Smith

Dr. Beck mentions me in his manuscript as one of several persons to whose writing he feels some indebtedness. As a matter of fact it is I who am indebted to him.

Recent years have seen the revival of some amazing supernaturalism, not all of it confined to the fundamentalist and revivalist congregations. Many speeches, essays, and books by scientists reveal lack of critical acuity and deficiency in historic and philosophic perspective as the authors seek to escape the impersonalism of nature by some speculation which enables them, and encourages others, to extrapolate from the phenomena of human personality to matters transcending the known, and perhaps knowable, cosmos. It is proving harder to stir man's ego out of its rut than it was to get the earth to move.

Such writers, I believe, represent a small minority of our scientific population, but for some reason they are the most vocal and make the best public speakers, essayists, and sometimes even the best university presidents, possibly because it is easier, and more profitable, to sell the public gold bricks than plain bricks, and there is and can be no law against this deception at the level of philosophy. Astronomy, anthropology, and physics have perhaps had the best representation, in both the literary and philosophic sense, before the general public, while biology seems to have had the worst. Astronomy has universal appeal and, despite the transmutation of elements in the sun and stars and some confusing details with respect to "ultimate particles," it has been ably explained by many writers. Anthropology offers vicarious adventure away from home and mores and is readily interpreted at the simply human level. Physics, in consequence of the advent of atomic transformation and the enormous energy content of the nucleus, has forced itself upon the public despite the technical difficulties of popular presentation. It is perhaps not too facetious to remark that if we are all to die, quickly or slowly, from this modern alchemy, informed people would like to know how and why.

But suppose we do not die, suppose that tempers cool off, that the world (despite some other difficulties) continues to be habitable for some centuries or millenniums to come—is it not cogent to ask how we are going to live, and even more cogent, why?

Some predict that one day biology will swallow up physics, or that physics will swallow up biology, but for the present we can retain the definition of biology as subsuming all the sciences dealing with living organisms. The history of biology, thus broadly conceived, can be roughly divided into three phases. The exploratory or taxonomic phase (the designations are mine) covers the period when the biologist was primarily concerned with becoming acquainted with and relating (classifying) the multitudinous members of the vegetable and animal kingdoms. There followed the organic phase in which he was learning anatomy and physiology, the structure and interrelatedness of the organs which comprise plants and animals. Lastly comes the analytic or molecular phase in which the problem of organization is being pursued down to the ultimate molecular level. These overlap to a considerable extent: the first reached its climax with the demonstration a hundred years ago of the reality of organic evolution. We have scarcely yet reached the zenith of the second phase, but we are nonetheless well started into the last, or molecular, phase and with strange consequences. If those who studied biology a generation ago returned to it now they would be surprised to find the subject almost as radically changed as is the physics of World War I.

Whether life is unique to the earth is at the moment an unanswerable question; it is doubtful if any of the other planets of this solar system have what we would call living organisms on them, but without recourse to science fiction a reasonable guess permits us to think that among the billion stars of our galaxy and the billion galaxies beyond the Milky Way there are probably millions of satellites not too dissimilar to earth on which life could and, given the proper conditions, would have evolved along much the same general lines as here. Then what is life? How does it work? How did it evolve?

Dr. Beck has wisely chosen to approach his story by the historical route, selecting only a few of many possible topics for discussion (many volumes would be required to cover the whole of historic and contemporary biology). By way of gross anatomy and microanatomy he comes to the cell theory and evolution. Two books, Charles Darwin's *Origin of Species* (1859) and Thomas Henry Huxley's *Man's Place in Nature* (1863), marked the climax and fruition of this phase.

At this point Dr. Beck for a moment turns philosopher: after the demonstration in the eighteenth and nineteenth centuries of the tautological nature of mathematics, philosophy abandoned profitless speculation about the transcendental in favor of the exercise of examining words themselves, searching for the meaning of meaning; and science abandoned the absolute in favor of tentative empirical examination. In tracing this philosophical reconstruction Dr. Beck shows us how the new philosophy of science came to influence all thought in the direction of clarity, testability, precision, and objectivity, and how in turn philosophy became more like science in its methodology. He makes it clear that science is not a sealed body of knowledge but a method, a method which is greater than the sum of its results. Philosophers call this method logical empiricism, biologists call it naturalism; nearly a century ago Thomas Henry Huxley called it agnosticism. In his orientation one sees Dr. Beck's indebtedness to Hans Reichenbach (who died in 1953), Herbert Feigl, and Ernest Nagel, all in the front rank of contemporary philosophy.

This critique of the scientific method (and of all-too-human scientists) brings us back to firmer ground for the examination of the problem of causality, the Cartesian doctrine of mechanism, and the nature of cells, chromosomes, genes, viruses. The significance of genes he deftly translates in terms of information theory as applied to cellular chemistry, at the heart of which is the master codifying agent of genetics, the complex compound, desoxyribonucleic acid (DNA), now the object of analytical methods which go beyond conventional molecular chemistry as the latter goes beyond the microscope and naked eye, and now on the threshold of laboratory synthesis. And so on to the origin of life, its manifold differentiation in evolution, and its ultimate synthesis, at least in an elementary form. So close are we to this synthesis that when it comes it may be something of an anticlimax, like "breaking through the sound barrier." At the other extreme, the biologist—an abstract composite of many interrelated sciences—will begin to make inroads on the problem of consciousness, without resort, this writer thinks, to Cartesian dualism or Berkeleian idealism; and then man, who possesses the most complicated thinking machine in the world, will come of age as a philosopher.

As for the future, and perhaps just over the horizon, is the problem of senescence: "I can see no reason why death, in the nature of things, need be inevitable . . ." but since there is a limit to the materials which conceivably can be turned into food, this, at least, "would prevent immortality from being widely practiced." And the problem of values: Dr. Beck stops short here, wisely I think, but I hope he will agree with me when I say that the assertion, so frequently heard, that science is ethically neutral, that human values must forever remain outside the realm of empirical examination and valuation, is old-fashioned nonsense.

Apart from his historical approach, many of the advances in biology which Dr. Beck describes are utterly new and have been made within the last ten years. Biology is exploding with new techniques and discoveries. "What then, in the name of Miserere, may we expect in the next ten years, in the next century and millennium? . . . Our new biology is an infant with a future unimaginable." So far as we can know at the present time, man is the most magnificently self-ordered creation in this expanding cosmos. He is not, however, quite as magnificent as we think he could be. Somehow or other we must find a way to communicate the essence of today's science—our only reliable corpus of knowledge —to young and old alike; somehow "thinking must again be made popular, and great thinking synonymous with high adventure."

I am indebted to Dr. Beck because he has written a thoroughly readable book on biology, one that is scientifically accurate, philosophically sound, and fired with humor, imagination, and the spirit of high adventure.

AUTHOR'S NOTE

I've learned one thing about the Universe. There's no money in astronomy.

—*New Yorker* cartoon

Of the many charges being flung at scientists these days, one is that they have failed in their duty to communicate, in a manner intelligible to nonscientific readers, a sense of what is going on in science today, where it is heading, where it is not heading, and why not. I think this charge is a fair one. The book that follows is an attempt to clear my own conscience on this score.

Scientists sometimes note wistfully that the huge and obvious reservoir of cordial interest in science among readers of books so often finds its outlet in science fiction, a genre of writing that is lately showing alarming signs of taking itself seriously. The pity of it is that *nothing* in "Sf."—from the Mutants loose among the galaxies to the trans-Aristotelian world of *Null-A*—nothing in this ersatz mishmash can stand up next to the truths of real science, either for human drama and suspense or for intellectual stimulation and meditation-making. Science is the living dynamic creature which is feeding the fiction writer; and it is science which yearns for and deserves the high regard of men.

In this book, I have tried to say something about modern science as typified by contemporary biology, the background of ideas, and the men who have helped make it what it is today—an incredibly exciting adventure story about the human mind and its subtly powerful enemy, ignorance. In an attempt to convey some of the sweep and grandeur of this extraordinary chapter of human history, I have approached the problems of biology, and science in general, from the point of view of the working scientist, raising questions more or less in the order he raised them, wrestling with the obstacles he has encountered and encounters still. This, it seems to me, is the most meaningful way to think about science because it makes one literally *feel* the spirit of scientific inquiry. And it deepens the cultural meaning of science; for it firmly teaches that *all that science has learned, it has learned from hypothesis and experiment.* The scientist learns from evidence, not from innate knowledge, though there have been times when accepted "evidence" was mere pious wish. The scientist must weigh his evidence, and often he has no way of doing so, possessing neither the tools, the plan, nor the ability to free himself from the preconceptions of his times. It is a fantastic story, filled with pitfalls and portents. It is ours to share.

Throughout the text, I have touched on a good many controversial questions—mostly because this is where the fun is. In all cases, I have taken the stand I believe to be the correct one, and I have tried to defend my positions on their merits. Needless to remark, the basic elements of science and philosophy are inquiry, argument, and evidence. Truth is sought by these means, and if one wishes to dispute another's position, one does so by presenting superior argument or evidence. By this procedure do we hope to arrive at a body of reliable knowledge. If one wishes to reserve judgment, to take a position of skepticism, one may justifiably do so only after examining and rejecting the available evidence. Skepticism then becomes a position in its own right and can be defended by argument. To do otherwise, to reject arbitrarily without examination, to deny the validity of existing thought is emotional behavior and is out of the realm of philosophical or scientific debate. It is clearly one's privilege to behave this way, but holders of such views have no place in the great search for truth. To these I say good-by and good luck. Because I am not a philosopher, but a philosophee, I may be proved wrong in my views on philosophical questions. In these cases, I will admit it.

A brief word on the materials upon which I have drawn for this study. A list will be found in the back of the book of the books, articles, and so forth, that are directly cited or quoted in the text. However, this list is not comprehensive, nor would it be possible for me to provide an accounting of the sources I have used. It is too diverse and includes too many books, journals, conversations, meetings, and musings. I have been especially stimulated by the writings of Homer Smith, Herbert Muller, Lawrence Kubie, and the late Hans Reichenbach—the last of whom gave me needed encouragement in the launching of this project. Knowing him was a very great privilege. I must acknowledge, too, the useful discussions on one topic or another I have held with Severo Ochoa and Robert Yost. To these distinguished individuals and others unmentioned, I am also indebted. But, in the usual phrase, I take little credit for the ideas given here, and full credit for my own interpretations and errors.

To my long-suffering friends Hans Meyerhoff, Norman Simmons, and Lee Pearce go my thanks for support and forbearance above and beyond the call of duty. Gentlemen, I salute you.*

Portions of the text—specifically the sections dealing with the cell, the matter of spontaneous generation, and the meaninglessness of "protoplasm"—were previously together in the form of an essay entitled *The cell: some*

* In the interest of accuracy, it should be noted that they were suffering long before they met me.

thoughts on cytology, psychology, and epistemology, which was awarded the 1954 Wenner-Gren Foundation Honorable Mention Award by The New York Academy of Sciences. Their courtesy is acknowledged in permitting this material to appear here.

WILLIAM S. BECK

New York City
January, 1957

CONTENTS

PART TWO
The First Great Modern Synthesis

PART THREE
Twentieth Century, the Age of Analysis

CHAPTER I

THE HALL OF MIRRORS: A PROLOGUE

I have a toe in the crack of my sepulchral door.
—Homer W. Smith

It is commonly said that ours is an age in crisis, a time which in a brief span of years has twice witnessed the human race commit mayhem upon itself, which has endured great political, economic, and cultural upheaval. While crisis has been the ever-present human condition through history, from Candide to Mr. Antrobus, the situation in today's world, its profound depth and immense scale, seems clearly to bespeak the rising tides of change. Our crisis is the crisis of transition between two worlds, the old that is dying and the new that is struggling to be born. Its pain is the pain of uncertainty.

Men have always had to endure misery. The essence of crisis, however, is a disproportionality between the amount of misery men suffer and the potentialities of their culture. It is a disparity between achievement and potentiality, a fettering of potentiality. Its hallmark is wasted and misdirected creative energy and its result is defective growth and conflict.

This book is being written in the belief that science and scientific methods are the best means available to us for solving the problems of our cultural crisis. Science is, beyond question, the outstanding feature of modern civilization. Our world is, to an increasing extent, dominated, if not by pure science itself, then by the conceptions of the public at large and its leaders concerning the nature of science. More and more, this idea of science, misunderstood though it is, has gained in influence, and, as its status has changed, great new problems have arisen, many of which have yet even to be identified as problems by the majority of people.

It can be argued, I think (and I intend to argue), that much of humanity's present difficulty stems from the paradoxically strained relations between science and the other areas of knowledge, and from the surpassing paradoxes within science itself, the very ingredients which make it such a frustrating and delightful mistress to its practitioners. These paradoxes are an important cause of the present crisis; they are its consequences and one of its best examples. For the essence of science is paradox and, in trying to explain science, this is one of the main points I hope to get across.

To the mid-twentieth-century citizen, science is an almost grotesquely ambivalent phenomenon: it is at the same time highly systematic in its approach to the real world, yet it is never complete and never reaches final conclusions. It is the model of certainty in its methodology and logic, yet its driving force is deliberate doubt, and its results are probable, never certain. It requires of its workers absolute discipline, yet it is the fountainhead of exciting new ideas and new ways of thought. Though it may be local in origin, its conclusions are universal. For its creators it is a supreme adventure of the spirit, while at the same time it is the sole basis of endless reams of myth and superstition. It is the healer and builder and the propagator of untold suffering and death. Is it any wonder that science, the strong, the promising, the unforeseeable, the anarchical force in our modern world, should be the cause of acute anxiety?

The remedy is understanding and maturity, and it is my purpose here to contribute what I can to a broader understanding of the essential nature of science, as typified by biology, and of life, as explained by science. What we will find will require a mature viewpoint, for we will learn that wherever we seek certainty, there we will not find it, wherever we establish rigid categories, classes, or concepts, no matter what the reason, these will soon fail us and, like sunken ships, become in time only lumps in the sea bottom. Because science is not an absolutist doctrine, its position is the hardest to defend in the unending battle with absolutism, and its defenders require a maximum of sympathetic understanding. It is their inability to give this understanding, to make the effort it requires, to find contentment in a world in which all questions have not been answered, which have turned men to theism, transcendentalist metaphysics, cynicism, and struggle.

We must recognize for what it is man's predilection for dividing things into tidy categories, irrespective of whether clarity is gained or lost thereby. Learning, thus, is scientific or humanistic. Within science, we have physics/biology/chemistry. We will come to realize that these boundaries have been established by us for our own reasons. They are man-made, and despite their long tradition, despite the problems of university organizers, book classifiers, and curriculum planners, despite the tribal instincts of professional men, fields of learning are ultimately surrounded only by illusory boundaries—like the "rooms" in a hall of mirrors. It is when the illusion is penetrated that progress takes place. To the cell or the atom, it matters little whether its pursuer is a biochemist, philosopher, or diplomat. Likewise, science cannot be regarded as a thing apart, to be studied, admired, or ignored. It is a vital part of our culture, our culture is part of it, it permeates our thinking, and its continued separateness from what is fondly called "the humanities" is a preposterous practical joke on all thinking men.

Science is indeed a hall of mirrors, complex, labyrinthine, glittering, and challenging. What is perhaps more to the point, it shows us what we look like from the side and the rear and this is something worth knowing.

In the pages that follow, we will speak of the nature of science, of the scientist, of ideas, and of life. It is my intention to connect science with the rest of our experience by interweaving the notions of biological thought with aspects of history and the philosophical and cultural climate of each age (including this one), and by showing the scientist to be a human being, not a wizard, demon, or lovable white-haired old man. He is not a caricature or a stereotype but a man who faces difficult problems (for a variety of personal reasons), who succeeds and fails, and who behaves as nobly or erratically as his neighbor—sometimes more so, sometimes less so.

An account of such breadth poses problems for an author who can say only one thing at a time; thus we will need to plant a number of ideas along the way in order to harvest them in later chapters. Accordingly, the book is divided into four parts. In the first, we will expand on the connection between science and culture, and we will talk about the nature of science, how it came into being, how biology separated off as a discrete branch of scientific inquiry, and why certainty—despite our dearest wishes—must forever elude us. In Part Two, we will sketch the state of biological thought at the end of its first great modern period, the nineteenth and early twentieth centuries, and we will relive some of the wonderfully acrid controversies which rocked that age. We come then to Part Three and the great revolution in thought which modern physics brought about. Here we will speak of some of the notions of modern analytical philosophy—the nature of language, models, explanation, causality, information, and the inquiring mind—all of which constitute the ground-stuff of the next great movement in biology through which we are living in this very hour. These dramatic developments and their implications for the future of man are the subjects of Part Four. Although most people are not aware of it, biology has lurched ahead into a climactic meeting with physics and chemistry and, under the guiding sanity of modern logic and epistemology, incredible new vistas have abruptly opened up for those who will raise their heads to see them. No longer is biology merely the life and loves of the North American horned grebe. Today it is at one with the totality of human knowledge.

We seem now to be living through a discouraging period of tension and estrangement between intelligent citizens and their science. It is a curious additional paradox that modern man, the unwitting ward and liege of science, should feel ill informed and little interested in science and its methods. Part of the trouble, no doubt, is related to a breakdown of communication between the specialist and nonspecialist. The rapid growth and consequent fragmentation of science decrees that each of us is a nonspecialist, whether we be scientist or layman, for we are nonspecialists in the other man's area, and a communication failure between scientist and layman is, for all practical purposes, the same as a communication failure between scientist and scientist.

One of the difficulties is what seems to me a failure in the technics of education. Educationists have failed to explain science and propagate its broader meanings, and, as has recently been bemoaned by Julian Huxley, particularly is this true for biological science. Not only has this failure been visited upon the average intelligent citizen who may not even know what he doesn't know, it is partly attributable to those responsible for the training of scientists. Scientists, too, must understand their culture, they must lead their fellow men to the light; for it still takes two to make a conversation.

Unfortunately, the problems of communication are not easily solved. We presume that since a passion for understanding characterizes man, it must exist in some form in all men. The difficulties then would seem to be largely psychological and semantic. In communicating knowledge, all sorts of emotional barriers exist, and if blame is to be assigned to anyone, surely it belongs equally to scientists, laymen, broadcasters, publishers, and editors—for they all have a share of responsibility for the ignorance on the part of the average person of the nature of science, its limitations and potentialities. As for the scientists, many seem to feel they are wasting their time in concocting "simplifications." They distrust the public's reaction to the tentative character of science and live in fear of colleagues who will peer down their noses in autocratic disapproval. Earl Ubell, science editor of the New York *Herald Tribune,* once remarked that scientists who get their names in the newspapers inevitably must endure the sneers of their fellows: "We saw your ad, Joe." The pressure is there and every scientist knows it is there.

Obviously, the scientist's symbols and vocabulary are partly to blame for that great "abyss" that isolates the expert. To the uninitiated, symbols are frightening, intrusive, hostile, and discouraging. I am certain, however, that exposition is possible without them. It should be remembered that symbols are simply word or sentence substitutes intended only as time savers. Cordiality follows familiarity, and only occasionally is one garroted by these useful helpers.

I have no illusions about the difficulties implicit in trying to reach a nonscientific audience with this sort of an account. A recent editorial in *Endeavour* spoke feelingly of the problems that face scientists who write of science for the general reader, pointing out that "travelers in foreign countries seem sometimes to believe that they will be perfectly understood if they speak loudly and clearly enough in their own language." This is true, and it is likewise true, as the editorial contends, that there are certain dangers in believing that all the mysteries of science can be made clear if only the scientist will take the trouble to explain himself in very simple terms. However, I don't think one should underestimate the intelligent citizen. Naturally, he cannot understand the theory of chemical kinetics without the proper background, but he can grasp the notion of biochemical specificity if it is made clear that such specificity means uniqueness and its basis is the same as that of a key or fingerprint. In other words, large and important areas of science are accessible to the uninitiated and much of importance can be said without entering into the nuances, details, and complexities which daily absorb the interest of the scientist. I believe, in fact, that because of his preoccupation with details (I should say *important* details), much can profitably be said about science at large to the scientist himself. We will do our best to stay on the straight and narrow and, if it is possible, to maintain an optimum mixture of rigor and palatability.

We will thus proceed by telling a story of quandary and discovery, of the long years of plodding, often misguided, effort punctuated by electrifying new insights and fructifying ideas. We will talk about the problems involved in arriving at knowledge of living things, and emphasize again and again that our conclusions are tentative because they are based on observations and these are continually subject to refinement and new interpretation. Partly in an effort to counteract the popular simplicities that have been inspired by the complexities of our age, I will try to foster an attitude toward science in general and biology in particular which will induce the reader to distrust the dogmatic statement and to ask always, What is the evidence and how was it obtained? We must educate ourselves to live amidst uncertainty and temporary truth. In probing the magnificent and overwhelming complexities of life, we must proceed humbly and with care.

Science is abstract. Sir William Dampier called it "the ordered knowledge of natural phenomena and the rational study of the relationship between the concepts in which these phenomena are expressed." But as the days go by, I am more persuaded that in a way *science is men*—complex men, courageous men, perceptive, vain, anxious, humble, ambitious, brilliant, arrogant, inconsistent, witty, withdrawn, weary, and contented men. Some are like Professor Henry Higgins (who, in his own words, is a "pensive, forgiving, quiet-living man"). A few are like the giant Prometheus.

The literature of biology abounds in awe-inspiring acts of iridescent genius. And, as we shall see, it contains many an authentic clinical example of extraordinary neuroticism on the part of scientists and public alike. Though emotion in science can be justified in the defense of truth and scientific method, scientists have not infrequently fought obscurantist and emotion-charged opposition with a passionate impatience all their own. In these ironic instances, the cause of science had to lose. As stated above, cool reason is the hardest position to defend on the field of controversy. Regrettably, humanly, entertainingly, *all* parties to many a celebrated dispute ended deep in the muddy water for failing to keep an open mind. Reflecting on this rich past can only strengthen our understanding of man and of truth.

Though a law of nature is phrased in abstract language and is itself devoid of passion and sensibility, the history of its discovery may be an epic worthy of Homer, into whose every page is stamped the personality of a man. We can defend scientific truth by cold logic but we cannot promote its discovery this way. The human factor in the creative equation is an important part of what I want to write about in the following pages. It is a story of irony and paradox and we will find that in the final analysis, there can be no final analysis.

PART ONE

NATURE, SCIENCE, AND MAN: HOW THE QUEST BEGAN

CHAPTER II

THE COMING REUNION OF SCIENCE AND CULTURE

Ana. But surely there is a great gulf fixed.

The Devil. Dear lady: a parable must not be taken too literally. . . . There is no physical gulf between the philosopher's class room and the bull ring; but the bull fighters do not come to the class room for all that. Have you ever been in the country where I have the largest following? England. There they have great racecourses, and also concert rooms where they play [Mozart]. Those who go to the racecourses can stay away from them and go to the classical concerts if they like: there is no law against it; for Englishmen never will be slaves: they are free to do whatever the Government and public opinion allow them to do. And the classical concert is admitted to be a higher, more cultivated, poetic, intellectual, ennobling place than the racecourse. But do the lovers of racing desert their sport and flock to the concert room? Not they. There is the great gulf of the parable between the two places . . . [and] the gulf of dislike is impassable and eternal.

—Bernard Shaw: *Man and Superman,* Act III

The scientist doesn't just do Science each day. He spends his hours trying to find answers to specific questions. Thus his first and most important task is to choose the question he intends to ask of nature. It is a decision into which many factors must enter. Among them are considerations of taste, training, the availability or nonavailability of technical facilities, and the prospects for success in the time available. But even more important in determining the outcome of this critical decision are factors which might be termed suprasubjective: the state of science at the moment, the problems and prospects then causing excitement along the laboratory circuit, the degree of freedom and permissiveness in the institution and the country, the general intellectual climate of the period.

It is most revealing, for example, to spend an afternoon in the library paging through the dusty bound journals of former years. There one can find innumerable papers on topics which somehow were never investigated further despite what looked like promising leads. Likewise, one finds in the published works of different countries curious variations and uniformities in the choice of questions, sometimes to the point of seeming fetishism, which have no clear explanation. The course of our interests through the years is an erratic one, and there are frequently no obvious reasons for the directions it takes. Auspiciously launched investigations sometimes die on the vine, their findings ignored and their conclusions yawned at. Certain topics seem at times actually to be distasteful to the majority of scientists. Other times, dead horses are endlessly beaten upon.

In other words, the scientist in making this first crucial decision is acting under the influence—or tyranny in many cases—of his times. Despite everything, his freedom of action is severely limited. He is, in fact, an individual interacting with his culture, its values and strictures, and what comes out of this interaction is of decisive importance for the course of science. It is as much influenced by the atmosphere of the times as the make-up of the individual scientist. If he is a follower or leader, a novice or seasoned campaigner, a dilettante or zealot, the result will vary accordingly. What we face then, at the very start, is the intriguing question of the scientist and the influence upon him of his age.

Science and the temper of the times

When Huxley published his views on the ancestry of humankind, a century stood aghast at the fancied insult and pious moral men told each other that science had gone too far. Similar events followed the appearance of Freud's scientific conclusions. Yet in the course of time, the theories of evolution and psychoanalysis gained wide acceptance; indeed, both contributions had an incalculably great impact on the culture, religion, art, and everyday thinking of almost all men. This is not to say that opposition to these scientific generalizations has completely disappeared. It hasn't—partly because some of their problems are yet to be solved (we still don't understand the evolutionary origin of man) and partly because special intricacies in the subject matter of both fields make *proof* extraordinarily difficult. One of the consequences of this difficulty has been the proliferation of countless schools of thought—those opinion-holding factions whose outward appearances in many cases suggest nothing quite so much as a frescoed mural depicting Struggle.

In any event, enlightened men now accept many of the ideas and implications of evolution and psychoanalysis, the ancient pattern having repeated itself, as enlightenment finally came to those who, wrongly as it turned out, considered themselves already enlightened. Even the most superficial backward glance at the history of ideas will reveal the monotonous repetition of this sequence. The daring innovation of an original thinker meets rigid opposition from traditionalists and obscurantists, until at last the pressure of evidence becomes irresistible.

What is not so readily seen, however, is the other side of the coin. There have been times in our past when novel ideas were quite properly opposed by traditional thinkers because the novel idea was either inadequately supported, erratic, or plainly and demonstrably wrong. These occasions, though probably far more numerous than the better-known struggles between genuine scientific evidence and outraged tradition, have tended to escape our notice, possibly because we are less well instructed and entertained not at all by the spectacle of moderate people walking straight roads in erect postures.

But if progress is to continue, and we assume that most men want it to, seemingly wild-eyed or unsupported ideas must be put to the test, and it is perhaps just as well that a touch of inflexibility taints us all. A new idea, particularly one that challenges old and long-held points of view, must endure the battle and win if it is to survive and become a tradition of its own. The battle is necessary, and sometimes it becomes intense.

Interestingly, the battlefield where the innovator struggles with his age is often within the mind of the scientist, and this is another aspect of scientific history that is commonly forgotten. Scientists are men and, like other men, they are brought up to hold the same views that other people hold. The importance of this fact is that the scientist, like everyone else, is a creature of his times, its prejudices, truths, and assumptions, and when the moment comes to make conclusions from the evidence at hand, the scientist may find it impossible even to conjure up, much less believe, a possible explanation for his data that conflicts with things that, consciously or unconsciously, he has always believed. If such a conclusion should seem inescapable, it may still be easier to believe that some error has occurred than that an eternal truth is false.

This is understandable and to some extent desirable. Yet, had such paralysis of the imagination afflicted all men of science, the world would have known no Copernicus, Galileo, Newton, Darwin, or Pasteur. Each of these pulled down an ancient temple of truth because the evidence made it necessary to do so and, in turn, each changed the course of history. How have such men arisen in history? Were they unbalanced geniuses or prodigal titans? Did they happen on their discoveries by chance? Were they so constituted psychologically that *they*, for some reason, could question authority more readily than could their fellow men, all of whom had often seen and satisfactorily understood the rising of the sun, the falling of the apple, and the fermenting of the wine? And one thinks of Darwin, a religious man, whose distress at the implications of his own discovery caused him to pass the remainder of his long life in physical pain and anxious retirement.

We wonder about these things because they hold a question for our time. We are the latest modern generation and we know vastly more than those who came before us. Ours is the age of analysis, and we have come to know a great deal about the processes of learning, the psychological pitfalls of prejudice and preconception, and the brute imperatives of logic which, among other things, keep reminding us that *every idea we have might be wrong*. We have brought our research tools to an unprecedented degree of sharpness and have anatomized every last step that falls between observation and conclusion. In other words, not only have we far surpassed the understanding of earlier generations, but we are now doing so at an accelerating rate of speed, a rate whose own rate of acceleration appears to be accelerating.

Why then are there problems that persistently elude the scientist? Obviously, there will always be a supply of unsolved problems, since each new discovery of science uncovers a host of new problems. Physicists, for example, could not now be puzzling over what holds the subatomic particles together in the nucleus if the particles themselves had not already been discovered. But why are we without the answers to a whole hierarchy of old and venerable problems of very long standing? Why, for example, do we know almost nothing about cancer? Is it because insufficient money has been spent in cancer research? Is it because there is a shortage of what newspapers call "scientists, engineers, and technicians"?

If the ingrained beliefs and attitudes of the modern world have somehow kept scientists from new and radical approaches to the problem of cancer, then it would follow that what we are waiting for is another Darwin or Pasteur. No doubt it is believed by those responsible for the current "crash program" in cancer research that larger expenditures of research funds will hasten the day when the lightning strike of genius will flash across the sky. On this day, it is thought, a Darwin or a Pasteur—perhaps yet unborn—will perform the crucial experiment or, in an inexplicable moment of deep insight, he will perceive a fallacy that a generation overlooked.

This sort of thing *is* going on today. Evidence has been presented, for example, that, on the face of it, seems capable of explanation only if mental telepathy or extrasensory perception exists. Most scientists reject this explanation, yet a few daring individuals have concluded that ESP does exist and have accepted all of the implications of this belief, among which is the view that telepathic waves pass between individuals that cannot be obstructed by physical barriers and cannot be detected by any manner of radiation detector. The doubters, recognizing that such a phenomenon is completely incompatible with modern physics and conceding that all of physics just *might* be wrong, nevertheless prefer to believe that the evidence is defective, either through error or—let's face it—through fraud, since to them it seems that, in this neurotic age, there is a higher probability that fraudulent or erroneous evidence has been produced than that all the laws of physics are invalid. And there the question stands, as the world awaits the incontrovertible experiment which will prove that ESP exists.

What then can we say of the age we live in? If this is the most golden of the golden ages of science, why do we not know the nature of matter and the secret of life? Is there a limit to what science can accomplish, beyond which men should ask no more of scientists and scientists no more of themselves? Because science is the mightiest force in the worlds of today and tomorrow, I think these questions are important. And because I see evidence suggesting that nonscientific men are becoming more and more estranged from and unfamiliar with what I believe to be the essential nature of science, I think it important that people look again at the leviathan in their midst, for in certain combinations of light and shadow it appears at times in danger of becoming icebound.

It is these questions—insofar as biology may speak for all of science—with which this book is concerned. We will talk about some of the problems of modern biology, the complex changing science of today whose workers are seeking still to understand the nature of life. And in exploring this unending mountainside, we will find, I think, that science is very much more than most of us thought it was, and something rather less than most of us would like it to be.

Man's place in nature and vice versa

Not only is man himself a living organism, he is, as well, surrounded by, dependent on, derived from, progenitor of, inhabited by, threatened by, and—in the inexorable course of time—devoured by an assortment of living organisms other than himself. To put it another way, life is a web of which man is a part and a prisoner. Little need be said, therefore, about the importance of all life to human life.

What of man, the organism? What is he? What is his origin, his state, and his destiny? Man, we know, is an animal which, like all animals, seeks food, shelter, and security, mates and reproduces, who fights off the encroachments of a hostile environment until it is possible to fight no longer. Then, like all animals, he dies. But man is unique among animals, for he alone has the ability—and apparently the compulsion—to build cultures. His growth is not completed by reproduction, nor is it fulfilled by death, because the biological pattern of man has made his nature self-surpassing.

Culture is that milieu of ideas, myths, and values which only the human animal can exude. It is the result of man's unique ability to create and respond to symbols. "Without symbols," wrote Lewis Mumford, "man's life would be one of immediate appetites, immediate sensations; limited to a past shorter than his own lifetime, at the mercy of a future he could never anticipate, never prepare for. In such a world out of hearing would be out of reach, and out of sight would be out of mind." For these reasons, man needs not only bread, but art, ritual, philosophy, science, myth, religion, dance, and drama. When, by ignorance or adversity, he is barred from these symbols of his culture, man is destitute and, thus malnourished, he languishes.

Presumably, then, a visiting observer from Betelgeuse wishing to sort out the Animal Kingdom would quickly notice the human predilection for culture-building and he might reasonably conclude that here was a reliable, if somewhat roundabout, method of telling men from other beasts. In other words, the tendency and ability to make cultures is a special property of one group of living things. It is, in fact, a biological phenomenon.

To those members of the species who feel proud of man's capabilities, it must be disconcerting to observe a colt walking away from its birth or a three-month-old puppy performing tricks, while the human infant seems to hold on to its tot-hood as though it were all music and sunshine. Childhood, it then appears, is the prolonged immaturity we *must* have in order to imbibe our culture and learn what went before us, before we can become a part of it in one or another of its many aspects.

Since its beginning, mankind has been interested in the source of its creation, the keys to survival, the pursuit of beauty (and more recently truth), and the secret of everlasting life. Cultural patterns differ widely from people to people, from age to age, and from location to location, the physical environment obviously having an important influence in shaping the ways of men. Eskimos, for example, don't wear grass skirts, and no one could predict a man's cultural behavior merely by identifying him zoologically as a member of the species Homo sapiens. Yet despite these differences, each human culture has concerned itself with these Big Questions and offered up its own answers. Cultures thus contain the truths, biases, mores, class distinctions, unconscious assumptions, and motivations of each age, those forces whose powers have led men in their times to defy the more primitive instincts for self-preservation and, instead, to give up worldly goods, to deny the existence of what the senses perceive, and to become martyrs and saints. And as the epochs have faded into the past, each has left its legacy to human experience.

We can say then that culture and biology are intimately interrelated in a number of ways. The creation of culture is a biological imperative and its character is shaped by the needs and limitations of the organism. Moreover, cultures are influenced by man's opinions, whether conscious or unconscious, of what he is and what life is—as was our culture by the impact of Darwinism. And, finally, *to understand culture one must have some understanding of biological thought.* If this book has two themes, surely this is one of them.

Human beings like to classify things on an *either-or* basis. An act is either good or it's evil. An object is animate or inanimate. One is conservative or liberal. And, if we are scholars, we are humanists or scientists—and likewise, if we are scientists, we are physical or biological. These are demonstrably false dichotomies, each of which has been harmful to human progress. When he has argued that scientific education is a critically important part of cultural education, J. Bronowski has often been stopped "by those whose education and tastes are literary, because they found these claims puzzling. They know what culture is: it is Sophocles and Chaucer and Michelangelo and Mozart and the other figures round the base of the Albert Memorial. And they know what culture is not: it is not laundry lists and sleeping pills and the proved reserves of oil and the *Statistical Digest.*

In short, culture is not a body of facts: but what is science but facts? How then, they ask, can science be a part of culture, and why should one learn science to become cultured? There is no scientist in the frieze of the Albert Memorial."

Well, science is not a set of facts but a way of giving unity and intelligibility to the facts of nature so that nature may be controlled and new facts predicted. I suspect the word *biology* bears a similar taint to most people. It is wriggling earthworms, or paradoxically lifeless portraits in ancient and frayed textbooks of lizards, spiders, and the like; it is a stern, strait-laced teacher and an utterly revolting, never-ending dissection of some lower form of life. We might do something about this now because I intend the word *biology* to have breadth of meaning, encompassing all aspects of the phenomenon of life from the gene to the superego, from metabolism to tool making, from the slime mold to the Irish setter. As for the word *culture*, I use this also in the broadest sense, to refer both to basic and universal human traits such as tool making, shelter building, and the wearing of clothing, and to that aspect of the word culture that implies refinement or advancement—art, letters, music, and the like—those things which stand in contrast to Philistinism. In both these senses, the point is clearly valid. Biology and culture are inseparable: they overlap; they are necessary to each other and mutually influence one another to an extent that is quite startling when one begins to think about it. Culture is influenced and conditioned by the facts and phenomena of biology, the needs and limitations of the human organism, just as our art and ideas are shaped by the ideas that men have about themselves and the nature of life. Conversely—and, though less obvious, this part of the interrelationship is no less important—the state of culture powerfully affects the content and course of scientific thought in biology.

One might cite innumerable examples of this sort of thing. Racial prejudice is one. Many men believe that the white, Nordic, or Anglo-Saxon races are innately superior to other races, many of whose members have pigmented skin and are called colored. Even those who are not openly committed to this idea are affected by it and, despite professions of tolerance, many are repelled by the thought of racial intermarriage, the ethical teachings of Christianity and the sacred principles of democracy to the contrary notwithstanding. Conversely, it is held by many of those who see evil in these attitudes that there is no such thing as race and there are no biological differences within the human species. It is wrong, of course, to overlook the disinterested conclusions of modern physical anthropology. Human beings *do* differ—in skin color, hair form, height and physique, and blood groups. There *are* recognizable physical types that are related to some extent to geographical origins and to a lesser extent to cultural and language groups. But there is no evidence to support a doctrine of racial superiority or inferiority. Actually, almost no human types are genetically pure, and all known groups are more or less poorly defined around the edges. It is fair to say that what differences there exist between racial groups are put there by the hostile cultures of men in the grip of cupidity and fear. The lesson of history is clear: all of civilization's golden ages have arisen from mixed races, including that of modern America whose foundations rest solidly on a mongrel antiquity. Yet racial prejudice remains a powerful force in our culture.

Another instructive link between culture and biology is found in modern psychiatry, a metaphorical tree that is growing in the rich ground common to both. Though today's model of the mind resides in the whole organism, the roots of psychiatry push down through the hierarchy of biological organization, past the organ, through the cell, into the subcellular level of biochemistry. There is an ancient and honorable tradition of thought—dating at least from the seventeenth century—to the effect that mind and body are separate entities.

In 1637, René Descartes declared the absolute separateness of mind and body, and Cartesian dualism has, in varying measure, greatly influenced all subsequent thought—from Spinoza and Leibniz to Mary Baker Eddy. Certainly the idea makes a modicum of sense—at first glance it is not self-evidently erroneous—but we know now that the mind-body dichotomy is just another example of the human weakness for "either-or-ism" and, with Ralph Gerard, we must agree that the mind needs the brain and that "contrary to Alice's experience in Wonderland, the grin cannot remain after the cat is gone."

When an experience leaves a memory there must be some material imprint in the brain (according to current evidence), since it is clear that brain function at all levels involves, not specters and poltergeists, but patterns of neuronal discharge. It is not necessary to visualize these material imprints as little scenic bas-reliefs scattered throughout the cranium: the phenomenon bears a closer resemblance perhaps to what happens in the course of magnetic tape recording. Thus memory—and consciousness too—has a physiological basis. At least, so believe many current workers.

It is plain also that the findings of psychoanalysis have strengthened the claim of psychology to stand within the domain of biology. Just as Darwinism challenged mankind to an act of humility, psychoanalysis confronted us with the fact that we are all compelled to live under the influence of powerful unconscious psychological forces having much in common with the emotional patterns and instincts of "lower" animals. Thereby has psychoanalysis reinforced the unity of biology. Since Freud, the psychiatrist has become the student of all human nature, and this may be regarded as the cultural fruit of our metaphorical tree. The problems of human happiness and discontent, of ethics and moral responsibility, the basic elements, in fact, of all cultures, have ceased to be solely of religious and philosophical concern. They are, we now believe, the subtler manifestations of the unconscious mind which itself stands close to the most primitive and fundamental of life's properties. It is perhaps not too much to hope that a clearer understanding of the mechanism by which normal frustration leads inevitably to discontent will in time free men from the residual hates and lusts of his childhood. This would yield a more productive, less gluttonous culture, free of the envy, rivalry, crime, war, and neurosis of everyday life, whose bitterness is born in the nursery and corrupts to the grave.

As for the reverse phenomenon, the influence of culture upon biological thought, I have already spoken of the importance of his "point of view" to the scientist who is mulling over his data in search of generalizations, and there will be more about this in a later chapter. But the influence works at many levels and in devious ways. Two examples come to mind which may illuminate the point. One relates to the conflict that rages quietly in the minds of scientists and of those who provide financial support for research over whether the scientist should seek knowledge for its own sake or for the direct purpose of relieving human suffering. It is a fact that much of today's biological research owes its existence to a society interested in the latter goal. Public health services and cancer, heart disease, and poliomyelitis foundations want results that are more or less directly related to what must be called an ethical aim: the prevention of disease and the healing of the sick. (Thus is ethics as much cultural as biological, for human benevolence has at least something to do with the instinct for self-preservation.)

On the other hand, it is not historically true that the major developments of science have been due to a specially strong determination to increase man's command over nature. The Greeks were not pre-eminent in technology but in "useless" abstract thinking such as geometry. Modern science has been more interested in experimental verification, but it has tried to carry on the tradition that valued exploration and understanding above mere usefulness. As we shall presently see, genuine scientific progress in the nature of things cannot take place when science is a wagon hitched to a practical star. And it is time that this realization became a part of our culture. Some hopeful signs suggest that in some quarters this is now happening.

A second example of what culture does to the content of biological thought has to do with the present deplorable state of knowledge concerning the physiology of human sexual intercourse. It is startling to realize how little is known of this fundamental process. The major textbooks of physiology and medical school courses of today barely mention it. The only imaginable reason for this state of affairs is that no one wants to or feels able to investigate such matters in the laboratory. In other words, an ancient taboo flourishes in the temple of science. How else can one explain the hullabaloo that followed the innocuous publications of Professor Kinsey and his associates a few years ago? A recent occurrence provides an even more vivid illustration. Over two thousand papers were read at the 1956 meeting of a national society for experimental biology. One of these dealt with certain physiological measurements made in the laboratory during human sexual intercourse. It is perhaps not surprising that, in the meager press coverage of this scientific congress, this modest contribution should have received headline prominence, including a story in a leading news magazine entitled "Wired for Love." What was a little startling, however, was the fact that, among the jaded scientists attending the meeting, this paper caused a minor sensation and was the subject of endless speculation and giggling in the bistros and coffee shops. I know because I was there. No wonder nothing is known on the subject.

Culture and biological thought *are* inseparable, and one wonders how they became alienated from one another, for they were not always so estranged.

The idea of biology and its fickle fortunes

For long centuries before the comparatively recent dawn of experimental science, whatever was known about living things was known by all men alike. Somewhat later, biology's interpreters and archivists were the literary men, theologians, and philosophers of each age. In those early germinal years, a single man of learning could know all there was to know throughout the entire province of knowledge. Thus, early speculations on the nature of life were more cultural sophism than science. And as the cultures of the passing eras ebbed and flowed, men's views on life and its place in the scheme of things now followed and now led the capricious parade.

In a way, the purest picture of human life in a biological framework is to be seen in the lives of our nameless prehistoric ancestors. They, by unbelievably arduous effort and ingenuity, made the human race a going concern. They discovered the tool, the seed, and the domesticated animal. They created the marvelous instrument of language by which man discovered and later disguised his humanity. Actually, our "savage" ancestors are still quite close to us, not only in our abundant talent for savagery, but in the superstitions and fetishes of simple men, as well as in the inner essences of modern respectability, the tabooed word, the national totem, and the ceremonial initiation.

Primitive man, no doubt, began speculating upon the meaning of life when he saw that life must end in death. The phenomenon of disease, of life ebbing from the body, must also have drawn attention to the living state and its vicissitudes. To the primitive mind, sun, wind, fire, and sea were alive and each became, at various times, the object of religious feelings and elaborate mythologies. But like an infant who can cry but who knows nothing of phonation, the knowledge of the times was a superficial practical sort of know-how which was crowded in by the thick mists of magic. The typical primitive man subsisting on his garden would manage it expertly, using well-made rudimentary implements, planting crops by the seasons, selecting soils and seedlings, and knowingly eradicating weeds and pests. For a man to do these things, he must have a strong conviction that they will work and that, barring droughts and locusts, a harvest will come in. Yet with all of this practical knowledge, primitive men performed elaborate sequences of magic rites at every juncture of their agricultural practice, thus revealing a deep division in their attitude toward the living world. On the one hand were the well-known factors governing the growth of plants—water, cultivation, and so forth—and these things one coped with by knowledge and hard work. While on the other hand lay the unknowable, the forces behind pestilence, famine, and drought, and these were staved off by magic.

Perhaps it is improper to speak of the primitive man and his tiny world as the originator of biological thinking. Biology is, after all, a science with the avowed purpose of investigating nature and elucidating general laws. Yet there *were* scientific elements in the culture of primitives, even though this age had no apparent intention to educe the laws of nature for their own sake. The primitive man's power to observe and record was often advanced, but, as we shall see, science is far more than observing and recording. We will agree, therefore, that the savage had no formal science, that although he knew a great deal about living things, he knew nothing about the nature of life and knew not of his ignorance.

Man had to reach a certain level of civilization before he could visualize the world at large, and many civilizations rose and fell before the golden age of Greece. During these years some isolated advances were made: the Babylonians dissected a human body, the Jews somehow decided that they would prosper better by renouncing "unclean" meat, and the Egyptians learned how to make mummies. And in some Egyptian art, we see the first evidences of racial awareness. For example, we are told that in the reliefs of the royal tombs of the Nineteenth Dynasty (1321–1198 B.C.), a complete classification of the races is found, with Semites painted yellow, Negroes black, Egyptians red, and Northerners or Europeans as white-skinned men with blue eyes. All told, a scanty output from a dozen millenniums! It is intriguing to realize how very much more we know of Greek thought than of its antecedents. The history of Greece was unusually well documented by contemporary historians and, perhaps for this reason, has been doted upon by 2,000 years of scholarship. Surely, much that has come down to us from Greek civilization was not originated by the Greeks but transmitted by them from their predecessors, for to the modern Greek student of 400 B.C., ancient history was the history of Egypt.

There is, however, a more substantial reason for the pre-eminence of Greek thought in intellectual history. As pointed out by W. A. Smith, "The Indians, initially a jolly and extroverted people, early fell under the sway of a sacred literature and a tyrannical priesthood. The Chinese escaped the sacred and the priestly, but succumbed to the past. . . . By way of contrast, the Greeks had no sacred book, no priestly hierarchy, and no authoritarian tradition to keep them from speculating about the nature of man and the world. Their geniuses were, therefore, relatively free."

It was a remarkable age, for almost every area of artistic and intellectual experience was entered and activated by irrepressible innovators. In philosophy, all of the Big Questions were asked: What is the nature of good and beauty? How did the universe begin? What is life and what is the meaning of human life? And, almost to the last *ism,* the age gave forth with the full gamut of answers, from cynicism to idealism. Ignorant of the theological doctrines which were later to remove man from nature, the learned men of Greece in their speculations on life went so far as to postulate the evolution of man from lower animals, though this was pure conjecture devoid of evidence. The point is that nothing in the culture of the age made such a suggestion outrageous.

In reflecting upon another age and in comparing it with our own, most of us make the natural error of overrating the past, by thinking of it only in terms of its symbols, its great monuments and heroic achievements, with no consideration of its everyday life, its meanness, sordidness, mediocrity, and foolishness. The loftiest ideal of a former age becomes its essence in our minds, so that the legacy hides the ancestor. Thus, the classical age of Greece reminds many of us only of Plato and Aristotle, the "father of science," and Herodotus, the first anthropologist, and a group of handsome masonry pieces in various stages of dilapidation. Greece couldn't have been all Plato because her demagogues led her to ruin, and we wonder what the golden age must have been like to the ordinary people, not all of whom were men of learning. The evidence suggests that the vaunted spirit of enlightenment was experienced only by the educated few. Schooling was meager, most people were illiterate, and learning was a privilege available only to those who were wealthy enough to journey to the feet of the masters.

As for the masters themselves, some have had no equal in history, if influence be the measure. Of Plato, for example, Whitehead has remarked, hyperbolically perhaps, that all of Western philosophy since his time has been only a series of footnotes to his writing. It may be that the same can be said of Aristotle with respect to biology, metaphysics, political theory, and law. The gap, however, was very large between the learned few and the ordinary man. It is therefore likely that the biological erudition of the man in the street resembled that of the primitive, while, at the same time, the great minds of the age, flourishing in insular splendor, asked the big biological questions, made beginning attempts at answering them scientifically, and set them down alongside of the major problems of culture and philosophy.

For the ancient and modern worlds to have been peaks, the Middle Ages must then have been a valley, and so it has been judged by most historians from their perches high up on the modern slope. It was a curious age, both for what it was and what it has variously been thought to be by its critics. Depending upon one's point of view, the Middle Ages may be dated from A.D. 500 to 1500, from Augustine to Galileo, from Charlemagne to Columbus, from the fall of Rome to the Renaissance. Literally risen from the ruins of the ancient world, the medieval world was characterized by the emergence of a strong and authoritarian Christian church. Urban life disappeared, to be replaced by a society sharply divided into feudal warrior-chieftains and the peasants and artisans, and, though a major legacy of the Middle Ages was the university, thought and culture declined deplorably during these centuries.

For those who kept alive the flame of learning in monastic centers and isolated universities, the quintessence of knowledge was theology, and the method of scholars was a bizarre hodgepodge of ornate pageantry, recourse to sanctified authority, and undisguised fabrication. Herbert Muller has quoted the following example of the lofty indifference to vulgar fact of a scholarly ninth-century historical biographer, the Bishop of Ravenna, who wrote, "Where I have not found any history of any of these bishops, and have not been able by conversation with aged men, or inspection of the monuments, or from any other authentic source, to obtain information concerning them, in such a case, in order that there might not be a break in the series, I have composed the life myself, with the help of God and the prayers of the brethren."

There is little question that the medieval period has been badly treated by Renaissance and modern historians. The burgeoning sixteenth and seventeenth centuries had nothing but contempt for their oppressive parent, and originated the slanderous clichés "a thousand years without a bath" and the statement that medieval philosophers were concerned primarily with how many angels could stand on the head of a pin. The romantic eighteenth century relented in its judgment because it saw excitement and color in the style of medieval architecture, calligraphy, chivalry, and the myths of Robin Hood. But the nineteenth-century pendulum swung back again when its historians filed new judgments, and today the period remains poorly understood. A number of recent writers have attempted to "set the record straight" by pointing out the large number of "modern" ideas that were articulated in the monasteries and universities of the Middle Ages, as, for example, Grosseteste's work in optics, Jordanus's in mechanics, and the skepticism of William of Occam concerning our ability to attain true knowledge of the "essences" of things.

For most of us, the Middle Ages is known only by a patchwork of contradictory symbols—knighthood in flower, feudal moated castles, and the burning of Joan of Arc by a sinister Inquisition. Perhaps this is the morning-after that must inevitably follow a historiographic binge. Modern critics do agree, however, that the scientific knowledge of the Middle Ages was meager, that what little progress had been made by the Ancients in developing the scientific method was allowed to recede into the dishonored past. Ecclesiastical authority was supreme, and when the High Church theologians who dominated the universities finally recognized what a superb ally they had in the same Aristotle they had earlier denounced as a heathen seer, Aristotelianism became for a thousand years the true scientific basis for the hierarchical aims of the papal power. The Church presumably approved of Aristotle's conception of the earth as the home of all imperfection because this nicely left heaven as the source of salvation. And whatever of

Aristotle's writings did not agree with the revealed Word could be easily explained by reference to the author's paganism.

Biology prospered little in these centuries, and what little that was done as a formal pursuit consisted of foolish compilations of ancient writings done in the service of theology and doctrine. Beyond this, the medieval mind was enmeshed in an almost unbelievable tangle of astrology, alchemy, magic, and sorcery. While it has been held that such preoccupations were perfectly reasonable in their time and that alchemy represented an "advance" over primitive and ancient occultism, it is difficult to acknowledge that science grew out of these intellectual errors, that it owed its existence to them. This would be like assigning parentage of the labor movement to the excesses and cupidity of management. Rather, we would agree with Dampier, who wrote, "The scattered seedlings of science had to grow in a vast and confused jungle which was always threatening to choke them, and not in the open healthy prairie of ignorance."

In the next few chapters we will speak of the Renaissance and the modern worlds. For the moment, we will merely note that the dawn of modern science took place in the seventeenth century—a century which Whitehead called "the century of genius," for, despite the murk of the immediately preceding millennium, it produced Francis Bacon, Harvey, Kepler, Galileo, Descartes, Pascal, Huygens, Boyle, Newton, Locke, Spinoza, Leibniz, and countless others of high distinction. It was the century in which scientific biology had its true beginning.

The Renaissance marked not only the birth of modern science, but a return to respectability of intellectual pursuits. Science had not, by 1700, become the most honored of occupations, and it remained for some time a gaudy and slightly disreputable parvenu in the academic curriculum. But scientific awareness did begin at last to seep down into the minds of the intelligent public. As we shall presently see, the new enlightenment swept the Western world like a wave of fire and shook men's imaginations to their deepest foundations. All that had once been believed was now suspect, and for the first time men challenged the notion that ancient culture must forever symbolize the ultimate in human aspirations. The idea somehow took hold that men were capable of progress! How strange it seems to us, the heirs of that new tradition, to imagine a world not working to improve itself.

Thus, all at once, there arose the great currents of thought which dominate our century: Protestantism, humanism, and—what was a truly dynamic part of the culture of the Enlightenment—modern science. An era had begun in which the intelligent public participated actively in the scientific debates of the day, particularly those marked by sharp controversy. With the forward lurches of scientific progress, a watchful public could taste the sweetness of a successful experiment and the gall of contrary evidence, the acquiescence to which, whenever it happened, must surely have been beneficial for the public mental hygiene.

The gap on the Albert Memorial

In discussing the theme of the increasing separateness of science in the modern world, J. Robert Oppenheimer wrote, "We live today in a world in which poets and historians and men of affairs are proud that they wouldn't even begin to consider thinking about learning anything of science, regarding it as the far end of a tunnel too long for any wise man to put his head into." James Killian expressed it more bluntly by reporting two intelligences that have been making the rounds of the faculty lounges—one the observation that the scientist knows nothing of the liberal arts and regrets it, while the humanist knows nothing of science and is proud of it. The other was an incident said to have occurred at a liberal arts faculty meeting. When a student named Cicero was reported to have flunked Latin, everybody laughed, but when a student named Gauss was reported to have failed mathematics, only the science professors laughed.

Since we seem then to be facing a deep, wide gulf between the humanities and science, uncrossed except by an infrequent intellectual frogman, it would be of interest—*scientific* interest actually—to inquire whether or not differences can be found in the character or content of the two domains which might help explain the present situation. And, as it turns out, there are some rather provocative differences.

For one thing, a useful distinction, though not a rigid dichotomy, can be made between two kinds of knowledge: cumulative and noncumulative knowledge (as pointed out by Crane Brinton in *Ideas and Men*). *Cumulative* knowledge is typified by science, since through the centuries it has been built up by accretions slowly added onto an original hard core of truth. Nothing, for example, has been substituted by modern physics for the truths discovered in ancient Greece by Archimedes, although physics has built upon this solid foundation to achieve its present size and strength. This is not to say that all seminal ideas are necessarily and forever correct. Sciences have been built upon erroneous ideas, and only later was error corrected. We may even assume that certain of today's fundamental truths will in time be proved erroneous. Such is the nature of the great scientific revolutions produced by the work of Copernicus, Einstein, and Darwin, for each of these was such that its reverberations carried back through the entire body of cumulated knowledge to shake the central core itself.

Noncumulative knowledge, on the other hand, is well illustrated by literature. Today's writers deal with questions of right and wrong, beauty and ugliness, human nature, and the universals of life, while the Greek playwrights of over 2,000 years ago wrote on exactly the same themes (as their scientific contemporaries were simultaneously working out the principles of plane geometry). Knowledge in this realm, then, has not, by the process of accumulation, increased in any clear fashion, though perhaps we should say only that the *rate* of accumulation distinguishes science from art, literature, and philosophy. Arnold Toynbee has written, "Human Affairs are still the Dark Continent of the Universe, compared to the realm of Physical Nature which has been so brilliantly illuminated by the discoveries of modern Western scientists in the course of the last three hundred years. We students of Human Affairs are like those explorers of Tropical Africa who were pushing their way into the interior from half a dozen different coasts in the middle years of the last century; and, when people are opening up a dark continent by a converging movement, it is a landmark in their progress every time that a Stanley meets his Livingstone."

We may assume also that these apparent differences (and others) play some role in determining which men and women enter which field. What we have called cumulative or scientific knowledge, for example, is better suited to experimental verification and hence is more clearly true or false. Such fields might be expected to attract the tough-minded, the realist, the skeptic. Noncumulative knowledge, conversely, is less (or not at all) accessible to clear tests of truth, is less likely therefore to alter the course of human history and hence might attract the idealist, the dreamer, the artist, and the optimist.

Needless to say, these remarks are superficial. More will be said on this subject later and here I must be hopelessly brief. The literature on this tantalizing subject is massive, ranging from the high plateaus of the psychoanalytic reviews to the trade journals that are wrestling bravely with the "scientist shortage." For the time being, we will note only how increasingly difficult it is for a gifted man to play his part in today's society unless he is something of a specialist; and we will concede the existence of deep forces which propel men of learning toward one or the other of the two great continents of knowledge. But let us also remember that the purpose of all scholarship is to project order into the external world and that it is our purpose here to see if somehow we cannot find a continental isthmus across which scientists and humanists might run a little light traffic.

Let us now turn our attention to science itself and see if we cannot learn something of its essential nature.

CHAPTER III

THE NATURE OF SCIENCE

The Newtonian having said, That Descartes was an Ignoramus, the Disciple of that Philosopher reply'd in a passion, You Lie.

—D'Argens' Chinese Lett., 1741

Consider the three following case histories.

1. A biologist decides that, since cancer is the scourge of mankind, he will dedicate himself to the task of discovering its cause. He approaches the problem by examining cancer cells carefully and determining their properties in an orderly manner. Upon retiring at the age of sixty-five, he has, in addition to having exhausted himself, demonstrated unequivocally that cancer cells contain 268 of the 302 enzymes that were looked for, that cancer cells can assume over 139 different shapes, and that they have a rather bland taste—all of which are facts not previously known. Unfortunately, this investigation had to end before it was possible to make any conclusions concerning the cause of cancer.

2. A well-known investigator seeks for many years to understand the essential nature of the living organism. He observes the marvelous complexity of the cell, and he is awed by the fact that when a cell divides, its progeny are absolute replicas of itself down to the last detail. He is struck by the "goal-seeking" properties of living

organisms, the metamorphosis of the tadpole, the incredible process by which a single-celled embryo becomes a man, the regeneration of amputated limbs by salamanders, the healing of wounds, the continued vertical growth of a young pine tree even after its trunk has been pulled down and trussed into an unnatural position. In trying to understand these observations, he concludes that the whole organism is very much greater than the sum of its parts and that the complexity of an organism is so unimaginably great there must reside within it some *principle* of life over and above its mere material structure. This principle, he concludes, is not a physical entity but a vital force that somehow wills or guides the cell toward its goal and the fulfillment of its biological purpose. And it is this force, he logically infers, that must distinguish the living from the inanimate.

3. A small white rat, known in the laboratory as Peter, is placed in a contraption that looks like this:

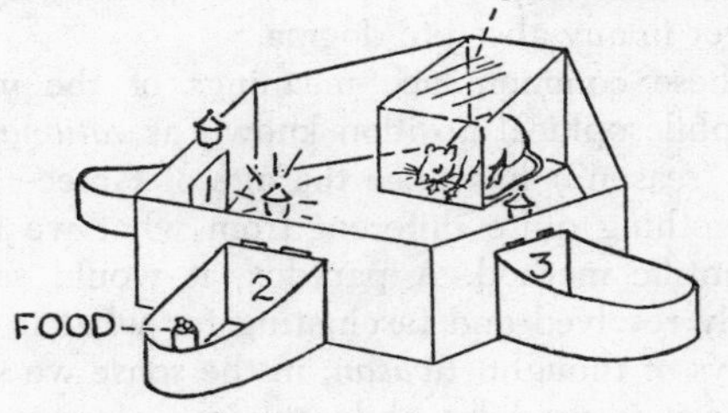

Compartment A is a glass-enclosed observation booth from which Peter may peer out at the three doors which we have labeled 1, 2, and 3. Above each of these is a light bulb but only one door leads to food. Things are arranged for a few weeks so that the food is always behind the one door whose light is on, and, of course, the door is changed from trial to trial. Peter quickly learns this fact, for after some practice he always goes, when released from A, to the lighted door and gratification. Now, however, the procedure is changed. He is detained in A and allowed to watch while the light outside the lunchroom is merely blinked on and off, and he is not released for a fair interval of time. The question then becomes: When released will he find the food, since he cannot now respond to a light that is not on, but only to something in his mind? We watch, Peter is released, he hesitates, makes his decision, and heads for the right door, his problem solved.

It is the purpose of this chapter to help us decide which of these three seekers of truth is using the method of science.

The decline and fall of speculation

In ordinary conversation, the word *reason* is seldom misunderstood. It means sound thinking, intelligence, sanity, and sense—and, in its various shadings of meaning, we contrast it with emotion, imprudence, and obtuseness. A "man of reason," in the ordinary phrase, is not a true believer in any absolute dogma.

Despite these commonplace meanings of the word reason, the philosophical position known as *rationalism* (from *ratio*, "reason") has since the age of Greece represented something quite different from what we now call the scientific method. A paradox, it would seem, but one easily resolved and fascinating for what it tells us of the ways of thought. *Reason*, in the sense we shall use it and as it is used by philosophers, refers to the processes of *logical thought* and not necessarily to the pursuit of truth. For example, if we are told "all philosophers are immoral" and "Democritus is a philosopher," we must conclude that Democritus is immoral. The conclusion lies inescapably within the given premises and, by the process of logical proof or *deduction*, we merely unwrap and expose it. Nothing new has been added and thus we see the essential emptiness of deduction. The point to be emphasized, however, is that logical deduction leads to a conclusion *regardless of the truth of the premise.* The above conclusion is logically sound, though the premise is possibly false.

The significance of this fact for the history of thought is very great indeed. What it means is that an internally consistent and logically impeccable system of ideas may be spun out of the reasoning mind whether or not the "given" or underlying premise is true. Thus did Euclid develop a logically faultless geometry based on an assumption—that parallel lines never meet—which 2,000 years later was found to be unjustified. Mathematics is, in fact, the ideal example of logic at work, for the mathematician proceeds by analyzing his given premises for their implicit meanings, and the mathematician's "truth" has no connection with the external world.

The difficulty with rationalism arose when men, impressed and awed by the power of reason, came to believe that all questions, even the Big Questions of philosophy, could be made to yield to the reasoning mind, that the mind, in fact, has access to all of the great and ultimate truths. We may exemplify this point of view by picturing the complete rationalist at work: he is seated in his study, a room without windows, in a deep comfortable chair; his eyes are closed, and his mind is hard at work. The only equipment he could possibly use would be paper, quill, and ink. And we wonder as we view this tableau how, if it is true that the sun always rises in the east, the rationalist could possibly discover it in a study without windows. For here is the crucial defect of rationalism. It needs nothing but mind and a premise and, since it sees nothing of the external world, the truth of its conclusions stands or falls by the truth of the premises. Truth, then, is not the same as logic.

Another point of view that rose to new stature in the seventeenth century held that the mind by itself commands no royal road to truth and that, in the words of John Locke, the mind is a blank page: it is *experience* that writes upon it. This thesis, so indispensable to science, is called *empiricism* (from the Greek words meaning "experience" and "trial"). It is the view that says if you wish to understand nature, look at nature, not at Aristotle. We see now why rationalism emerged as a countercurrent to science. Though the mother lode of reason, it denied to the mind the harvest of its senses. And it is sense data, what he sees, feels, hears, tastes, and smells, which starts the empiricist on his road to truth.

Rationalism, it should be noted, is not necessarily the same as pure speculation. Neither is it true that rationalism and empiricism were born in the seventeenth century, for both points of view were alive and kicking in the ancient world. The empirical approach to knowledge is discernible in some of the works of Archimedes, Ptolemy, and Hippocrates, and we know from their technology, their houses, architecture, sailing ships, and, to some extent, their medicine that ancient men learned some of what they knew by reaching out and touching the world. Rationalism prospered too, for the philosophies of Plato and Aristotle were in large part rationalistic, seeking truth by the power of reason alone. But the rationalists of the ancient world gave their brand of thought a stripe of its own. In constructing their world views, they needed a given premise and this they usually obtained by pure and unvarnished speculation. They fabricated the bases upon which whole philosophies rested out of the gossamer of imagination. Hence, through speculation and the fatal fascination it held for them, the ancients were swept into colossal error.

Imagination took over, and huge authoritarian cosmologies arose, packed with exquisitely detailed and utterly false generalizations. While it is true that error is inevitable in an age whose means of acquiring knowledge are primitive or nonexistent, and we must not too harshly criticize the ancients from the vantage point of today, it is still impressive how universal was the willingness to step forward with explanations for observed phenomena in the total absence of knowledge and the reluctance even occasionally to concede ignorance. Reasoning, for example, was based on *analogy* with human behavior, and conclusions were drawn from the human traits supposedly belonging to inanimate objects. Great forces of nature were embodied in complicated mythologies, phrases were used such as "planetary attractions" or "evil humors" which had connotations of humanness or animateness. It was obviously impossible, for example, for Aristotle to have observed microscopic objects such as spermatozoa. It was his view that the female contributed matter to the embryo while the male contributed nothing material, only the principle, soul, power, or—to use a typically Aristotelian concept—form. There can be no reproach for the contemporary ignorance of microscopic life. But surely this unverifiable, speculative statement, scarcely even a hypothesis, represented a misleading error which, because of the stature conferred upon Aristotle by others, doubtless hindered progress for many centuries.

The loose language, the empty verbalisms and doctrines, the intense desire for universal knowledge are all phenomena which are undoubtedly attributable to emotional needs. Psychology explains the universal human propensity for mythmaking, servility to authority, desire for security, and what we will say of the further progress of thought shows how these ancient errors have at last been recognized and to some extent purged. Only "to some extent" because modern man is no freer of these psychological impulses than the man of ancient times. Furthermore, having insight into the nature of human compulsions is not quite enough to liberate one from them. (Jules Masserman has referred to the disquieting paradox of people who supposedly have achieved the various brands of self-understanding, yet are unable to apply this vision to the solution to their problems. The condition of those who "cruise about submerged in oceanic depths of 'insight' who are in touch with reality only by a thin throatful of air" he calls *status schnorkelis.*) We still are men, and, in our desire to make the world more like the heaven we wish it, we still must lean toward beliefs and denials which inescapably shape the course of science.

Later rationalism recognized the consequences of a basic premise made of foolish fancy, and the complete and thoroughgoing new rationalism that emerged in the seventeenth century was obsessed with the importance of finding basic axioms which, though self-evident and therefore knowable without recourse to experience, are nevertheless true and suitable starting points for logical constructions. These would be the a priori truths that the rationalist conceived, or better preconceived, us to be born with. In the rationalism of medieval Christianity, God was the basic given truth, and it was held that the human mind without benefit of the senses had the ability to fathom at least in part God's plan for the universe. Not so for the new rationalist. In searching for indubitable basic propositions, he had no need of a supernatural being, nor of ancient authority. He banished God from the processes of truth-seeking in the belief that the mind was all-powerful, and he made as symbols of his century the great rationalistic systems of thought that in their own completeness gave answers to all questions of man and metaphysics.

Here we can but mention in passing a few of the greatest of the rationalistic system builders. Spinoza, for example, the philosopher's philosopher, who devised a system of *ethics* in which mathematical proofs patterned after the geometry of Euclid were used to establish theorems on God and the nature of true goodness. And the brilliant Leibniz, who wrestled earnestly with the nature of the relationship between "truths of reason" and "truths of fact" and concluded that harmony between the two depended solely upon pure laws of thought. In his great construction, Leibniz devised a general system outlining all possible forms of thought and the "universal laws" connecting them. All truths, however complex, could then be extracted from these elements, so it was claimed, by combining them according to the prescriptions of logic.

And there was Descartes, perhaps the greatest of the rationalists—the man many have called the father of modern philosophy. In establishing his method of inquiry, he temporarily became a true skeptic. Believing only in the power of reason and in the idea that he was born to set right the muddled beliefs of his time, Descartes recognized the importance of an unshakable base for a rationalistic philosophy. By systematically doubting, by rejecting, in his words, "as absolutely false all opinions in regard to which I could suppose the least ground for doubt, in order to ascertain whether after that there remained aught in my belief that was wholly indubitable," he came at last to the proposition that his doubt could not conquer. He could not doubt that he was doubting, and from this came the famous *cogito, ergo sum,* I think, therefore I am. This was Descartes's hard-won premise, and upon it, by the power of his logic alone, he proceeded to build a system of thought that went right on up to God. The basic axiom, then, was found by *intuition,* the key feature in the method of Descartes. Unhappily for him, modern logicians have exposed the fallacy in his basic statement and have picked to pieces his logical technics. The Cartesian system, though powerfully influential upon later generations both for its content and grandeur, is now a shattered hulk, for its basis and structure were in error.

Interestingly, the style of Descartes's life matched his philosophy and probably had a lot to do with the picture we have of the armchair life of the rationalist. His career is filled with charming vignettes of the master at work: in bed, in a warm oven, in a snowbound hut where, alone one day while returning from the coronation of the Holy Roman Emperor, Ferdinand, he had his greatest insights. As a soldier in the Thirty Years' War, he spent most of his time discussing mathematics with the army engineers. When finally he was appointed tutor to the young and romantic Queen Christina of Sweden, the rigors of lecturing on philosophy while horseback riding at sunrise led to his final illness.

The work of Descartes in the seventeenth century and of later philosophers such as the great Immanuel Kant brought rationalism to a high-water mark in its sophistication and in the attractions it held for thinking men. It prospered in an age to which order and system were all important, not only in the pursuit of knowledge but in the political actions of all-powerful princes and the formation at last of stable churches from diverse denominational factions. But rationalism, though it has deductive thinking in common with science, is not science, and in this century the fully developed method of science finally saw the light of day. To understand the nature of science, one must understand why rationalism failed.

The rise of science

It happened quietly, for Europe was being convulsed by religious wars and most people, by and large, are not interested in such things. But a profound revolution was launched when, in the midst of a rationalist ground swell, the first positive and clear statements of the empiricist position began appearing around 1600. The age soon gave way to philosophical struggle, for though at one in their contest with the arid expositors of Aristotle, the fathers of modern science, like many another revolutionary clique, ended their unanimity once they had named a common enemy.

Much of the groundwork for empiricism was laid by the great Galileo, perhaps the most famous of scientific martyrs. A worshiper of facts, Galileo was an ingenious experimenter first and a theoretician second. Clocks were not yet known, yet he discovered two of the laws governing the velocity of falling bodies. To determine time intervals, he used the weight of the water accumulating from a dripping basin. With wily genius, he worked out the mechanical laws governing the motion of objects rolling down inclined planes, so that, centuries later, Bergson wrote, "The concept of time came down an inclined plane from heaven to the modern world through Galileo." He enlarged the visible universe by developing better telescopes and, by careful observation of the planets, showed conclusively the error of the astronomy of Ptolemy which was based not on observation but on one man's conception of what the universe ought to look like if it were to be elegant and simple. Galileo's observations bolstered the Copernican theory that the earth revolved about the sun, at a time when the church was committed to the opposite idea, that the earth, the scene of Christ's sacrifice, was the center of the universe.

Even Galileo had a touch of Cartesian rationalism in him (as do we all), for he must have believed in his deepest mind that the universe is arranged with mathematical precision and that if we could only grasp the true underlying axioms, we might somehow unravel the laws of nature without the need for experiment. He is said to have boasted on occasion that he used experiment only to prove to those less wise than he what he already knew to be true. He was ultimately tried for heresy before the Inquisition and he chose to recant rather than accept its judgment. No one will forget the words Galileo is said to have muttered as he rose from his knees in the chamber of penitence: "And yet it moves. . . ." If the story is apocryphal, it is history's greatest rumor.

While Galileo was one of the first to practice empiricism, Francis Bacon was its first philosopher, and let no one assume that because a man can do science, he is necessarily able to explain in abstract terms the nature of the scientific method.* Bacon has been a highly con-

* Einstein once remarked, "If you want to know the essence of scientific method, don't listen to what a scientist may tell you. Watch what he does." Morris Cohen qualified it,

troversial figure in the history of ideas. His life had many unsavory episodes, of which much has been made by latter-day critics under the leadership of Lord Macaulay. But, if a blackguard, he was a brilliant blackguard, for his monumental treatise *Novum Organum* revolutionized thought.

Bacon tells us how, while an undergraduate at Trinity College, Cambridge, he became disgusted with Aristotelianism because, though centuries old, it had yielded not progress but barren dispute. He then and there resolved to establish a new philosophy which would reform all human knowledge and allow man to regain the control of nature he had lost with the fall of Adam. It was a task, however, which he never lived to complete, for it did not begin in earnest until a fantastic political career had climaxed in exile. Although he failed to achieve his goal, his lasting fame was secured by the *method* which he suggested be used in his great crusade. The method was new and the title *Novum Organum*, or *New Method*, was a direct challenge to Aristotle, whose theory of method was titled *Organon*. The work was a magnificently written attack on medieval thought, rationalism, and the defects of Aristotelianism. His rejection of a medieval legacy that argued causes and ignored facts was so vigorous it awoke his contemporaries to high enthusiasm. He bluntly stated that philosophy is not a science of things divine or human, nor is it a search for abstract truth; it is rather a practical seeking to improve our condition of life by increasing our power over nature and forcing her to yield us her fruit. In ringing phrases, he declared that our knowledge of the external world

---

"Watch what he does when engaged in scientific work, not when he is taking a holiday or is on a picnic, or discoursing on something beyond his competence." Scientists may or may not clearly grasp the essential nature of the scientific method and still be successful in their scientific activities, as illustrated by the nonscientific character of many of their utterances on nonscientific topics.

comes only from our sense impressions, and the only way we can discern true knowledge from the flux of sense impressions in which we are swimming is by systematic and orderly observation of nature. We must observe phenomena, record them, and classify them, and, in time, enough knowledge will have been acquired to give us a firm grasp upon nature's laws. Nor should this pursuit of data be left to chance and whim. Societies should be formed, which under competent leadership should send forth armies to win the great battle for knowledge.*

Could anything be further from rationalism? It was the apotheosis of empiricism—but was Bacon's *novum organum* the method of science? Let us consider the point carefully. In emphasizing the limitations of deductive logic, Bacon stressed the value of *inductive* logic, the difference between the two being the great hinge upon which empiricism hangs. Inductive thinking does not depend upon a given premise but upon observational data, and its conclusion tells us something not implicit in the premise. Therefore, it is something we did not know before, it is new knowledge. Consider the inference "all cases of Gok's disease *so far observed* have proved fatal, therefore Gok's disease is a fatal disease." Our inference carries us from the cases we *have* observed to those we *have not* observed. Consequently, the truth of the conclusion cannot be guaranteed, for there is always the possibility that in time we will encounter a nonfatal case. We know now that we should not speak in inductive logic of the truth of a conclusion, but rather of its *probability* of being true. This probability can be high or low. It would be high if our conclusion was based on a wide experience with Gok's disease which had known no exceptions. It would be low if we'd made our conclusion after seeing only four cases. For some inductive conclusions, the probability of truth is so high there is

* This proposal to regiment scientists as an army was elaborated in Bacon's philosophical romance *The New Atlantis*.

practically no chance of future contradiction (though mathematically its probability is never zero). Thus, we are justified in saying the sun will rise tomorrow, not because we are oracles, but because we and others have observed it rise each morning many, many times without exception.

Inductive logic is really the basis of the many decisions that we constantly make in everyday life. Every hour of every day, whether we realize it or not, we make big and little decisions that are based on short-range predictions having specific probability values. Most of the time, little importance attaches to the success or failure of these low-pitched inductive conclusions. If this morning the sky looks gray and I decide to wear my raincoat, I am basing my decision on some previous observational data to the effect that this sort of sky is usually followed by rain. If today it clears up, I have made an unsuccessful prediction, I have had to drag along a heavy raincoat, and my future reaction to gray skies should lead to an inductive conclusion whose probability rating is one notch poorer. Even in the face of highly improbable outcomes, we like to stay on the safe side when the outcome would be catastrophic should it happen to occur. Thus, we buy insurance though houses rarely burn down, and have bone x-rays taken even though bruises are relatively common and fractures relatively rare.

It was Bacon's merit to have recognized that empiricism leads to new knowledge via the inductive inference. Bacon's failure—and it is a failure only by today's standards—is his belief that empiricism would yield *certain* knowledge. He failed to recognize the probable character of truth as we now know it. Moreover, he believed that his method would provide answers for the Big Questions of philosophy. He advocated making long lists of random facts from which, he felt sure, nature's laws and eternal truth would spring forth when the lists became long enough.

It was Robert Boyle and later Newton and Locke,

however, who fostered the marriage of reason and empiricism, whose timely offspring was modern science. Of these three pioneers in the development of the scientific method, chief credit probably belongs to Boyle. Although Boyle was born in 1627 (the year of Bacon's death), Locke in 1632, and Newton in 1642 (the year of Galileo's death), Boyle had established his commanding reputation by the publication of his *Spring and Weight of the Air* in 1660 and *Sceptical Chymist* in 1661, some thirty years before the appearance of Newton's *Principia* and Locke's *Essay Concerning Human Understanding.*

When Boyle returned to London after his service in the continental war, he joined a group of scholars who met weekly to discuss philosophy and further experimental science. Boyle termed this Baconian group "The Invisible College" and when the war forced them to Oxford, he joined them and there earned his reputation as the final foe of alchemy and the founder of modern chemistry. When the Restoration brought peace in 1660, the Invisible College became the Royal Society, the very society Bacon had urged into existence. In many ways, the founding of this society marks the true beginning of modern science. Its motto, *Nullius in verba,* pledged its Fellows to reject all doctrine in favor of experiment.

As a youth, Boyle was dismayed at the lip service paid to Bacon's method and the meager effort that went with it. Like Bacon, he resolved to demolish wrongheadedness and, at Oxford, he organized laboratories, secretaries, and all manner of assistants (one of whom was Robert Hooke) into an army of investigators quite in keeping with the Baconian prescription. Between 1660 and 1673, Boyle published fifteen treatises whose success and scope are virtually without parallel in the history of science.

Boyle's contributions to chemistry cannot detain us here. Let us merely make note of the viewpoint which he brought to his investigations as illustrated in *The*

Sceptical Chymist. The treatise is a dialogue between an Aristotelian (who believed in four "elements"—earth, fire, water, and air), a Spagyrist* (who believed in the three "principles" of Paracelsus—sulfur, mercury, and salt), and the "sceptical chymist." The meeting occurs under the chairmanship of Boyle, who early addresses the others: "I am not a little pleased to find that you are resolved on this occasion to insist rather on experiments than on syllogisms. For I, and no doubt you, have long observed that those dialectical subtleties, that the schoolmen too often employ about physiological mysteries, are wont much more to declare the wit of him that uses them, than increase the knowledge or remove the doubts of sober lovers of truth." Boyle died in 1691. The epitaph on his Irish tombstone reads: "Father of Chemistry and Uncle of the Earl of Cork."

Boyle had made complete the cleavage between material and spiritual phenomena. There was a God who was creator and ruler, but man, his unique creation, had the power to reason and observe. God created the material world to operate under rigorous mechanical laws that were unaffected by the wishes and feelings of men. We will come back again to this view of a mechanical world, for it was the hallmark of the natal century of science, it was the necessary precondition for Newton, and it soon settled at the heart of a great question of physics, the nature of causality, and the greatest question of biology, the nature of life. The physical universe was conceived by the natural philosophers of the seventeenth century as a vast machine, a material entity made of atoms possessing mass, position, size, and shape, whose behavior follows ascertainable laws. The cosmos was autonomous. Being material, it was real and hence of-

* Spagyrism or alchemy was rampant in the century preceding Boyle. A typical example of the sort of thing that went on is a chapter heading in the 1596 edition of *Paracelsus' Experiments & Cures:* "The Spagericke Antidotarie of the preparation and making of medicines against Goonshot."

fered resistance to the senses. Though Boyle and his contemporaries attributed the mechanistic world to a higher divinity, it is noteworthy that their contributions to knowledge had a mechanistic not a divine derivation.

The thought has been expressed that this world view was far from original, that it had, in fact, begun in ancient Greece with Epicurus, Democritus, and Zeno, and had it not been for barbarian hordes, the collapse of classicism, and a pious, other-worldly, Christian millennium, the flourishing Greek culture would have led to the discovery of the laws of nature so that a later revolution would not have been necessary. But a later revolution was necessary and, with Newton, we reach its climax.

It was said of Newton in the seventeenth century that he was like the River Nile, whose powers were gigantic but whose source was unknown. In the eighteenth century, an age that all but deified Newton, Alexander Pope exclaimed:

> Nature and Nature's laws lay hid in night:
> God said, Let Newton be! and all was light.

And in recent times Newton has been acclaimed, perhaps unwarrantably, as the greatest thinker of all time, whose authority and influence have been paralleled only by Aristotle's. The reason for such encomiums can be easily stated. Newton laid the foundation for three separate fields of inquiry: higher mathematics, celestial mechanics, and physical optics. And what is more fantastic is the fact that these great contributions were all made within a period of eighteen months when Newton was twenty-three years old. It was unquestionably the most fruitful eighteen months in the history of creative imagination. Newton spent the remainder of his scientific career merely elaborating these discoveries. What he accomplished in this period is described in his own words:

> In the beginning of the year 1665 I found the method for approximating series and the rule for re-

ducing any dignity [power] of any binomial to such a series [*i.e.*, the binomial theorem]. The same year in May I found the method of tangents of Gregory and Slusius, and in November [discovered] the direct method of Fluxions [*i.e.*, differential calculus], and the next year in January had the Theory of Colours, and in May following I had an entrance into the inverse method of Fluxions [*i.e.*, integral calculus], and in the same year I began to think of gravity extending to the orb of the Moon . . . and having thereby compared the force requisite to keep the Moon in her orb with the force of gravity at the surface of the earth, and found them to answer pretty nearly. . . .

Thus came immortality to a man who, tortured at times with despair and self-doubt, seemed to court controversy and flee adulation; who for some reason preferred not to make public his discoveries; who, convinced that Leibniz had plagiarized the calculus, quarreled for years with him over the question of priority; who, in a state of collapse after completing the *Principia*, began writing angry denunciatory letters to friends, including John Locke, whom he accused of trying to "embroil him with women"; and who, as Master of the Mint, was buried in Westminster Abbey not for the *Principia*, which few have read, but rather because he had stabilized the coinage and restored national credit at a time when England was striving to build a vast mercantile empire against Dutch and Portuguese opposition. On Newton's tombstone are the words: "Mortals, congratulate yourselves that so great a man has lived for the honor of the human race."

The circumstances leading to the publication of the *Principia* are harrowing to consider. In his first scientific publication, Newton had communicated his theory of light and color to the Royal Society in 1672. It aroused a storm of criticism, some from men of stature such as

Christian Huygens and Robert Hooke. Of the absurd criticism by a man named Linus, Newton wrote, "I see I have made myself a slave to philosophy [science], but if I get free of Mr. Linus's business I will resolutely bid adieu to it eternally, accepting what I do for my private satisfaction, or leave to come out after me; for I see a man must either resolve to put out nothing new, or become a slave to defend it." He was already convinced that Leibniz had pilfered his discovery of the calculus.

In 1674, Hooke wrote Newton a pleasant letter soliciting a paper for the Royal Society. In this letter, Hooke casually mentioned thoughts he had been entertaining about a rule of inverse squares. The discussion apparently aroused Newton from his sulks and he began to consider the problem of planetary motion. In 1684, there occurred the famous visit to Newton of the astronomer Halley. Halley asked Newton to describe the orbit of a planet attracted to the sun by a gravitational force obeying an inverse-square rule. Newton immediately replied, "An ellipse." Halley asked Newton how he knew that, and Newton replied, "I have calculated it!" These four words convinced Halley that Newton had worked out the mathematical basis for the law of gravity. Overjoyed and realizing that his own and Hooke's concepts had been no more than intuitive, Halley cajoled Newton into relenting and publishing his work.

Just before publication, however, trouble with Hooke started. Hooke heard that Newton was going to publish the inverse-square law and he concluded that this was the fruit of his earlier letter to Newton. When Newton learned that Hooke wanted to be acknowledged, he exploded, contending that he had developed the theorem long before Hooke had ever mentioned it. Moreover, Hooke had never been able to solve it mathematically. He wrote an angry letter to Halley bitterly attacking Hooke for "this new provocation" and threatened to suppress the crucial chapters. Somehow Halley mollified him, the classic went to press intact, and Newton retired to have a nervous breakdown. As it later turned out, the book was published largely at Halley's own expense. To the discoverer of Halley's comet, therefore, the world owes eternal gratitude. His vision and self-sacrifice made possible the greatest single monument of human learning, the *Philosophiae Naturalis Principia Mathematica* of Isaac Newton.

What interests us in the achievements of Newton is the fact that his discoveries were made by an unusual method. And it is of some interest again that to discern his method we must examine what he did, not his writings about what he did, for, though his novel method was one of the first and surely the greatest use of the scientific method and though he himself was aware of his remarkable methodological discovery, still his writings did not fully discuss in general terms the method from which resulted his various discoveries.

First Newton made empirical observations in the tradition of Bacon and Boyle. From *observations* of his own and others, one of which, legend insists, was a falling apple, and in the belief that the universe was a mechanism that functioned according to mathematical laws, Newton concluded that some law of nature must govern the phenomena he observed. He formulated a simple mathematical equation (now known as the law of gravity) which would make sense out of the observations at hand by fitting them into a *generalization*. The abstract statement, we must remember, was in Newton's mind, it was not something he saw, nor has anyone ever witnessed an equation at work. It was, in fact, a *hypothesis*. Here we encounter the crucial feature of the method of Newton. If the general hypothesis was correct, he reasoned, it implies what behavior should be expected in other areas of experience, such as the motion of the moon, whose monthly revolutions should be governed by the hypothetical force. In other words, Newton used deductive logic and reason to extract an implicit conclusion from the tentative premise that was his hypothesis. This part of the procedure could be carried out in his study, for it required only reason, as in the rationalist tradition. Now to verify and bolster the hypothesis, Newton returned to empirical observations. If the equation carries an implicit prediction of the moon's behavior, let us look at the moon: *it* cannot be in error. If the moon's behavior fails to agree with the prediction, it was wrong, the logical correctness of the deduction notwithstanding. For the deduction's premise was wrong as proved by the demonstrable untruth of its conclusion. If, on the other hand, the moon's behavior has been successfully predicted, the hypothesis gains in strength and will continue to do so with each such successful test.

Interestingly, there was irony in the events that actually took place when Newton looked to the moon to verify the hypothesis of gravity. The observed motion failed to agree with his prediction and, realizing that brute fact must always win over beautiful hypothesis, Newton placed his papers in a drawer where they remained for twenty years. When finally a French expedition had made a more accurate measurement of the circumference of the earth, Newton saw that his original calculation had been based on an erroneous conception of the size of the earth. With the new figures, the old observations of the moon agreed precisely with the theory. Only then did he publish the law of gravity, a law of nature which no Bacon could have extracted from long lists of random observations of the world and which no Descartes could have brought forth by pure reason. We will note, parenthetically, that Newton's curiosity was stimulated not only by a small falling apple, but by the puzzling spectacle of a very large apple, the moon, which for no good reason is found hanging in mid-air.

The law of gravity continued successfully to explain and predict the motion of material bodies, achieving its most dramatic success (and thus support) when, in the nineteenth century, astronomers observed certain disturbances in the motion of the planets. It was assumed that *if the law of gravity were valid* these perturbations might be explained by postulating the existence of a large body of matter in a certain spot in the heavens. When the telescopes were fixed on the indicated point, a large new planet was found, exactly according to prediction. Thus was Neptune discovered in 1846.

The scientific method, so beautifully displayed in this discovery of Newton's, *combines* the technics of empiricism and deduction. Experiments or simple observations lead to individual facts without status as generalizations. The scientist examines these facts and attempts to make sense of them by devising some general explanation to account for them. This is the hypothesis, and if the scientist omits to frame a hypothesis, as did Bacon and the first biologist at the beginning of our chapter, he can proceed no further. For the hypothesis and not random chance should guide the scientist to his next observations. If the hypothesis is true, reasons the scientist hopefully, thus and so should be taking place in the observable world, and the hypothesis can be put to the test. If the predictions are confirmed, a new scientific generalization is on its way into being; if the test fails, the hypothesis needs to be mended or abandoned.

At times in science, as we shall later remark, hypotheses have been formulated that are effectively empty because they are impossible of experimental refutation. For any proposition to embody a possible truth about the world, it must also embody a possible falsehood. Since we proceed by asking nature questions, we learn nothing from her answers if the question is formulated so that the answer must be "yes." One example of this sort of thing from psychology is the improper use of the concept of reaction formation. If the observer postulates that an individual has a certain pattern of emotional impulses and then examines him and finds this pattern, all is well and the hypothesis is correct. But if he examines him and does not find the pattern, as often as not it is concluded that the individual does have the pattern but is covering up by reaction formation, so that the hypothesis still remains intact. Employed in this way hypotheses are useless, for they lead to no progress in the acquisition of knowledge. Clearly, this was the error of our second biologist. His hypothesis involved a metaphysical "principle of life," and no matter what he observed next the hypothesis would endure, for there could be no way of knowing whether the observed phenomena were or were not compatible with the existence of such a principle. We presume that the principle could do anything and hence no event could refute it. This procedure is not science, but, in the phrase of Needham, mere gap-filling after the fashion of Columbus's mapmaker who wrote, "Where Unknown, there place Terrors."

We are left then with Peter, the rat, as the last defender of the bastion of science. He, it seems, made an observation when he saw the blinking light, and we cannot deny that he formed a hypothesis when he decided that the light meant food. Its confirmation by trial led him to the discovery of a little "law" of nature. A scientist is rather like a rat in a maze. Both proceed by observation, insight, hypothesis, and trial, and for both, the hypothesis may arise from mere hunch. As we shall see, the invention of hypothesis is the truly creative part of science. It is perhaps this phenomenon that most emphatically distinguishes Peter from Newton.

CHAPTER IV

BIOLOGY BECOMES A SCIENCE

Perish those who said our good things before we did.
—Aelius Donatus, fourth century A.D.

With the Renaissance came a newer closeness to nature. For reasons that continue to intrigue scholars, the new age was marked by a return to classical culture, and a knowledge of classical literature became the mark of an educated gentleman. The culture of the period triumphantly crossed national boundaries and flourished in the exuberance of its freedom, for the new culture was outside and independent of, indeed sometimes hostile to, the Church. The new man was an independent man, an autonomous, versatile, creative man, and, for the first time, his interests turned toward nature, humanism, and art. Painting began to display nature with painstaking and unaccustomed realism, and the observational accuracy of the painter gained new dimensions with the first use of perspective and realistic treatments of light and shadow.

The new interest in nature revealed itself on every side: in the artist's landscapes, his nudes, and in the bawdy tales of Rabelais. And inevitably it became part of the new science as men began to inquire, for the first time in centuries, into the nature of life.

The paradox of William Harvey

One of the disquieting things about writing history, especially intellectual history, is the almost universal absence of clear boundaries between periods of darkness and light. Instead, we find in the cases where some individual is considered the "first" to have expressed a revolutionary idea that more often than not his greatness was conferred upon him by a posterity that could appreciate the achievement in the light of what came after. But in the immediate times of great thought and great works, one often witnesses the puzzling spectacle of an era oblivious to its own innovations or, what is more distracting to those of us who like our heroes unsullied, we find the great men themselves taking inconsistent positions, suggesting that they failed fully to understand the essential meaning of their own contribution. And, of course, we can almost always find, if we look hard enough, intimations of a novel idea in the thought of earlier times, so that we may feel deprived of the high drama which rightly befits the excelsior cry of genius.

Such considerations have particular relevance when we set about attempting to ordain someone the "father of modern biology." Usually this designation is given to William Harvey. In the early 1600's, Harvey observed that the beating heart expelled the blood within it. He then reasoned: if the heart contains two ounces of blood and beats sixty-five times each minute, then it must eject into the body over ten pounds of blood per minute. It had previously been thought that blood was derived from the food that is eaten. But one cannot imagine ten pounds of blood being formed anew each minute from the amount of food a man consumes. Reflection on this observation and simple deduction led Harvey to postulate that blood expelled by the heart must circulate through the body whence it returns to the heart. He then performed experiments to investigate the hypothesis. He showed that obstruction of a vein causes pooling of blood on the side of the obstruction away from the heart. He showed that the bleeding arises from the nearest end to the heart of a severed artery and the farthest end of a severed vein. And he demonstrated with elegant simplicity the function of the venous valves, concerning which he wrote that "so provident a cause as nature had not so plac'd many valves without design."

Harvey's discovery of the circulation of the blood in man was a monumental and many-sided contribution to science. In the first place, it discredited the beliefs of fourteen centuries that the heart was not a muscular organ and that the blood passed through the septum between the right and left ventricles. In addition, Harvey knowingly or unknowingly utilized the scientific method in almost astoundingly modern fashion; and, finally, he bolstered his already incontrovertible claim to immortality by conceiving the heart as a pump, for in this notion Harvey heralded a new view concerning living organisms—though as we will see he did not appreciate the meaning of his own work on this score. But to his successors his work gave proof to the concept that life, like the rest of the universe, could also be viewed as a material machine. Descartes was quick to praise Harvey for "having broken the ice in this matter," and in his own discourses he relied heavily on the work of Harvey to illustrate the mechanical nature of living objects. Their only difference from man-made machines, he insisted, was in the degree of complexity. With these assertions, sudden new excitement entered the realm of biological thought. For it now seemed reasonable that if the living organism were a material mechanism then it, too, could be investigated by the new method of science.

The paradox I have referred to arose in the following way. We have noted that antagonism to Aristotelian philosophy was the great common denominator of all the currents and trends of thought which led to the beginnings of modern science in the seventeenth century. Yet despite his weighty achievement and despite the powerful currents in the main stream of thought, Harvey considered himself fundamentally not to have broken with the past. It turns out when we examine his words that he believed himself finally to have proved the main tenets of the physiology of Aristotle:

> I begin to think whether there might not be a motion, as it were, in a circle. Now this I afterwards found to be true. . . . Which motion we may be allowed to call circular, in the same way as Aristotle says that air and the rain emulate the circular motion of the superior bodies; for the moist earth, warmed by the sun, evaporates; the vapors drawn upwards are condensed, and descending in the form of rain, moisten the earth again; and by this arrangement are generations of living things produced; and in like manner too are tempests and meteors engendered by the circular motion, and by the approach and recession of the sun.
>
> And so, in all likelihood, does it come to pass in the body, through the motion of the blood; the various parts are nourished, cherished, quickened by the warmer, more perfect, vaporous, spirituous, and, as I may say, alimentive blood; which, on the contrary, in contact with these parts becomes cooled, coagulated, and, so to speak, effete; whence it returns to its sovereign the heart, as if to its source, or to the inmost home of the body, there to recover its state of excellence or perfection. Here it resumes its due fluidity and receives an infusion of natural heat–powerful, fervid, a kind of treasury of life, and is impregnated with spirits, and it might be said with balsam; and thence it is again dispersed; and all this depends on the motion and action of the heart. . . .
>
> The heart, consequently, is the beginning of life; the sun of the microcosm, even as the sun in his turn

> might well be designated the heart of the world for it is the heart . . . which . . . is indeed the foundation of life, the source of all action.

This is florid and fanciful, and one recent writer (Wightman) dismisses this passage with the observation that Harvey was simply a man of his times and did not easily throw off the wordy inanities of scholasticism. But Walter Pagel tells us that in this passage the main thesis of Aristotle's world view is defended: the excellence of the circular motion and the parallelism between the macrocosm and the microcosm, that is, the universe and the living organism.

It thus appears that Harvey not only launched the great biological debate between mechanism and mysticism that rages to the present day, but, grotesquely and paradoxically, he became the leader of both sides of the argument. Descartes, for example, although anxious to avoid offense, for he well knew the fate of Galileo, did nevertheless displease many churchmen by his defense of the mechanistic view implicit in Harvey's work. Samuel Parker, Bishop of Oxford, declared that "mechanical philosophy is quite unfit for solving the problems of phenomena" and that Descartes along with Gassendi and Hobbes was one of the three most dangerous atheists of the age! Likewise, segments of secular opinion rebelled at the thought of a living machine.

Yet, Harvey himself leaned away from mechanistic ideas toward vitalism. He spoke often of life residing, revealing itself and the soul, in the blood where "the vital principle itself has its seat." Just as there exists in the semen, says Harvey, something which makes it generative and exceeds the powers of the elements in building an animal, there dwells in the blood some power which acts beyond the power of the elements. We have already encountered this notion in the thought of Aristotle. The vital principle, says Harvey with Aristotle, is nonmaterial.

Perhaps, then, it is proper that the great Harvey be

known as the father of biology, for the paradox he represents has been a leitmotiv behind all that has happened since. Two main currents of biological thought have crossed the centuries: the vitalistic view and the mechanistic. And, though neither originated with Harvey, both received substantial nourishment at his hands. The scientific method attests to the validity of Harvey's brilliant mechanistic discovery. What value we may place upon his nonempirical ideas is another matter. It is difficult to say how one can evaluate any vitalistic conception since no observation that could be made would rule it out. But, as we shall later observe, this has been no bar to believers in vitalism. In thinking of Harvey, one is reminded of the remark that Einstein is said to have made when asked for his opinion of Schrödinger's treatise on wave mechanics, whose conclusions Einstein felt were not justified by the data: "I enjoyed the data, but I didn't read the novel."

In any event, Harvey's great discovery did what too long needed doing. It launched biology as a science.

Corpse dissection: the decline and fall of Galenism

A debate over whether life has a special mystical nature is, in one sense, a debate over whether biology is fundamentally different from physics as a field of inquiry. The physicist looks at the inanimate world and, using the scientific method, elucidates its laws. If there is no difference between the two, the biologist should do likewise and with equal success. With Harvey, he began doing precisely that.

And yet there are differences between biology and physics. Biology faces a more difficult problem, for the complexity of life is built upon the complexity of matter and hence longer years were needed to scrape away the thicker shell of myth to get at the core of valid inquiry. For this reason alone, philosophy in the seventeenth century was dominated by physics, while the science of living organisms has only recently begun to make its impress upon philosophy. Biology offered grave difficulties to the early experimentalists who desired to use the scientific method on the problem of life but who possessed no unifying theories or hypotheses to guide their efforts. For long years, the only generalization that biology could claim was that life existed in many shapes and guises, and it was precisely this meager conception that dominated most of the early work. Its long early years were devoted to the task of *description*, for, as in all sciences in their formative phase, one must look and examine before seeking explanations.

Description flourished in the first century of scientific biology, and the hallmark of the new awakening became *anatomy*, the very epitome of systematic description—and if we must name a "father of anatomy" it is the inexhaustible Andreas Vesalius, who lived from 1514 to 1564. The Renaissance was the heir to a medical orthodoxy whose force and supremacy exactly paralleled the phenomenon of Aristotelianism in philosophy. The great physician of antiquity who remained unquestioned for 1,300 years was Galen, who lived from A.D. 130 to 200. A courtier of rank, a fashionable practitioner of imperial Rome, the last great physician of the ancient world, Galen began his career as surgeon to the gladiators and ended it as physician to the Emperor Marcus Aurelius. For thirteen centuries, Galen stood as the final authority on anatomy despite the fact that the nearest creature to man to be dissected by him was the ape, and he was not always careful to avoid drawing conclusions from one to the other despite his warnings to other anatomists of the dangers of such a practice.

Why was his influence equaled only by Aristotle's? George Sarton suggests that there were many reasons, most of them irrational. Galen endeared himself to the early religionists, who saw in him an ally who could bolster their theological views with the authority of science. And again, we must remark on the difference between a man and the dogmatism erected in his name. We cannot blame Galen for the idolatrous acceptance of his erroneous views by men who had every opportunity to learn the truth for themselves.

But practically no one thought of doing so until Vesalius. It is a remarkable fact, as Ashley Montagu pointed out, that the two books which most scholars agree mark the end of the Middle Ages were published within one week of each other. The first, *De revolutionibus orbium coelestium* by the Polish canon Copernicus, was published in Nürnberg on May 25, 1543, when the author was seventy years old, while the second, *De humani corporis fabrica libri septem,* was published at Basel on June 1, 1543, when its author, Vesalius, was twenty-eight years old.

It is difficult to fathom the real nature of Vesalius's contribution, for one can scarcely imagine why the world had to wait so long for a man who could write down what his eyes perceived. Vesalius was not the first to dissect the human body. Dissection and the witnessing of surgery became part of the curriculum of the Italian medical schools as early as the eleventh century, and by the middle of the thirteenth century the practice was fairly well organized in the universities of Salerno, Bologna, and Padua. One might suppose that the misleading errors of Galen could have easily been corrected by several hundred years of firsthand dissecting experience. But though the old editions of Galen became encrusted with marginalia, the medieval respect for classical authority knew no limit. Progress, it seems, was not to take place.

One reason for the stalemate should amuse anyone familiar with the inmost secrets of modern medicine, for the situation has not changed very much. It was the antagonism between the physicians and surgeons. In those days, the physicians, having received an essentially literary and philosophical education, looked with contempt upon the surgeons, who were mere technicians. In the dissecting theater, the surgeon would wield the knife while the professor lectured platitudes and "demonstrated" items of interest as they were dug up by the surgeon. Occasionally, to the delight of the students, great flatulent professorial debates would arise between visiting philosophical disciples of Aristotle and the medical followers of Galen. And while the discourse ebbed and flowed, the poor surgeon hacked away with his miserable implements, unnoticed except for an occasional epithet hurled from the cathedra. Is there any wonder that anatomy made no progress?

In considering the work of Vesalius, we again encounter the question that was raised in discussing Harvey —about the difficulties surrounding any effort to trace an innovation to its source. In a stimulating essay called "Vesalius and the Galenists," Ashley Montagu points out that for some reason Vesalius has become the romantic hero of an allegory about good and evil, a knight-errant who with sudden clear-mindedness struck down the living remnants of the Middle Ages who had lingered on into the Renaissance.

The truth is, however, that early sixteenth-century anatomists had already begun drifting toward a reliance upon observations rather than authority. The new spirit was clearly evident in the work of Carpi, Massa, and the brilliantly versatile Leonardo da Vinci, all predecessors of Vesalius who must surely have influenced him. In the *Fabrica,* therefore, Vesalius was, in fact, continuing an existing trend. Nevertheless, the work of Vesalius was prosecuted on a grand scale, and his individual contribution was gigantic.

In the *Fabrica,* Vesalius determined not only to give a systematic and accurate description of all parts of the human body but to present his work in as elegant a setting as graphic art would allow. He fretted over the publication, insisting on the finest engravers, that the paper should be strong and of uniform thickness, that every detail of every picture must be clearly visible. The work was based on the experience of five years' dissections, some of which were performed on decaying corpses taken from the gallows. The volume as published in 1543 contained 663 folio pages, 278 magnificent woodcuts, and numerous decorative historiated initials, one of which depicted a "resurrection" scene in the dissecting room. Truly, it is one of the great books of the world. Anatomy books to this day stand or fall by the quality of their drawings. From this standpoint, the *Fabrica* remains the most superb anatomical treatise ever to have been published.

Perhaps the tendency of later generations to fictionalize upon Vesalius is an inevitable consequence of his extraordinary bumptiousness and the staggering torrent of controversy engendered by his work and personality. The publication of the *Fabrica* shook the medical world to its foundations. His old teachers, among them Sylvius of Paris (who had been planning an anatomy book of his own) rose up in fury at this mad young usurper who dared challenge not only their own but Galen's authority. Although Vesalius mentioned no names, Sylvius felt the sting of words such as these, wherein Vesalius, speaking of his attempt to make his anatomy complete, writes:

> But this effort could by no manner of means have succeeded if, when I was studying medicine at Paris, I had not myself applied my hand to this business, but had acquiesced in the casual and superficial display to me and my fellow-students by certain barbers of a few organs at one or two public dissections. For in such perfunctory manner was anatomy then treated in the place where we have lived to see medicine happily reborn . . . except for eight muscles of the abdomen, disgracefully mangled and in the wrong order, no one (I speak the simple truth) ever demonstrated to me any single muscle, or any single bone, much less the network of nerves, veins, and arteries.

Of the hysterical and continuing attacks that were launched against Vesalius, Montagu assures us that the resentment was a personal one directed against the objectionable imperiousness and youth of its object. "It was not a school of thought," says Montagu, "which through its followers was hostile to Vesalius but frustrated individuals who seized upon Vesalius's criticism of Galen as a peg upon which to hang their abuse of the critic." The vaunted break with Galenism does not withstand scrutiny. Vesalius, like Harvey, considered himself to have remained in the antiquarian tradition. Though he criticized Galen (sometimes unfairly), he remained a Galenist, and this kinship is clear in Vesalius's work which held continuously to most of Galen's metaphysical ideas.

A first-class historical mystery surrounds the life of Vesalius subsequent to his triumphant publication of the *Fabrica* at the age of twenty-eight, for this event marked the end of his achievement in the history of science. Although anatomy now became Vesalian, Vesalius passed into the background. He left his chair as Professor of Anatomy at Padua and became physician to the Emperor Charles V, an unexplained withdrawal from a brilliant academic life that has caused much conjecture among historians.

Some have suggested that in such an appointment Vesalius hoped to find protection from the persecutions of his enemies. Another theory was that he needed money after the expensive publication of the *Fabrica*. Others have guessed that he feared ecclesiastical retribution as a result of having rifled graves and desecrated bodies. One unsupported story has it that Vesalius, while in the Court of Spain, undertook the dissection of a young woman whom he had attended. When the body was opened, the spectators were horrified to see the heart beating. Following this catastrophe, Vesalius undertook a pilgrimage to the Holy Land in order to avoid the Inquisition, a journey on which he met death at the age of fifty.

The most reasonable speculation seems to be that of O'Malley and Saunders, who consider Vesalius's rejection of his pre-eminent position to be entirely logical behavior for a man whose world was "guided by conceptions of a universal order derived from Platonic thinking." To him, therefore, the ultimate aim of the physician was the perfection of the medical art, attainable only through its practice. To modern physicians who cling to the academy, such an idea may come as an inspirational challenge.

And so, regardless of the identity of its author, a break had now taken place with the meager but powerful tradition of ancient biological thought. It began when anatomy became a systematic body of observational data upon which the questions of how, why, and whence could be intelligently asked.

The microcosm grows smaller

There is something magnificently obvious about cutting a man open and peering at his insides. Even a child contemplating his navel might think of trying it. But how could anyone reasonably be expected to assume the existence of a subworld of living creatures too small to be seen by the naked eye? The fact is no one did assume it until long after the lens grinders and spectaclemakers had placed into the hands of curiosity mongers powerful magnifying glasses of very short focus.

Although a number of individuals glimpsed at seeds and bugs through their new lenses, two men may be singled out as the first to realize the full importance of studying nature with instruments capable of increasing the power of the human senses. One was the brilliant Malpighi of Bologna (1628–1694), whose long catalogue of microscopic discoveries included the tiny capillaries—which elegantly completed the circulatory pathway discovered by Harvey—and the fine structure of the kidney. The other was the Englishman Robert Hooke.

His point of view was put forth convincingly in a remarkable book published in 1665 under the imprimatur of the Royal Society. We have already encountered Hooke as the assistant of Boyle and a source of irritation to Isaac Newton. Hooke, who lived from 1635 to 1703, had a fascinating career. "Curator of experiments" for the Royal Society, Hooke was a master mechanic in an age when there were still a few laws left which a mechanic could discover. In the early days of the Royal Society, its meetings were rather like circuses at which the members demonstrated their latest discoveries. Hooke was the fuss-budget who could always be seen tinkering with the equipment and superintending its operation. He became enamored of metal springs, invented carriage springs and the spiral watch spring, and, by observing that within the limit of elasticity the stretch of a spring is proportional to the stress put upon it, he discovered the law which bears his name. He drollishly published this discovery as an anagram, *ceiiinosssttuu,* and waited two years before disclosing its solution, "*ut tensio sic uis*" ("the power of any spring is in the same proportion with the tension thereof"). It is a manner of scientific communication which never became popular.

The treatise on microscopy was called *The Micrographia; or Some Physiological Descriptions of Minute Bodies Made by Magnifying Glasses and Enquiries Thereupon.* With this work, Hooke launched his study of microscopic anatomy, a purely descriptive voyage through an unknown sea, but one destined in later years to lead to the central discovery of biology, the cell. Upon examining a piece of cork, Hooke perceived it "to be all perforated and porus much like a Honey-comb, but that the pores of it were not regular; yet it was not unlike a Honey-comb in these particulars: first, in that it had a very solid substance, in comparison of the empty cavity that was contained between; next in that these pores, or cells, were not very deep, but consisted of a great many little Boxes, separated out of one continued Long pore, by certain Diaphragms." He was viewing, of course, only the thickened walls of dead cells, but in later notes he recorded similar divisions in the surfaces of living nettle leaves. Hooke was the first to have described living cells but not the last to fail to understand their true nature. It is, incidentally, often lamented that he termed these structures *cells*. Cell means "little room" and that is what Hooke thought these spaces were. In the light of later developments, corpuscles—"little bodies"—would have been more appropriate.

Hooke's contemporaries viewed this new world with considerable excitement, although Samuel Pepys complained that the cost of his microscope, £5/10/–, was a "great price for a curious bauble." The microscopic century was climaxed by the classic contributions of three great men: Johannes Swammerdam of Amsterdam, who saw the red cells in the blood of a frog; and the London physician Nehemiah Grew, who rediscovered the cells of Hooke, calling them "utricles" and "vesicles" but still failed to see the contents of the little rooms. The third was Leeuwenhoek.

Antony van Leeuwenhoek, the lens grinder of Delft, was as eccentric a character as one is likely to meet in the chronicles of science, although at times I suspect his biographers of making too much of a good thing. That he was garrulous, suspicious, gossipy, and contentious is obvious from his own writings, but as Paul de Kruif depicts him in *Microbe Hunters* his performance borders on the slapstick. This is, of course, far from a scholarly book, but it does seem to have colored and to have been colored by the stereotyped image of poor old Leeuwenhoek. It is my impression that his eccentricity vanishes as soon as one ceases making foolish comparisons between this man and his contemporaries of the Royal Society of England, many of whom have passed irretrievably into oblivion. Fortunately, Latinity was not then and is not now a prerequisite for intelligence and skill.

What we do know is that Leeuwenhoek's contributions were monumental. Using lenses of his own making, he patiently examined the microscopic structure of everything he could place his hands on, and, at the request of the newly founded Royal Society, reported his discoveries in a series of communications that went forth without interruption for over fifty years. He found in rain water a subvisible world of swimming creatures and wrote the first description of bacteria. To doubters, he offered affidavits from prominent citizens of Delft who had seen the "wretched beasties." He did not, of course, relate them to human disease. He discovered blood cells, and as de Kruif so turgidly put it, "The most sacred and improper and romantic things in life were only material for the probing, tireless eyes of his lenses. Leeuwenhoek discovered the human sperm, and the cold-blooded science of his searching would have been shocking, if he had not been such a completely innocent man!" At one point, he declared he had seen within a sperm a whole tiny man. In his famous letter of 1674, Leeuwenhoek first described protozoan organisms of pond water. Before dispatching his last communication at the age of ninety-one, he had told the Royal Society of an infinite variety of microscopic life. To the end, he refused to disclose his methods of study.

Curiously, the death of Leeuwenhoek in 1723 ended the first inquisitive phase of biological microscopy. The age had achieved the pioneer discoveries in a wide range of fields; in general, however, it emphasized what we now call histology rather than cytology. According to Woodruff, the attempt of that time to envisage biological truth from the data at hand was premature because of their superficiality. As Peattie wrote, "We have the feeling that the men of that age were coasting along golden shores that were hidden from them in thin mists, and that with a little more perseverance, vision, and daring, they would have had a landfall of twentieth century discovery." Although cells had been seen, their nature remained unknown until 1838, 173 years after Hooke's examination of a piece of cork.

The power of the past was now broken and the new groundwork laid. With the piling up of triumphs for the scientific method, with the realization that living things were accessible to scientific investigation, with the proliferation of printing, books, and writing, modern biology came at last into its own.

CHAPTER V

THE FUTILE SEARCH FOR CERTAINTY

An idealist is one who, on noticing that a rose smells better than a cabbage, concludes it will also make better soup.

—H. L. Mencken

It has been stated that, compared to the mathematical and physical sciences, biology is an immature youth. Perhaps this is so. But when they start off in search of certain knowledge, biologists and physicists start together and, in the course of things, they meet the same fate.

Sigmund and the amoeba: a scientific fable

There once was a very earnest young man whom we shall call Sigmund. For some deep-seated psychological reason, he was determined to learn the secret of life, and, in pursuit of this goal, he studied long years in three or four great universities. He drank deep from the well-springs of knowledge and, in time, read just about every word that had ever been written on the nature of life. His plan was ambitious but simple: first he would learn everything that was already known; then, with this behind him, he would enter the laboratory and there, by the force of will and intelligence, wrest life's secret from the limbo of ignorance. The great new edifice of learning that he dreamed of building would be clean and compelling, free of ancient controversy, and—this was the important part—*devoid of all uncertainty.* From his studies, he was confident, would come ultimate knowledge. No one before had ever prepared so diligently for a great crusade against ignorance and error.

The truth of the matter is that Sigmund was obsessed. For example, he simply could not examine the work of other scientists without finding fundamental defects. Either experiments were improperly designed or they rested upon unproved suppositions; he found frequent failures to control the variables in an experiment and occasional failures even to recognize what the variables were. His judgment in such matters was usually quite sound, but, lamentably, he *always* had some fault to find.

In his hunger for broad, wonderful, consummate understanding, Sigmund laid plans for the perfect experiment in which everything would be controlled and which, therefore, would of necessity yield ultimate knowledge. Though otherwise an entirely admirable young chap, this singular resolution was his undoing, as we shall see.

When he was finally ready to begin his experiments, Sigmund said, "The basic unit of life is the cell. Therefore, the best procedure would be to start off by elucidating the nature of the cell. Let me see now. . . ." And he began to consider how best to procure a single cell for his experiments. He realized, of course, that most living things contained many cells, but he knew of no tools that could be relied upon to snip one off without damaging it. True, bacteria are single-celled organisms, but it seemed likely that their ceaseless reproductive activity might be a source of distraction. How could one make any headway with a microbe if, while being observed, it insisted on dissolving into two offspring and, in a manner of speaking, ceasing really to exist?

But the year was growing older and a choice had to be made, so Sigmund finally selected the amoeba as his experimental object. It, too, kept multiplying, but there were periods of quiescence. Perhaps one could get something done in these occasional intervals. After a number of maddening encounters with the university purchasing office and several fruitless trips to nearby stagnant pools, he finally succeeded in obtaining some amoebae from a wholesale supply house—that is, what he obtained was a bottle labeled "amoebae." Sigmund peered at them under a microscope: they certainly looked like what amoebae are supposed to look like. But were they amoebae *beyond all doubt?* The question flustered Sigmund, for he realized he was standing face to face with his first test of mettle. He could not permit his work to be questioned on the ground that he hadn't proved he was working with amoebae.

And so he began a systematic investigation to prove that the tiny organism was indeed an amoeba. It is of incidental interest that for the first several months of his laboratory career, Sigmund made one asinine blunder after another. He dropped glassware; he burned his elbow in the Bunsen burner flame one day; once he accidentally swallowed a few of his best specimens while transferring them with a pipette; and there was the time he knocked a whole tank of amoebae onto the floor and had to get a new supply which he couldn't be certain were the same as the ones he'd already been studying so that he had to start all over. These unfortunate errors, inevitable in the life of every beginner, were perhaps slightly more frequent in Sigmund's early experience because his previous training had been only in theory and not in the use of the hands. Nevertheless, Sigmund's department chairman defended him at an emergency meeting of the university's Research Committee, and privately he said, "Pull yourself together, boy! You've got what it takes!"

And in time Sigmund did learn. In fact, he eventually

became a master of laboratory technic, an ingenious and resourceful perfectionist. The work began to move along rapidly. He succeeded in demonstrating that the best descriptions that had ever been given of amoebae did indeed apply to his specimens but he wisely realized that *all* the characteristics of the amoeba had not yet been described because these were limitless. An organism has as many characteristics as the human imagination could think to look for. This was followed by the realization that the word "amoeba" was defined in the first place by someone who pointed to an organism, listed a few of its traits—such as shape, motility, littleness —and then exclaimed in a public place, "This thing here is to be known as an amoeba!"

It must then follow, Sigmund reasoned, that every possessor of these few characteristics must be an amoeba. But he quickly found that it was far from simple to show with certainty whether the organism before him did or did not have the qualities amoebae are supposed to have. Some were a little too large, others seemed the wrong color, and, on the day in question, there was a chill in the air, and they were anything but motile. Sigmund tried another batch which someone had brought him, and joyfully he found that these creatures *did* have the right qualities—but, the next afternoon, in the silence of his laboratory, Sigmund realized they were singing! There they were, looking for all the world like amoebae, but if you listened carefully at the mouth of their bottle, you could hear piping little voices. This was something whose presence or absence the original definer of amoeba had not even mentioned, and it was now too late to have another look at his specimens, since they had long since died or divided down the middle. And so it was a bit difficult to say *with certainty* just what was and what was not an amoeba. "It doesn't make any difference," cried Sigmund. "This is a verbal question and I shall call these beasts anything I please! They're alive and that's what matters."

It was a wise decision because within the group of amoebae which he had obtained from the supply house, Sigmund soon found that some contained enzyme X and others didn't. So he classified the organisms as *amoebae (Sigmund type) strain X* and *strain O*. Then he discovered that some contained enzyme Y and others didn't, but this had no apparent connection with X since some of the X's had Y and some of the O's had Y. He made a large chart to list these findings and it soon became very complicated, suggesting either that there were many types of amoebae *or* that the word "amoeba" referred only to an arbitrary minimum number of traits—in which case "amoeba-ness" was all in the way you looked at it.

A psychoanalyst acquaintance who occasionally looked in on Sigmund would always scowl at the chart and mutter significantly, but Sigmund courteously said nothing. "If I can't recognize an amoeba when I see it," he thought to himself, "what, in the name of Heaven, must this poor man be up against in his work?"

Wearying of classification and tabulation, Sigmund decided he could delay no longer. He would select one amoeba, determine its type, and use it for his serious studies. He examined the chart and picked out the category: *amoeba (Sigmund type) strain* $X\text{-}Y\text{-}Q^{+}_{r}$, *subgroup Φ, bilobed nucleus, life span 2.3 days, master IBM number 21–6095–N*. At this point he had a major setback, for he found that in order to select an amoeba of the desired type, he would have to test many, and in the testing he would make the organisms unfit for further study, fatiguing them dreadfully as he put them through their paces and, in the end, destroying them (in the life-span test). He was literally forced to reach into the tank, select something that looked more or less like an amoeba, and accept the bitter fact that he could not both know its type and study it. Because of his desire for certainty, this development was most upsetting. He decided to brazen it out and somehow repress his anxiety. "Intellectually," he told himself, "I am capable of reaching my goal."

The months went by and the experiments became more and more frustrating. Sigmund found out many interesting things about his amoebae, but the only experiments that seemed to yield information contained also the seeds of doubt. No matter what happened, Sigmund could always ask *why* it happened and a new chilly vault of ignorance would swing open. For example, every experimental manipulation disturbed the amoeba and introduced an unnatural factor into its environment. Sigmund wanted to know how it behaved in its natural environment but he could know nothing unless he examined it—and to examine it he must take it from its natural environment. Despite the brilliance and subtlety of his technic, his amoebae had to be prodded, illuminated, asphyxiated, peered at under ultraviolet lamps and otherwise distracted. He scorned statistical methods of analyzing results because, by their very nature, they gave approximate answers, not certain ones.

Self-doubt gnawed away at Sigmund's emotional structure. He developed migraine and insomnia, and two doctors (he always consulted two doctors) told him he had colitis. For one week he switched from amoebae to white mice but hysterically switched back again. He grew more intense and worked longer and longer hours. Each night he worked later in his laboratory and, though young couples could sometimes be seen strolling across the starlit campus, Sigmund never saw them. To control every last factor in the environment, he wheeled in larger and larger pieces of electronic equipment. If the amoeba excreted something into its surrounding fluid, an electronic device would detect this, quickly withdraw the fluid, and replace it with a fresh medium, impeccably correct in composition. Sigmund began to realize that if he could not soon bring his experiments to a successful conclusion, he would have a serious breakdown. And so he sat down to plan the culminating experience of his life, his perfect experiment. Sitting there at his desk, Sigmund looked rather like a plant that had been grown in a cave.

At last came the night, the night of the climactic experiment. He entered his crowded laboratory and looked around with satisfaction. The experiment would utilize all his equipment, skill, and judgment. There could be no failure because every circumstance had been allowed for. From this night, thought Sigmund, will come the secret of life. He adjusted the dials with loving care and introduced the amoeba into its chamber, convinced that every possible whim of the tiny animal had been foreseen. Here it would be comfortable and in its gratification would reveal all its mysteries to the now trembling scientist.

The experiment began. Recording devices began clicking efficiently. Large tubes glowed and flickered on and off. Sigmund maneuvered the micromanipulator and looked intently at the cathode-ray oscillograph. The seconds ticked by and Sigmund knew that his fingers were now circled round the answer he sought. In a split second more, he would clench them closed and seize it forever.

But suddenly a spark flew between two inadequately insulated wires that were hanging just behind and to the left of Sigmund's head. He had badly overloaded the electrical circuits despite repeated warnings from the university engineer. The flash of fire ignited the vapors that were seeping out of an improperly constructed solvent locker, and within seconds the laboratory was a roaring inferno. Poor Sigmund, along with the entire Science Building was quickly burned to a crisp. As the raging flames thrust skyward, a thunderous explosion rocked the sleeping campus, producing a crater in the ground of sizable proportions.

The next day the university authorities, surveying the tragic scene, couldn't help but feel that the whole regrettable affair was not without its redeeming features. In order to build a new Science Building, they had been planning at great cost to tear down the old one and now this had been done for them. As a matter of fact, the excavation in the basement for the new cyclotron had also been seen to, and, despite the fact that Sigmund's research grant had been irrevocably lost, they were some thirty or forty thousand dollars ahead, not even counting the insurance. This, they decided unanimously, would be put into the new building and into its research programs and fellowships.

They gave the first grant to a fellow named Glickman, a brilliant young fellow, who had some rather advanced ideas about biology. It was he who launched the first experiments in the new Science Building when, at last, it was erected.

Our most cherished illusion

If men had either to be Romanticists or Classicists, Sigmund would surely have been a Romantic, for it is clear that he thought of his crusade in terms of the Infinite, and that to him science was the highroad to omnipotence. Certainly no resigned, inflexible, pipe-smoking, Classicist sense of proportion ever tainted his point of view. True, he was a misfit, an inner-directed Outsider in all likelihood, and yet had it not been for ill fortune, he might have achieved his mission and immortality—or so it would seem. As it turned out, however, Sigmund's sublime moment turned him into a cinder instead of a saint.

Can this melancholy tale instruct us? Can we find in Sigmund's footsteps a clue which will spare us his fate? Was his end, as in Greek tragedy, decreed by Inevitability? We must seriously ask these questions because if science is the ascendant force in the modern world, if we are to live with it and by it—or even for it—we must deepen our understanding of what it is and what it is not. For, despite his brilliance, Sigmund's understanding of science was as unsound as his understanding of himself.

As we view the brilliant successes that science and the scientific method have achieved, are we not entitled to conclude that here is the true pathway to certain knowledge? Sadly, it is not, as all its travelers must inevitably discover. To understand why this is so is to understand science, for, in one sense, the history of science is the history of human opinion on the question of certainty.

It is easy to see how the exuberant age of Newton might have come to believe that nature and reason held the key to certain knowledge. In those years, the air had the tang of the concept of progress and the times were imbued with the exciting new belief that human beings could achieve here on this earth a state of happiness and perfection that previous centuries thought possible only for deceased Christians in a state of grace. Reason—in its ordinary meaning—was the new nirvana, for it would lead man to an understanding of nature and supreme truth concerning what is good and right. John Locke emerged as a great philosopher of the new method, vigorously (and often uncritically) defending the principles of empiricism and inductive logic. The age idolized Newton and even Locke in his *Essay Concerning Human Understanding* referred to himself beside the "incomparable Mr. Newton, [as] an under-labourer, employed in clearing the ground and removing some of the rubbish that lies in the way of knowledge." Likewise, the great Laplace remarked that Newton was not only the greatest genius that ever lived, he was also the most fortunate, since there is but one universe and it can therefore be the lot of but one man in history to be the interpreter of its laws.

As the new idea spread through the world of affairs, its impact was felt in every sphere. Free trade replaced protective tariff practices because the way of nature was the way of free and independent competition. Monasticism began to disappear because celibacy made no sense. Men gave up believing that demons caused mental illness and the problem entered the realm of science. Even the high rational standards of the framers of the American Constitution were spiritual exemplars of the Age of Reason. Reason linked with experience was to be the guide to certain truth.

Yet it was not long before a voice of caution was heard in the din. How can one justify the use of inductive logic? asked David Hume, perhaps the greatest of all philosophers who have written in the English language. The answer one thinks of is that it has worked. But, Hume points out, what we are saying is "induction has so far proved successful, therefore it is justified" and this is itself an inductive inference. This is circular reasoning and the argument breaks down: we cannot justify induction and empiricism by induction and empiricism. And with this declaration, Hume brought to a ruinous end the classical age of empiricism. It was Hume's steadfast position that none of man's beliefs can be given the stamp of certainty.

This onslaught on the inductive inference has been answered by modern philosophy. We need say little on the nature of mathematical truth, for all seem agreed (including Hume) that mathematics in no wise contributes anything to the *content* of our knowledge of the world, but is rather an indispensable and powerful instrument for the validation, understanding, and even linguistic expression of such knowledge. But the defense of induction leaves us a little uneasy if certainty is what we desire. Part of the defense rests on the probable character of knowledge that has been mentioned. However, it is clear that a system which yields probable knowledge is vulnerable to the same critique brought by Hume against a system claiming certainty. Perhaps the clearest account of today's thinking on this question is that of Hans Reichenbach, who wrote:

The man who makes inductive inferences may be compared to a fisherman who casts a net into an unknown part of the ocean—he does not know whether he will catch fish, but he knows that if he wants to catch fish he has to cast his net. Every inductive prediction is like casting a net into the ocean of the happenings of nature; we do not know whether we shall have a good catch, but we try, at least, and try by the help of the best means available.

We try because we want to act—and he who wants to act cannot wait until the future has become observational knowledge. To control the future—to shape future happenings according to a plan—presupposes predictive knowledge of what will happen if certain conditions are realized; and if we do not know the truth about what will happen, we shall employ our best posits in the place of truth. Posits are the instruments of action where truth is not available; the justification of induction is that it is the best instrument of action known to us.*

We begin then to perceive how deep go the reasons which bar us from certainty. But other factors also contribute to the folly of such a quest. We have said that an experiment is an act or procedure carried out for the purpose of establishing knowledge. Consider: What do we do when we conduct an experiment? The key word in the answer to this question is *interaction*. Experiments are procedures deliberately designed to produce the *interaction* of some agency under our control with

* This reply of Mr. Reichenbach's to Hume's broadside, though it pleases me, has nevertheless failed to please a number of contemporary philosophers. Witness, Ernest Nagel's critique of Reichenbach's epistemology in *Sovereign Reason* and, more recently, Roy Harrod's brave attempt in *Foundations of Inductive Logic* to show that there are fully valid inductive arguments that require no support from any presupposition whatever regarding the uniformity of nature.

the system or object we are studying. It is the result of these interactions which we perceive. We seldom or never see (or in any way sense) the thing or event itself, but only the results of our manipulations of it. The reason for this is that our senses are incapable of perceiving the phenomena which illustrate most of the general laws. We can see falling objects and, if we are made of the stuff of Newton, we can suspect a natural law. Much is still being learned in biology by pure observation and brute description. This is the basic technic of the taxonomist, and even he is becoming a meddlesome experimentalist. But we cannot see the amount of acid in a test tube unless we add an indicator which becomes colored in the presence of acid (and if we wish to be quantitative we can measure the depth of the color). We cannot see the thyroid gland controlling the body's oxygen consumption unless we intervene and measure the oxygen consumed as we somehow manipulate the thyroid function to make it increase or decrease.

Interaction of some agency with a natural object or system, producing some visible measurable result, is the essence of experiment. It is the implications of *interaction* which spell despair for the one who would seek certain knowledge.

If you look at a cell under the microscope, in most cases you are looking at colored and easily discernible structures made visible by a process of fixation and staining. The fixative hardens the cell in its natural position at the moment of contact (at least we think it does, but how can we be sure without looking at "natural" cells and how can we look at them without fixing and staining them?). Stain reacts chemically with certain substances in the cell making their architectural pattern clearly visible in the microscope (that is, we assume the pattern is not disturbed by the stain, but to verify this we would have to compare the arrangement with that of an unstained cell, where, unfortunately, the pattern is only seen with difficulty).

Thus, we have had to infer what is going on in the unmolested system, an inference often difficult or impossible because we do not know to what extent the experimental intervention disturbed the system under study. Nor can we ever know except by further experiment, and this involves a further dislocation of the phenomenon of unknown and unknowable extent. The interactions we are producing are thus *obstacles* in the quest for certainty. This source of uncertainty is of momentous importance in biology.

It is easy to think of examples which make clear the difficulties involved in this situation. How do we know that the removal of blood from a vein for the purpose of counting the blood cells does not alter the blood count? To check this would necessitate doing blood counts in some way which would not require removal of blood from the body, undeniably, a formidable task. But let's imagine that someone conceived a way of counting the cells in the blood by passing a beam of light through some blood vessels, say, for example, in the ear or finger, and enumerating the cells as they went by. This would require considerable adroitness because the rate of flow of blood through even the smallest capillaries is known to be rapid and erratic. Now, of course, the problem is one of proving that the light which transilluminates the capillaries either does not disturb the blood count in that area or disturbs it to an extent which is uniformly consistent and proportional to the true count. To prove either of these assertions requires some knowledge of the true count and we are right back where we started.

Instances of this sort occur all through biological science. Every experiment or observation is subject to limitations in interpretation imposed by the inexhaustible sources of uncertainty. It is "certainly" true in psychiatry that the chief investigative technic of this science, the interviewing or testing of subjects, imposes influences of greater or lesser psychological importance on the subject —what the subject says, it must be remembered, he is saying in a test situation. What we know of his memory is based on what he tells us. He may not tell all. If he is given a drug to rid him of inhibitions, we must consider that the drug may alter either the faculty of memory or the subject's ability to relate the content of his memory. And so on. Yet, despite the unshakable enigma of the inherent uncertainty in all experiments, why do we talk as though a great deal is known with certainty in biology? We do indeed know a very great deal and are learning more each year. The point here is that everything we know has a *probability value,* an attached tag upon which is written the probability or likelihood that this fact is correct. Never is the fact so certain that the probability of its being false is zero. The probability of truth in many cases is great and rests securely on very good observations, repeatedly made in different laboratories by different investigators. Often, similar results come from several experimental approaches permitting us the reasonable inference that if our manipulations are disturbing the experimental object, at least they are doing so to a similar extent in each of the different types of experiments. For example, if no matter which of the many fundamentally different methods we used to determine the molecular weight of some compound we always got the same answer, probably—very probably—the answer is close to the truth.

It is therefore apparent that any conclusions based on "probably valid" experimental observations will themselves bear the taint. They, too, will have a probability rating, and there is no way in the world of bettering their status except by bettering the data upon which they are based.

A whole new science has arisen to deal with the probability problem: statistical analysis and the science of experimental design. Since the conclusions of scientific research carry an inherent probability rating and are based on experiments that have a certain inherent error, it becomes mandatory to turn to an old reliable helpmate, mathematical analysis, to give us some notion of the value—the degree of probability—of our conclusions. Statistical analysis gives us no new knowledge of the world but it delineates, sometimes in highly quantitative fashion, the *extent of uncertainty* attaching to the knowledge we have elsewhere uncovered. The devices of this type of analysis provide the scientist with accurate statements of the variance of his data, the probability that the results could be attributable to pure chance, clues as to the amount of work or number of experiments he must do in order to make the error of rejecting a correct hypothesis only once, say, in twenty times, an arbitrary decision. (It is surprising how inefficient scientific research can be, unguided by the principles of statistics.) Most important is the direction of the scientist's attention to methods of increasing the sensitivity of succeeding experiments or in some cases to the abandonment of a series of experiments because the factors producing imprecision are clearly beyond control. Finally, statistical methods, generously blended with portions of common sense, are instrumental in determining the design of the experiment.

Experimental design, particularly in a field as complex as biology, is no simple matter, as the late lamented Sigmund found out. It is essential to the experimental method that every system under study be compared with another system with *all* conditions identical except one. In this way, the role of the one factor may be reflected in the index we have chosen to observe. If we are interested in studying the effect of a certain drug in the treatment of some disease, the proper controls must be rigidly set up. If the disease is like most, it will eventually end in spontaneous recovery. Thus, if our unknown drug is administered to the patient, we will necessarily judge it favorably if no more is done. Presumably, this is the kind of "proof" behind the therapeutic use of holy oil, amulets, prayer, and the killing of a goat. For scientific evaluation the needed control is a sufficient number of people of the same age with the same malady each given an imitation of the drug (to control the emotional component in drug-induced recovery) followed by careful comparison of the duration of illness and percentage recovery in the treated and untreated groups.

The one factor being evaluated may be very complex, as typified by sociological problems where, for example, one might wish to compare and analyze the political beliefs of Negroes and white men. The individual components of this factor may or may not be accessible to further clarification, hence the unending contemporary debate: Is sociology a science? Such complexity, as we shall presently see, is not unique to sociology.

PART TWO

THE FIRST GREAT MODERN SYNTHESIS

CHAPTER VI

THE UNIT OF LIFE

> Give me six lines written by the most honorable of men, and I will find an excuse in them to hang him.
>
> —Richelieu, 1625

Physics early achieved a sweepingly unifying conception in the discovery of the indestructibility of energy. And this was precisely what the new biology lacked. Succeeding generations of biologists sought desperately for some point of view which would bring uniformity into the welter of data that had begun to accumulate. Men looked at living organisms, those islands of life which somehow manage to stay afloat in the great sea of nonlife, and wondered. How did life originate? How did "simple" atoms and molecules arrange themselves in elaborate parcels and then come alive? How did they develop the intricate machinery for profitably exchanging matter with the inanimate environment, sucking in food and oxygen, using what is needed and rejecting what is not? How did they acquire the ability to "breed true," men propagating men and microbes microbes while at the same time evolving into millions of different species? How did they learn to repair their wounds, to resist stress, to think, feel, and reason?

We cannot here enter into the details of the history

of biology to which so many have contributed in the years since the Renaissance. Instead, I should like to sketch the emergence of what might be called the modern point of view in several of the key areas of biological thought. The first of these is the notion that the cell is the unit of life, for this was the realization that finally brought to biology its long-wished-for unity.

The cell theory is born

The basic units of matter are atoms, and, true to their etymology, they cannot be split and still retain the attributes of a chemical element. Splitting the atom produces new and incredibly diverse smaller particles, and it is true that some among the subatomic particles do have certain properties in common with intact atoms of elemental matter—mass, for example. But, as we know the elements by their chemical and spectroscopic behavior, we know also that subatoms are not elemental matter but only parts, further divisible perhaps, of enormously more complex wholes. If nothing else, the particles lack the great empty vastnesses of the atom, abysses made of pure vacuum which occupy all but $\frac{1}{1,000,000,000,000}$ (or thereabouts) of the atom's volume.

Those basic properties which we ordinarily associate with the phenomenon of life are *all* possessed by nothing less complex than the cell. Many of the components of the living cell, the "sub-living" systems, may likewise share some of the properties of the living system itself, but the subsystems are not living organisms. The cell is. The biologist's broadening effort to comprehend the cell by intellectually reconstructing it from carefully isolated subsystems and fragments is a major theme of today's biology.

We are taught in school that the cell theory was formulated in 1838 by Schleiden and Schwann; yet the speakers at the 1939 centennial celebration of the cell theory were at great pains to deny that "the idea sprang Minerva-like, fully formed and original from the substance of their brains." The biological historians insisted that a closer reading of the literature of the century indicates that these men had many predecessors who had stated, directly or obliquely, that cells were the units of life. "In spite of all these antecedents," wrote Professor Conklin, "one of the most surprising facts in the history of science is that many texts of biology consider Schleiden founder of the cell theory."

Again we face a familiar question. It is true that by 1835 the cell was beginning to emerge as an entity possessing a life of its own and a complex structure. The time was ripe for a unifying theory stating the cellular nature of all living things—and, as has happened over and over again in science, when times are ripe, realizations come to several individuals simultaneously. If species must evolve then surely so must ideas.

It was in October 1838 that a famous dinner conversation is said to have occurred. Matthias Schleiden was an erratic, volatile character who turned to biology only in 1831 after having already attempted suicide in despondency over his failure as a lawyer. The story is told that shortly after the appearance of his monograph on the microscopic anatomy of plants in *Muller's Archiv*, Schleiden described his work over the coffee cups to Theodor Schwann, the German physiologist who, biographers insist, was a "simple" man. Schwann recognized the similarity of Schleiden's plant cell nuclei to structures he had seen in animal nerve tissue, and the two went immediately to Schwann's laboratory at the Anatomical Institute. Schleiden, too, recognized the similarities of structure. This, according to the more rhapsodic historians of biology, was the dawn of the cell theory.

Actually, Schleiden, in his famous monograph of 1838 and without acknowledging his indebtedness to his predecessors, proposed three conclusions: 1) that plants are composed entirely of cells which are *units of structure, physiology, and organization,* 2) that cells possess *duality,* that is, they are independent lives within a higher form of life, and 3) the main thesis, that there is a common mechanism of cell formation whereby new cells arise by a process analogous to crystal formation. Professor Karling points out that the last conclusion, Schleiden's false theory on cell origin, was also not original. "At that time there were two outstanding views as to how cells arise: first, the view that the nucleus and cell develop from an aggregation and confluence of granules of various sorts in the viscid content of the cell; and second, the view that new cells arise by division of a pre-existing cell." The second view, of course, is the correct one, as we shall mention momentarily. "How unfortunate," wrote Karling, "for biological research of that decade and the reputation of Schwann that Schleiden did not choose the alternative and correct view of his contemporary botanists." Since Schwann agrees with Schleiden on the mechanism of cell formation, he must on this issue stand or fall with Schleiden. As the falsity of the Schleiden and Schwann thesis of cell origin gradually came to light, this part of their work tended to be forgotten and in time their fame was secured by the erroneous belief that they had originated the doctrine of the independence, individuality, and duality of the cell and that it is the fundamental unit of all organisms.

"On the whole," wrote Conklin, "one gets a very unpleasant picture of Schleiden's relations to his predecessors and contemporaries, and the question forces itself on us, 'How did he come to be recognized as the founder of the cell theory?' I once heard a distinguished physiologist say that there are two ways to gain recognition, either brag or fight. It seems to me that Schleiden did both."

It seems to me regrettable that even in science there exists the need to create heroes where none exist. The compulsion to engraft a man's name onto a vast scientific movement seems to lead only to decades and centuries of quibbling. I strongly doubt that Schleiden and Schwann foresaw that their work would raise this issue and I doubt that they would have claimed paternity to the cell theory. It seems sufficient to say that their work was of value, their theory of cell division reasonable in its time. On that question, they were merely wrong. The detracting tone of the centennial essayists would perhaps have been better directed at the anamnestic errors of Schleiden and Schwann's successors.

It has occurred to me that the cell theory is a curious anomaly in the history of science. At no time in its early years did the theory ever seem a theoretical necessity. Instead, it just dribbled into existence, dawning slowly and simultaneously upon many men's minds, unlike the great discoveries of great individuals. Confronted with brute experimental data, Dalton established the basic laws of modern atomic theory. To explain his observations, Darwin was forced to his theory of natural selection. But the cell theory, which surely ranks beside these two, had no such nativity. As we have noted, cells were seen centuries before they were given special meaning by Hooke and Leeuwenhoek. Surely there was no good reason to suspect a priori that life could be divided into unit lives. The atomism of the ancient Greeks had long since gone to the philosophical nether world, and although Democritus had clearly stated that all life and growth and human behavior arose from "the conjunctions and dispersions of atoms," he had no good reason to think so. The sixteenth-century physician Fernel, who was brought so vividly to life by Sherrington, wrote that, for his part, divide a bit of muscle and you will merely get smaller muscle. He assumed, in the absence of the microscope, that such subdivision could continue indefinitely—there was no reason to think otherwise. Yet, when the microscope arrived and achieved the discovery that had merely been awaiting its arrival, men's imaginations failed to comprehend these specks of life. Their existence scandalized Buffon. Life seemed degraded if it could exist in such lowliness. It could be argued, I think, that this is yet another example of the conditioning of scientific thought by the philosophical climate and the psychology of an era.

If for no other reason than its heuristic value, the cell theory quickly began to prosper. It was promptly extended to unicellular organisms with the pronouncement of von Siebold in 1845 that protozoa are simply animals consisting of one cell. The majority of observers came to abandon the doctrine of the free formation of cells as expounded by Schleiden and Schwann, and, by mid-century, it was firmly established that cells alone can originate new cells. "*Omnis cellula e cellula,*" intoned Virchow. And, in 1861, simultaneously with the beginning of the great period of histological staining researches, Max Schultze proposed the essence of the modern "protoplasm theory." He presumed a fundamental similarity of the basic jelly-like substance of plant and animal cells and, extrapolating to all living forms, concluded that the material called "protoplasm" is the "physical basis of all life," differing from species to species only in specific details of structure and composition. To Schultze, we owe the oft-quoted definition of a cell as a "mass of protoplasm containing a nucleus." Thomas Huxley's famous Edinburgh lecture of 1868, which was called *On the Physical Basis of Life* (a title destined to become a cliché of biological literature), supported the unifying idea of protoplasm and stressed the universality of its form and function throughout the range of living systems. The concept of the universality of protoplasm became part of the first general synthesis of biological phenomena, and its most penetrating presentation was the 1892 edition of Hertwig's *The Cell and the Tissues,* which brought to a close a fruitful century.

I do not mean to suggest that opposition merely evaporated in the face of these theories. Their abstractions were tenuous and failed to predict or explain a huge number of facts. Many continued to support the idea that there are simpler units of life than cells, and this list included (with their verbal inventions) Haeckel's "plastidules," Nägeli's "micellae," Darwin's "gemmules," and Hertwig's "idioblasts" plus a welter of other conceptions based on the notion of superfundamental subcellular units of life.

Although much had been learned by direct microscopic examination of living cells, the great bulk of information on cellular structure was collected by painstaking examination of fixed and stained cells. Since fixation means killing and hardening the cell with chemicals, the static quality of this body of knowledge is understandable. Interestingly, the study of cell structure had its golden age in the last half of the nineteenth century in direct consequence of great new discoveries in the theory and technology of dyes. Germany was the center of activity in the field of dye chemistry, and we find that early cytomorphology was advanced by those biologists who had learned their chemistry well, the Germans. By skillfully applying to the chemically heterogeneous inner structure of fixed cells the principles learned in dyeing and mordanting wool, silk, and cotton fibers, microscopists were able to emblazon individual cell elements in brilliantly contrasting colors. And, in addition to the mere dying of nonliving tissue elements, cytologists and histologists learned to use coloring agents as a means of identifying specific chemical substances within the cell, as, for example, the recognition of starch by its iodine reaction. In its full flower, this technic came to be known as ***histochemistry***. Nineteenth-century workers also learned to render visible certain structures by ingeniously impregnating them with opaque materials, a technic akin to but distinctly different from dyeing. With special care, the most ultrafine structure of the cell could be brought into view by coating it with a delicate film of silver or gold. This technic was brought to its highest art by men like Golgi, Cohnheim, and Cajal.

Of course, like its biological substratum, staining theory was for long years not exactly crystalline in its clarity. Every bottle on the dye chemist's shelf was taken down and tried out as a cell stain, and although there emerged from this zealotry the standard stains of today—carmine, haematoxylin, eosin, and others—most of the early work was exuberantly haphazard. A reviewer in 1902 wrote, "The method of staining once having taken root in the animal histologist, grew and grew, till to be an histologist became practically synonymous with being a dyer, with this difference, that the professional dyer knew what he was about, while the histologist with few exceptions did not know, nor does he to the present day." Even now, fifty years later, we can still complain that much of the literature on staining technics reads like a witch's vade mecum. Long on cook-bookery and short on rationale, many published methods can often be duplicated but rarely interpreted.

There still persists debate on the question of whether cells are the simplest units of life, some of which retains the flavor of the nineteenth-century word tournaments. In the summer of 1954, there appeared a paper by the well-known Canadian endocrinologist and neologist Hans Selye declaring that the cell theory has become "too deeply ingrained in the minds of biologists to be displaced by other concepts." And as an "other concept," Selye offered a new fundamental element of life—a subcellular unit he calls the "reacton." Reactons are defined as the smallest entities capable of "selective biological reactivity." The thesis is defended not by data but by verbal analogy and teleological argument, the latter epistemological principle receiving a ringing and entertainingly wayward commendation. Happily, the piece ends by supplying the seeds of its own refutation:

> Vagueness of terms and concepts passes unnoticed, as long as there are not sufficient objective observations to which these should refer. Indeed, it

> would be a futile dialectic exercise to aim at conceptual or terminologic precision in reference to a field which has not been subjected to that degree of laboratory analysis which makes such theoretical precision possible, or even necessary. Yet, the theory must always be a little ahead of the facts, otherwise it cannot lead us to them.

Selye, of course, may be right—after all, Democritus was.

The matter of spontaneous generation

Biology, like physics, now had its atoms. They were the cells, and it became clear that the perpetuation and increase of the living world depends entirely on the production of cells and more cells. But a long and fundamental and rather tedious controversy had to take place before it was possible to state just where cells came from. When they were first recognized, it was evident that many kinds of cells could arise only by division of a parent cell—a case of "multiplication by division" according to the traditional professorial joke. Yet it was far from clear whether cell division was *the* method or merely *a* method for cell formation. Thus, though it was generally accepted by 1860 that fermentation and putrefaction were caused by living microorganisms, science still could not decisively answer the question: Where do microbes come from? This is not to say that no one had a hypothesis. Of two obvious possibilities—that like other cells they came from parent microbes identical to themselves or that they arose *de novo* from inanimate matter—for some reason few doubted the truth of the second.

From ancient times, men have believed that, under certain peculiar circumstances, life could arise spontaneously: from the ooze of rivers could come eels and from the entrails of dead bulls, bees; worms from mud, and maggots from dead meat. This belief was held by Aristotle, Newton, and Descartes, among many others, and apparently the great William Harvey too. (Harvey once wrote: "*omne vivum ex vivo*"—all life comes from life—but, in a famous address before the 1870 meeting of the British Association, Thomas Huxley remarked, "It is commonly counted among the many merits of our great countryman, Harvey, that he was the first to declare the opposition of fact to venerable authority in this, as in other matters; but I can discover no justification for this widespread notion!") The weight of centuries gradually disintegrated men's beliefs in the spontaneous origin of maggots and mice, but the doctrine of spontaneous generation clung tenaciously to the question of bacterial origin.

In association with Buffon, the Irish Jesuit priest, John Needham, declared that he could bring about at will the creation of living microbes in heat-sterilized broths, and, presumably in propitiation, theorized that God did not create living things directly but bade the earth and water to bring them forth. In his *Dictionnaire Philosophique*, Voltaire reflected that it was odd to read of Father Needham's claim while atheists conversely "should deny a Creator yet attribute to themselves the power of creating eels." But, wrote Thomas Huxley, "The great tragedy of science—the slaying of a beautiful hypothesis by an ugly fact—which is so constantly being enacted under the eyes of philosophers, was played, almost immediately, for the benefit of Buffon and Needham."

The Italian Abbé Spallanzani did an experiment. He showed that a broth *sealed from the air* while boiling never develops bacterial growths and hence never decomposes. To Needham's objection that Spallanzani had ruined his broths and the air above them by excessive boiling, the Abbé replied by breaking the seals of his flasks. Air rushed in and bacterial growth began! But the essential conflict remained. Whatever Spallanzani and his followers did to remove seeds and contaminants was regarded by the spontaneous generationists as damaging to the "vital force" from whence comes new life.

Thus, doubt remained, and into the controversy came the titanic figure of Louis Pasteur. Believing that a solution to this problem was essential to the development of his theories concerning the role of bacteria in nature, Pasteur cheerfully acknowledged the possibility that living bacteria very well might be arising anew from inanimate matter. To him, the research problem was largely a technical one: to repeat the work of those who had claimed to have observed spontaneous generation but to employ infinite care to discover and exclude every possible concealed portal of bacterial entry. For the one that contended that life did not enter from the outside, the proof had to go to the question of possible contamination. Pasteur worked logically. After prolonged boiling, a broth would ferment only when air was admitted to it. Therefore, either air contained a factor necessary for the spontaneous generation of life *or* viable germs were borne in by the air and seeded in the sterile nutrient broth. Pasteur designed ingenious flasks whose long S-shaped necks could be left open. Air could pass in and out freely but its bacteria-laden dust particles were trapped in the sinuous glass tube. Broths boiled in these flasks remained sterile. When their necks were snapped to admit ordinary air, bacterial growth would then commence—but not in every case. An occasional flask remained sterile presumably because the bacterial population of the air is unevenly distributed. The forces of spontaneous generation would not be so erratic. Continuing skepticism drove Pasteur almost to fanatical efforts to control the ingredients of his experiments to destroy the doubts of the most skeptical. He ranged from the mountain air of Montanvert, which he showed to be almost sterile, to those deep, clear wells whose waters had been rendered germ free by slow filtration through sandy soil. The latter discovery led to the familiar porcelain filters of the bacteriology laboratory. With pores small enough to exclude bacteria, solutions allowed to percolate through them could be reliably sterilized.

The argument raged on and soon spilled beyond the boundaries of science to become a burning religious and philosophical question of the day. For many, Pasteur's conclusions caused conflict because they seemed simultaneously to support the Biblical account of creation while denying a variety of other philosophical systems. The public was soon caught up in the crossfire of a vigorous series of public lectures and demonstrations by leading exponents of both views, novelists, clergymen, their adjuncts and friends. Perhaps the most famous of these evenings in the theater—competing perhaps with that great debate between Huxley and Bishop Wilberforce for elegance of rhetoric—was Pasteur's public lecture at the Sorbonne on April 7, 1864. Having shown his audience the swan-necked flasks containing sterile broths, he concluded, "And, therefore, gentlemen, I could point to that liquid and say to you, I have taken my drop of water from the immensity of creation, and I have taken it full of the elements appropriated to the development of inferior beings. And I wait, I watch, I question it!—begging it to recommence for me the beautiful spectacle of the first creation. But it is dumb, dumb since these experiments were begun several years ago; it is dumb because I have kept it from the only thing man does not know how to produce: from the germs that float in the air, from Life, for Life is a germ and a germ is Life. Never will the doctrine of spontaneous generation recover from the mortal blow of this simple experiment." And it has not. Today these same flasks stand immutable: they are still free of microbial life.

It is an interesting fact that despite the ringing declaration of Pasteur, the issue did not die completely. And although far from healthy, it is not yet dead. In his fascinating biography of Pasteur, René Dubos has traced the later developments which saw new eruptions of the controversy, new technical progress and criticism, and new energetic figures in the breech of the battle such as Bastian, for, and the immortal Tyndall, against, the doctrine of spontaneous generation. There was also new "sorrow" for Pasteur as he read years later, in 1877, the last jottings of the great physiologist Claude Bernard and saw in them the "mystical" suggestion that yeast may arise from grape juice. Even at this late date, Pasteur was stirred to new experiments again to prove to the dead Bernard and his followers the correctness of his position.

Dubos wrote:

> It is unrewarding for a philosopher to demonstrate his thesis with too much thoroughness and too convincingly. His ideas soon become part of the intellectual household of humanity, and the genius and labors which had to be expended in establishing them either are forgotten, or their memory becomes somewhat boring. For this reason, one often reads and hears that Pasteur and Tyndall wasted much talent and energy in a useless fight, for the belief in spontaneous generation was dying a natural death when they took arms against it. In reality, they had to overcome not only the teachings of the most eminent physiologists of the day, but also the emotional prejudices based on philosophical convictions.

Actually, despite the brilliant work of Pasteur and Tyndall, it has not yet been proved that each claim of its occurrence was scientifically invalidated by experimental error. In the heat of the battle, Pasteur complained that every source of error played into the hands of his opponents. "For me, affirming as I do that there are no spontaneous fermentations, I am bound to eliminate every cause of error, every perturbing influence. Whereas I can maintain my results only by means of the most irreproachable technique, their claims profit by every inadequate experiment."

In most accounts of these matters, it seems to me that this one point is often overlooked. The chronicle has become a fable preaching the supremacy of reason over emotion, and, as exponents of reason, reasonable men have always said, as Pasteur did, that spontaneous generation *is* a possibility. With what seems to be the traditional self-contradictoriness of the liberal point of view, many writers, in denouncing the emotional origin of the doctrine, have displayed their own brand of irrational argument. In Castiglione's *History of Medicine,* it says, "The perennial problem of spontaneous generation, which should have been disposed of by Spallanzani's successful refutation of Needham's contentions a century earlier, reappeared at this time." This simply is not so. Spallanzani's work *was* open to legitimate scientific criticism and was therefore unconvincing to perfectly rational skeptics. It seems to me that spontaneous generation is not only a possibility, but a completely reasonable possibility which should never be relinquished from scientific thought. Before men knew of bacteria, they accepted the doctrine of spontaneous generation as the "only reasonable alternative" to a belief in supernatural creation. But today as we look with satisfaction at the downfall of the spontaneous generation hypothesis, we must not forget that science has rationally concluded that *life once did originate on earth by spontaneous generation.* It was really Pasteur's evidence against spontaneous generation that for the first time brought the whole difficult question of the origin of life before the scientific world. In the above controversy, what was unreasonable was the parade of men who claimed to have "proved" or who resolutely "believed in" spontaneous generation in the face of proof—not that spontaneous generation cannot occur—but that their work was shot through with experimental error. The acceptable evidence also makes it clear that spontaneous generation, if it does occur, must obviously be a highly improbable event under present conditions. Logic tells us that science can only prove an event improbable: it can never prove it impossible—and Gamow has appropriately remarked that nobody is really certain what would happen if a hermetically sealed can were opened after a couple of million years. Modern science agrees that it was highly improbable for life to have arisen in the pre-Cambrian seas, but it concludes, nevertheless, that there it did occur. With this, I think, Pasteur would agree.

Aside from their theoretical implications, these researches had the great practical result of putting bacteriology on a solid footing. It was now clear how precisely careful one had to be to avoid bacterial contamination in the laboratory. We now knew what "sterile" meant and we knew that there could be no such thing as "partial sterilization." The discovery of bacteria high in the upper atmosphere, in the mud of the deep sea bottom, in the waters of hot springs, and in the arctic glaciers established bacterial ubiquity as almost absolute. In recognition of this, Lord Lister introduced aseptic technic into the practice of surgery. It was the revolution in technic alone that made possible modern bacteriology and the subsequent research connecting bacteria to phenomena of human concern, research which today is more prodigious than ever. We are just beginning to understand the relationship of bacteria to certain human diseases, to soil chemistry, nutrition, and the phenomenon of antibiosis, wherein a product of one organism (*e.g.*, penicillin) is detrimental to another.

It is not an exaggeration then to say that the emergence of the cell theory represents biology's most significant and fruitful advance. The realization that all plants and animals are composed of cells which are essentially alike, that cells are all formed by the same fundamental division process, that the total organism is a whole made up of the activities and interrelations of its individual cells, opened up horizons we have not even begun to approach. The cell is the microcosm of life, for in its origin, nature, and continuity, resides the entire problem of biology.

CHAPTER VII

LIFE EVOLVES

One often hears of writers that rise and swell with their subject, though it may seem but an ordinary one. How, then, with me, writing of this Leviathan? Unconsciously my chirography expands into placard capitals. Give me a condor's quill! Give me Vesuvius' crater for an inkstand! Friends, hold my arms!

—Herman Melville: *Moby Dick*

As the primal molecules of the ancient seas wove themselves into the web of life, so began the slow, pulsing, ceaseless advance of organism, flowing and fusing across the epochs of time, emerging hesitantly from the sea, and then thriving, at last, on dry land. From that time to this, the earth has witnessed the rise of perhaps many millions of species of living organisms, ranging in size from the invisible virus to the giant sequoia. Without even counting the vast numbers of extinct species, there are in the world today over a million varieties of animals and almost half as many plants. What explanation can there be for such incredible diversity? What forces or patterns underlie the bewildering torrent of living forms?

These questions, among the most challenging and incendiary in the intellectual history of man, have aroused controversy since the dawn of recorded history. Since the earliest times, there have been two main streams of thought on these questions: there are those who believe in the divine Special Creation of fixed and unchanging species and who, thus, deny the fact of evolution, and there are those who accept the view that life has evolved and that species are inconstant. Among the latter, there should be, but often has not been, a clear distinction between the questions "Has evolution occurred?" and "By what mechanism has it occurred?" Today, most people in possession of the scientific data (but, as we shall see, not all) agree to the fact of evolution. On the question of mechanism there is much disagreement. It was not too far in the past when an advocate of the mere view that some sort of evolution took place was the object of stormy protest and public ridicule.

Darwinism and controversy

Nuances of evolutionary ideas are to be found in the earliest writings of philosophers and naturalists in the sixth and seventh centuries B.C., although no doubt it is true that in these great meadows of speculation are to be found the inklings of almost any idea. Thales (640–546 B.C.) believed that life sprang from water, and Heraclitus, a century later, held that all things flow and change, life presumably included. The notion that life arises from nonlife, and animals from plants, a clear-cut evolutionary concept, was postulated by Empedocles (495–435 B.C.). While these views were speculative, they may not have been entirely unscientific. It is possible that early thinkers postulated biological evolution—that is, continuous change, step building on step—because they *observed* that indeed all things change in this manner. Clothes, laws, buildings, language, and mountains, all gradually unfold new patterns and yet often retain mute and functionless vestiges of the old, remnants of past form and design. As we shall see later, modern evolutionists think that even the *mechanism of organic evolution* has undergone evolution, modifying and improving itself through the ages.

The erudite Aristotle evolved a theory of descent and skirted close to the doctrine of inheritance of acquired characteristics although he never actually articulated this idea. Though such a view would have been totally erroneous, it would at least have been a bona fide evolutionary concept. Little more was written in this vein for the long duration of the Middle Ages.

The recognition of fossils in the early years of the Renaissance gave rise to a perfectly fascinating series of churchly contortions in defense of the Mosaic account of creation. Each new finding generated its own meticulous explanation in the name of unyielding orthodoxy. These were memorable years in the annals of absurdity. The argument of Leonardo da Vinci that fossils were the actual remains of living organisms embedded in the earth's crust was taken to indicate that these remains must have reached their positions during the great flood because everyone knows that the Creator finished the earth's crust before He made the fishes. The finding of shells on high mountains signified the monstrous proportions of the flood, or, alternatively, they were the fanciful result of God's inscrutable whimsy.

In his remarkable book *Man and His Gods,* Homer Smith wrote:

> It was the whimsy view that brought the geologist Johann Beringer to grief. So definitely had this professor in the University of Würzburg committed himself to the theory that fossils are "stones of a peculiar sort, hidden by the Author of Nature for his own pleasure," that some of his skeptical students determined to give his faith a thorough trial. They prepared and baked a number of sham fossils from clay, depicting reptiles and fish, birds in their nests, and imaginary creatures, and these they buried where Beringer was sure to find them. The Professor was so enthusiastic over his discovery that his tempters elaborated other fossils figuring the sun and moon, as well as Syrian and Babylonian script. With each successive find Beringer was increasingly

convinced that he had come upon irrefutable evidence of the hand of God, and he published (1726) his discoveries in a treatise illustrated by twenty-one folio plates, devoting a chapter to the refutation of those among his skeptical colleagues who asserted that the fossils were fakes. Only later, when one of them turned up bearing his own name, was his faith in the divine origin of fossils, and in human nature, shattered.

The probings of the geologists of the eighteenth century, Werner, Hutton, Lyell, and others, forced into consideration the evidence that the earth's history extended back millions and millions of years and not, as Archbishop Ussher had carefully computed, to 4004 B.C., and it was in the eighteenth century that, at last, we find clear, strong statements of evolutionary belief. The inventor of the first satisfactory system for naming plants and animals,* the Swedish professor Linnaeus (1707–1778), although impressed with the likenesses of living things, saw no need to postulate kinship. He was a confirmed believer in Special Creation, and yet there is reason to believe that through caution and prudence his true views were never firmly stated. His early statement that "there are no new species" is deleted from the 1766 edition of his great book *Systema Naturae*. It appears that Linnaeus arrived at a limited acceptance of evolution.

In eighteenth-century France, the France of Voltaire, a contemporary of Linnaeus, the imaginative Comte de Buffon (1707–1788) pruned a few more branches from the tree of Special Creation. He noted that deeply bur-

* The "two-name" or so-called *binomial* system which gives first the genus and second the species, *e.g., Rana pipiens,* the familiar frog. In the whole animal kingdom, there is only one genus *Rana,* and among its more than two hundred species, only one called *pipiens.* In assembling this catalogue, Linnaeus prepared the first systematic compendium of plants and animals since Aristotle.

ied fossils bear less resemblance to modern animals than do shallow ones. While believing early in life in divine creation of immutable species and returning approximately to this position in his old age, he detoured for several years through a strong belief in the mutability of species by environment. That his advocacy of this view exposed him to ridicule persisting long after his death is evident in this account of George Bernard Shaw. "One day," he wrote, "early in the eighteen hundred and sixties, I, being then a small boy, was with my nurse, buying something in the shop of a petty newsagent, bookseller, and stationer in Camden Street, Dublin, when there entered an elderly man, weighty and solemn, who advanced to the counter, and said pompously, 'Have you the works of the celebrated Buffoon?' . . . The celebrated Buffoon was not a humorist, but the famous naturalist Buffon. Every literate child at that time knew Buffon's *Natural History* as well as Aesop's Fables."

A disciple of Buffon was Cuvier (1769–1832), soon to become a master anatomist. He obstinately defended Special Creation and, because of his scientific reputation and high rank in the French Academy, was able successfully to belittle and denounce those with opposing views. With remarkable skill, he assembled the fossil bones found by the geologist Smith into reconstructions of the great vertebrates of the past, recognized that they were extinct and yet refused to accept a time scale that differed from that of the good Archbishop Ussher. He reasoned that extinct species had been destroyed by cataclysmic forces and that new species had been created to take their places.

Cuvier is remembered partly for his famous denunciation of an imaginative countryman, Lamarck. Lamarck, in 1814, popularized the doctrine (which now makes the word Lamarckism almost synonymous with nonsense) that since certain organs may change as a result of use or disuse, new environmental conditions can place demands on animals such that new organs develop which, in turn, are passed on to the offspring. He chose as an example the giraffe's long neck, which he attributed to its appetite for tender treetops. Though grievously in error, these superficially reasonable arguments did much to popularize the idea of progressive change, hence Lamarck's abuse at the hands of Cuvier and the clergy.

Into this arena came the immortal Darwin. It was a time when microscopy was poorly developed, when paleontology, the science of fossils, was in its infancy, and when mathematics had no place in biology. Charles Darwin (1809–1882) was the grandson of Erasmus Darwin, a physician, poet, and early evolutionist, whose book *Zoonomia,* published in 1794, obliquely anticipated both the doctrines of inheritance of acquired characteristics of Lamarck and natural selection, later to be formulated by his grandson. The story has often been told of how Charles Darwin's life hinged on the most extraordinary coincidences: his distaste for medicine brought on by the sights of the Edinburgh operating rooms, his transfer to Cambridge to study for the ministry just in time for a fateful meeting with the botanist Henslow, and, of course, the narrow margin by which he almost missed boarding the H.M.S. *Beagle* for the voyage of exploration that now belongs to history.

Darwin seized the opportunity to study the plants and animals of the South American coast, and for five laborious years he made careful notes and gathered priceless specimens. He was overwhelmed by the natural riches of this part of the world, the rivers and layers of sedimentary rocks, the coral reefs and lava beds. On his long field trips, he encountered strange new animals, insects and beetles, lovely orchids, and new grasses and trees. He was like Alice in a strange Wonderland. From this stronghold of life derived his lifelong preoccupation with the problem of species.

Though a confident Creationist upon leaving England, Darwin's doubts grew. His geological findings were incompatible with Archbishop Ussher's date of creation.

He was struck by the endless variety of life and pondered its origin. In 1838, he wrote, he read the Malthus essay on population which declared that man's ability to propagate was so great he would eventually outrun his food supply. If he did not check his fecundity, war, pestilence, and famine would do it for him. Here Darwin found the clue to a comprehensive dynamic theory on the riddle of the origin of species.

The tale of Darwin's discovery is classical to those interested in the ways of genius. A mighty creative intelligence turned from the accumulation of data to the formulation of theory, and there occurred a great moment in the history of thought. In attempting to see a solution to the species problem he decided to explore the field completely. He wrote in his *Autobiography:*

> By collecting all facts which bore in any way on the variation of animals and plants under domestication and nature, some light might perhaps be thrown on the whole subject. My first note-book was opened on July, 1837. I worked on true Baconian principles, and without any theory collected facts on a wholesale scale, more especially with respect to domesticated productions, by printed enquiries, by conversations with skillful breeders and gardeners, and by extensive reading. . . . I soon perceived that selection was the keystone of man's success in making useful races of animals and plants. But how selection could be applied to organisms living in a state of nature, remained for some time a mystery to me.

How could selection operate in nature? The Malthus essay gave the clue. Darwin wrote:

> Being well prepared to appreciate the struggle for existence which everywhere goes on from long-cultivated observation of the habits of animals and plants, it at once struck me that under these circumstances favorable variations would tend to be

> preserved, and unfavorable ones to be destroyed. The result of this would be the formation of a new species. Here then I had at last got a theory by which to work.

Although this decisive idea came to Darwin in 1838, he remained to the end his own severest critic. He waited almost four years to draft a first sketch of his theory and did not publish the *Origin of Species* until 1859, almost twenty years later. The kernel of Darwinism is simplicity itself:

1. The reproductive power of animals is much greater than is necessary to maintain their numbers. Only if a very large part of the offspring is destroyed will the numbers remain constant.
2. There must be, therefore, a "struggle for existence" between members of a species and between the different species in the case that several species have the same habitat and food supply.
3. Animals vary widely—and, presumably, such variation is inherited.
4. In the struggle for existence, favorable variations have survival value. Unfavorable variations will lead to extermination. This is *natural selection,* the selection of the favored by nature. By accumulation of favorable variations, natural selection leads to gradual change in animals tending toward better and better adaptation and thus to evolution.

Here we have a remarkable example of the fruitful interplay of induction (reasoning from observation with deference to the law of probability) and deduction (reasoning by logic). The argument went something like this: first observation: some animals vary; first inductive conclusion: all animals probably vary; first logical deduction: variations must be inherited. Second observation: some species overproduce; second inductive conclusion: all species probably overproduce; second logical deduction: there must be a struggle for existence. And from the two logical deductions comes the third deduction, the major one: natural selection.

No account of this era can pass over the hullabaloo that followed the publication of *Origin of Species*. Ecclesiastical critics, members of Parliament, fellow scientists descended upon Darwin. The disingenuous Bishop Wilberforce, widely known as an orator, condemned the book outright and, at a memorable meeting of the British Association in 1860, engaged in debate with "Darwin's Bulldog," Thomas Huxley.

"In conclusion," said Bishop Wilberforce, "I should like to ask my honorable opponent whether he considers himself descended from a monkey on his grandmother's side or his grandfather's." Huxley, white with anger, rose to reply. "A man," said he, "has no reason to be ashamed of having an ape for his grandfather. If there were an ancestor whom I should feel shame in recalling, it would be a *man*, a man of restless and versatile intellect, who, not content with an equivocal success in his own sphere of activity, plunges into scientific questions with which he has no real acquaintance, only to obscure them by an aimless rhetoric, and distract the attention of his hearers from the real point at issue by eloquent digressions, and skilled appeals to religious prejudice."*

With the publication of *Man's Place in Nature* in 1863, Thomas Huxley became the true author of "Darwinism" and its central figure. For here interest was focused from first to last upon *man*, as Huxley proclaimed in exciting phrases and compelling arguments the descent of man from ape, while pleading with his doubting generation to abandon its vanity. Though Darwin had been timid,

* This story, always quoted for its entertainment value in accounts of this era, may be apocryphal. According to a recently unearthed letter, Huxley once wrote: "I said my say with perfect good temper and politeness—I assure you of this because all sorts of reports have been spread about, e.g., that I had said I would rather be an ape than a bishop, etc."

Huxley did not falter and, by placing man firmly within the evolutionary scheme, he fashioned a movement which extended far beyond the range of Darwin's immediate personal interests.

The impact of evolutionary ideas on the intellectual world was monumental. In the sixth edition of the *Origin of Species,* Darwin gave his scientific theory connotations of human progress and goodness, suggesting that evolution is pointed toward an ultimate perfection. This line of thought passed rapidly into the cultural stream where it has since modified every minor current.

Evolutionary ideas swept into explorations of human life and values, social institutions, religion, and morality. Great debates started which in many cases have still not quieted. It was a half-century of great writings bearing the evolutionary stamp: Spencer's works on sociology and ethics, Frazer's *Golden Bough* which traced the evolution of religious rite, Westermarck's *Origin and Development of Moral Ideas.* The trend was toward explaining the higher as evolving from the lower, mind from life and life from matter. On these questions, on the question whether the evolutionary drive was necessarily toward perfection, there were grave disagreements. Surely the evidence of history on mental and moral evolution helped to divorce the concepts of evolution and progress. The "naturalistic" movement in moral philosophy soon split down the middle. One faction courageously supported the reducibility of mind and morals to the organic level and eventually formed the vanguard of modern materialism. The other, led by men like William James and John Dewey, insisted on the reality and separateness of moral ideas, but accepted their natural conditioning. This doctrine wove itself into the great American philosophical movement of pragmatism, which in its various forms has so profoundly affected education, law, and human life in general.

As for the response of the Church to the onward surge of evolutionary thinking, this varied with the various formulations of Christian doctrine. The Protestants, committed to the literal interpretation of the Bible, found Darwinism in flat disagreement with the Biblical account of creation. Following the famous Scopes trial in Tennessee in 1925, several American states tried to legislate evolution out of existence by forbidding its teaching in public schools. Catholicism earnestly tried to make fine distinctions between evolution as applied to animals and as applied to man and between theistically oriented evolution and that based on materialism and atheism, the general position being that science, properly interpreted, does not conflict with sacred dogma. A splinter movement from Catholicism, which became known as Modernism, attempted to reformulate Christian doctrine in the light of new knowledge, but this uprising was terminated in 1907 by papal encyclical implemented by a certain number of excommunications. The movement has since been confined to the Protestant Church. As recently as 1953, His Holiness Pius XII, addressing a scientific audience at Castel Gandolfo, took an ultraconservative view toward evolution, admitting it only as a possibility, a hypothesis yet to be verified, an opinion of some scientists and not others. To this, the eminent geneticist T. Dobzhansky replied, "[The statement] does not hold evolution to be contrary to or incompatible with Divine Revelation. But regrettably, it does not show evidence of being well advised concerning the actual state of knowledge in biological science. . . . This is injurious both to science and religion, keeping up several centuries of misunderstanding."

It was in biology, however, that the great transformation took place. The field was galvanized by its sudden conversion from a static classificatory discipline to a dynamic, integrated, autonomous science with its own philosophical understructure. The changes that occurred in physiology, psychology, and biochemistry were tremendous. There arose the new science of ecology. It should be remembered that Darwin did not originate the idea of evolution. His work, however, made it reasonable and provided a starting point from which science could proceed to further inquiry. In the scientific controversies which raged and spumed, there was frequent confusion between the fact of evolution and natural selection, its postulated mechanism. Darwin quickly attracted a small cordon of staunch defenders, Huxley and Hooker in England, Asa Gray in America, and the brilliant German Ernst Haeckel. There were also articulate opponents, notably von Kölliker, Richard Owen, and the Swiss-American Louis Agassiz (who, it is said, embraced evolutionism on his deathbed), and these objected variously to evolution, natural selection, or both.

A number of modifications of the natural selection idea did appear in later decades. At the turn of the century, strong reaction against the theory almost drove it into disesteem but it staged a vigorous recovery and is today, at least among geneticists, almost universally accepted. These later developments in evolutionary theory overlap and are intimately bound up with the science of genetics.

The modern point of view

Evolution is a *process*, a scheme of events occurring in time, and because of its indolent tempo is itself invisible to the human eye. We know of it through indirect evidence, the results of its workings that remain available to us for examination, and we are precluded from manipulating it experimentally. There is ample experimental evidence bearing on the mechanism of evolution, largely from genetics, but we will defer this until after we have had our formal introduction to the gene. Here let us sketch in the evidence for evolution, those empirical observations that demand a theory of evolution as their only plausible explanation.

There are several main types. First, there is the pattern

of order that runs through the diversities in living things. Despite the vast array of differences between organisms, there are unmistakable groupings of similar types. Shull has shown the following diagrams to illustrate the differences between utter randomness of events and a pattern that implies some connection between individual events.*

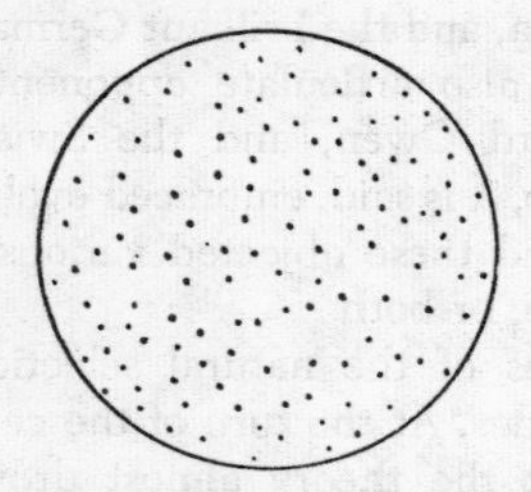

Random distribution of shot on a target

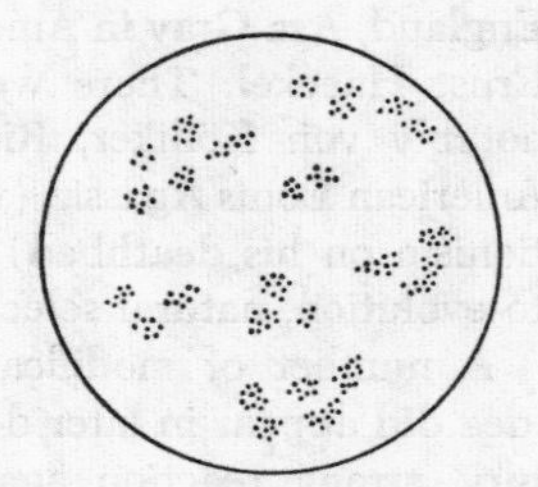

Grouping of shot on a target which indicates some connection between the separate shots

Some sort of theory of evolution is immediately suggested as a possible explanation for these groupings. Close examination of these patterns reveals that there are higher and higher categories, larger and larger groups which are made up of smaller groups. In the living world, the individual on the lowest classification is a member of a *species* and may differ from members of other species only in minor ways such as color of fur or shape of wings. When several species have strong resemblances to one another which distinguish them from another cluster of similar species, we have two higher groups, each a *genus*. The same is true for genera and up the scale through *family, order, class,* and *phylum*. Thus taxonomy has given us a table of organization that looks something like this:

* Figures are redrawn from A. Shull, *Evolution,* 2nd ed., McGraw-Hill, 1951, and Remington Arms Co., by permission.

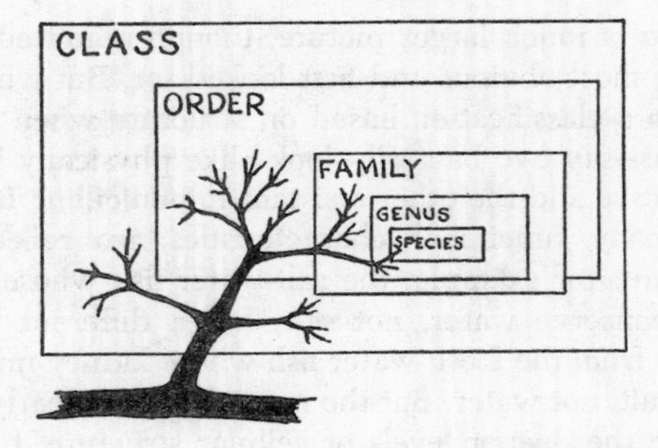

The big animal phyla, of which there are over a dozen, include the worms, the insects, jellyfishes, single-celled organisms, and backboned animals, the last including man. The plant kingdom has a similar taxonomic scheme.

Classification is a tricky business. First of all, let us agree that it is probably necessary: to be understood, all variable phenomena must be sorted into categories wherever it is possible to do so. In any system of classification, there are two steps: first, defining and describing the units to be classified and analyzing for their diagnostic differences, and, second, arranging the units into a classificatory scheme, a hierarchy of ever-larger groups. In biology, as elsewhere, we use names as recognition symbols. At first, names like "skunk" or "catfish" were entirely adequate, but the establishment of the biological classifications of Linnaeus introduced the binomial system of nomenclature according to which the second word of the name indicates species or *distinctness* and the first word indicates genus or *relationship*. Clearly, such a system must be based on a sound knowledge of the items being named and classified. The better our knowledge, the more meaningful the classification.

Classification was long based on the most obvious characteristic of the organism, structure—how the animal is built and what he looks like. This approach is plainly full of hazards. Appearance and structure are but facets of a much larger picture, though admittedly they are the most obvious and first looked for. But what happens to a classification based on structure when two organisms—say two bacteria—look alike physically but one is sensitive and the other resistant to penicillin? It is true that many functional characteristics are reflected in structure: for example, the salt-water fish whose kidney must conserve water, not salt, has a different kind of kidney from the fresh-water fish whose kidney must conserve salt, not water. But the newer science clearly shows that on the deeper levels of cellular structure, function, and chemistry, fundamental differences occur between organisms (sometimes within the same species) which have no gross structural counterpart. Are we then to designate several new species?

This should make it evident that species, the lowest common denominator of classification, cannot be simply defined. Even if structural similarity were the sole criterion, there has to be some decision on how rigid one wants to be. As it is, no two living beings are exactly alike. And so we are left with a concept of species that lacks preciseness. Species, the books tell us (and the vague words are italicized), are made up of *similar* individuals, *differing* from other species, which breed *mostly* among themselves, are *quite* permanent and yet are *flexible* and *plastic,* tending to change in the course of many generations. What we can unhesitatingly accept is that there are likenesses among living beings, and from this we infer kinship.

There are likenesses, too, between genera and classes. Much study has been devoted to anatomical analogies between the different types of living things: the ear of the frog and the ear of the dog, the human arm and the bird's wing. Many organisms possess vestigial remnants, such as the human ear-moving muscles, present but functionless, and these hint at remote consanguinity with present-day ear-moving animals. Impressed by the resemblance of the early mammalian embryo successively to a single-celled organism, a hydra, and a fish, Ernst Haeckel outlined what he called the "biogenetic law," according to which each individual in his own development recapitulates all the stages through which the entire race has passed. The validity of the "biogenetic law" is open to doubt* but the data which it seeks to explain show clearly that embryos possess what must be "inheritances from the past." This is evidence of common ancestry and, together with the grouping into species and genera, is evidence that somewhere along the line of descent, change took place. *Common ancestry plus change equals evolution.* The deduction cannot be avoided.

If species arose by evolution, they did so in a world that was itself evolving. In the course of geological time, continents have heaved up and subsided while the land bridges between them have often come and often gone. The peculiar distribution of certain species throughout the world is good evidence that evolution took place. This is illustrated by the striking differences between the large mammals of North and South America. Geological evidence indicates that at one time Panama was submerged so that no exchange of species could take place between the two continents. By the time the land bridge was established, mammalian evolution had reached an advanced stage. Remote islands such as the Galápagos, which Darwin visited in 1835, have species of insects, birds, and reptiles that are to be found nowhere else. The distribution of life in the world indicates that species must have originated everywhere and on many occasions. This in turn substantiates the fact of evolution.

Perhaps the most impressive evidence for evolution is

* It is currently believed that the individual does not pass through the *adult* stages of its evolutionary ancestors but through their *developmental* or embryonic stages. Thus, the gill clefts of the human embryo more resemble those of the fish embryo than they do the gill slits of the adult fish.

the fossil record. Paleontologists have been probing around in caves and potholes for over two centuries and have assembled a remarkable collection of fossilized remains of extinct species. From these, they have made deductions about the course of evolution. For certain species, the lines of descent are very well known from direct fossil evidence. But, interestingly, paleontology has its methodological problems too. It is at its best in the fortunate circumstance when it has uncovered a *series* of fossils, neatly laid down in successive, uninterrupted geological strata, giving a strong probability commendation to the inference that C evolved from B and B from A. As it happens, findings of this type are rare and few have been extensive enough to show more than the appearance of new species. For the formation of new genera, families, and classes, the major changes of evolution involving true novelty, such series provide no evidence.

In the usual case, the paleontologist is forced to deal with isolated fossils from widely separated geographical locations and geological eras. He can do no more than deduce the nature of intermediate forms. In addition, he must wrestle with other problems connected with fossils: they derive mainly from animals with hard shells and skeletons; because they have been embalmed in the earth in somewhat random fashion, they reflect chiefly the dominant species of an era and not the rarer forms whose recognition is highly important to an evolutionary theorist; and, of course, they can be formed only where sedimentation is taking place, such as sea bottoms and coastal areas. This is not to mention the technical difficulties in piecing together fossils that have been broken, baked, or squashed by the weight of time. These problems, however, should not discountenance the positive evidence of paleontology. Nor should any theory of evolution conflict with it, for this evidence is direct.

Paleontology has perhaps made its greatest contribution to our knowledge of the phylogeny* of vertebrates, the subphylum of backboned animals of which man is a prominent if not always chauvinistic member. The fossil record suggests that the vertebrates have been the most successful of animals and hence have evolved the most rapidly, extending their dominance over the widest range. By assembling the fragments, we can picture the emergence of the earliest known vertebrates following the Cambrian Revolution some four or five hundred million years ago. These were the heavily armored, bottom-living, jawless fishes of the fresh, continental lakes. In turn came actively swimming fish, the "cartilaginous" fishes, whose modern descendants are the sharks, and the "bony" fishes who were the ancestors of most modern fishes. Events had by then established the survival value of the segmented, flexible backbone, the power of fast swimming, and the location of major sense organs at the head end of the body.

But times changed and the heaving earth brought invasions of salt water into the continental areas. Inland fresh-water fish were forced to choose between an alien salt-water habitat and a shrinking fresh-water pool. Some took to the sea, and those who remained behind had to modify themselves in order to survive. Thus came the dawn of the age of air breathing and the prologue to the lung-possessing, terrestrial vertebrates.

Evolution was also advancing among plants and insects, and the world was entering the coal ages. Under the pelting rain and blazing sun, the lowlands became stretching green seas of vegetation, populated with spiders, snails, and scorpions and, at last, the vertebrate amphibians who lived half on land and half in water.

Soon came the glaciers and the careening, expanding earth grew cold and dry. Amphibians passed slowly into landlocked reptiles who, via stages of unsurpassed grotesquerie, evolved into the great dinosaurs. At about

* Phylogeny means development of race (genesis of phylum).

the time of the formation of the Rocky Mountains, a hundred million years ago, the age of the reptile came to an abrupt end. Up to this time, birds and mammals had remained in the background. They may have been evolving in small local groups and hence failing to represent themselves adequately in the fossil record. But whether the dwindling of the reptiles was caused by the prosperity of the mammals or vice versa remains an open question.

In any case, the mammals arrived, furry and warm-blooded to resist the cold and capable of nursing their young to protect them from egg-hungry predators. They grew better teeth and larger heads and in due time gave rise to upright, walking forms, the primates. Not until fifty million years later, a mere million years ago, is there any sign of man. The few available fossils of early transitional man have been widely publicized and, of course, disputed: the discovery in Java of the famous *Pithecanthropus erectus,* the celebrated "missing link" whom the late Ernest Hooton in his delightful book *Up from the Ape* called the low-brow who took a chance on the ground; the "Peking man," a Chinese giant with slightly larger cranium; and the mysterious "Heidelberg man" of whom, regrettably, we have found only the lower jaw. And then the finding of Neanderthal man, surrounded by tools, the citizen of 100,000 years ago, human in every particular. Until recently, the oldest human remains to be found in the Western Hemisphere date back only 11,000 years. Every sign indicates that the primate stock which gave birth to man did not live in the New World. In all probability, the cradle of man is central Asia.

The fascinating problem of fossil man and his disputed passage to the present is far too complicated to receive more than brief mention here. As seems generally the case in other branches of science, this one, too, has moved from simple clear "principles" to confusions and profound paradoxes. As Professor Loren Eiseley has pointed out:

> In the 1890's all that was needed to tell the story of human evolution was to arrange on a classroom desk the skull of a chimpanzee (with certain generally unheeded cautions), the skull cap of *Pithecanthropus* and the skull of Neanderthal. If the instructor placed his own head at the end of the line, a student could comprehend in a glance the full course of human evolution. There were then no obscurities, no anomalous apes, no poor relations whose genealogy was obscure, no little men with enormous teeth, no structural ancestors who persisted in fooling everyone by living beyond their time.

The last-mentioned discoveries and many others are the reasons we now recognize our ignorance. We are today confronted with myriad unanswered questions: the newer evidence that man may have arisen in Africa, the recent findings indicating man may have existed in North America earlier than was previously thought, the whole problem of the seemingly explosive origin of the human brain. It is clear that the origin of modern man is a problem both of taxonomy and of dating, and both must await better fossil evidence, particularly in the interval between 50,000 and 150,000 years ago.

Unfortunately, the anthropologist's problems are not limited to the inscrutability of nature in the raw. In recent years, the field was thrown into an uproar by an episode which could reasonably be presumed to have been invented by Gilbert and Sullivan. The "Piltdown man" has always been a riddle. Consisting solely of a skull and a jaw, the authenticity of their association has been vigorously disputed since they were found together between 1908 and 1912 by the amateur English antiquarian Charles Dawson along a country lane near Piltdown Common. The newly discovered fossil pit contained a variety of fragments, and during the following decade these were assorted into two assemblies called Piltdown I and Piltdown II. The announcement of their discovery before the Geological Society of London in 1912 touched off a controversy which boiled ceaselessly on until its unexpected denouement in 1953. The basic dispute—which in the light of later developments reflects credit on the conceptual solidity of this field of science—was between those who regarded the skull and jaw as part of the same individual, who must have been a very old man-ape (indeed the "dawn man" and "first Englishman," as his proponents called him) and those who considered the parts to be two other fellows, having originated separately from man and ape. The question was asked: What was a great ape doing in England in the first place and wasn't it remarkable that his jaw should have appeared in a cache of bones including interlocking specimens of human origin?

I cannot include all the details of this controversy. To make a long and intriguing story all too brief, the anthropologists Weiner, Oakley, and Clark announced in 1953 that the "Piltdown man" was a fraud! They found by means of modern analytical technics that the jawbone had been treated chemically to make it look old and the ape's teeth had been filed down to plausible human proportions. As to the validity of their findings, there could be no doubt. The scientists concluded that "the distinguished paleontologists and archaeologists who took part in the excavations at Piltdown were the victims of a most elaborate and carefully prepared hoax" that was "so extraordinarily skillful" and which "appears to have been so entirely unscrupulous and inexplicable, as to find no parallel in the history of paleontological discovery." The identification of the villain will be a nice conundrum for a new generation of scholars.

Following this announcement, the anthropologists of the world devoted a number of special meetings to the Piltdown hoax, and the published accounts of their proceedings communicate equal parts of consternation and relief. At least the evolution of man now seemed slightly less cryptic. To quote Straus:

> The Piltdown story is a significant one in the history of ideas, more particularly as it bears on the concept of the precise course of human evolution. For, if man's biological history be likened to a book, it is seen to be composed of both blank and written pages and, by those who note them carefully, many if not most of the written ones will be seen to be in the nature of palimpsests—pages that have been rewritten after their original writing has been rubbed out. Of this, the Piltdown affair is a striking demonstration. It is a demonstration, furthermore, that the palimpsest nature of the pages of man's history is not always due directly to new fossil discoveries but can also result from changes in the philosophical climate of the science. That this phenomenon is peculiar to anthropology, however, is seriously to be doubted.

Thus the likelihood of evolution is great. Save for a few shrill dissenters, all accept this fact. And there *are* dissenters, although few can be taken seriously. A Dutchman named van Houwensvelt published a book in 1931 called *Darwinism Has Deceived Humanity* in which he violently repudiated the scientific argument for evolution. His chapters, one of which is decisively titled *Scholars Have No Proof of Darwinism and Their Theories Are Wrong!*, are so acrid with contempt, they make amusing reading. Between salvos, things are kept lively with sly anecdotes such as the one about the International Zoological Congress of 1895 in Leiden where scholars had gathered to view the bones of the *Pithecanthropus erectus*. "At this congress the learned Rudolph von Virchow was so excited when he took the femur (thigh-bone) of the *Pithecanthropus* in his hands, that he flourished it about like a madman, and Dubois, who had become famous through its discovery, was frightened to death lest all at once the prehistoric bone should fall to the ground in pieces."

In a more recent and much more temperate book called *Is Evolution Proved?*, Arnold Lunn wrote:

> Influenced as I am by the mental fashion of the day my bias is in favor of evolution and I should accept evolution as proved but for the following facts: (a) the difficulty of reconciling the suddenness with which new types appear in the geological record with any theory of slow mindless evolution, (b) the impossibility of tracing any family into another family by means of true lineage series of fossils, (c) the impossibility of reconciling the alleged imperfection of the geological record with . . . statistics which suggest that most genera are represented in that record, and, finally, (d) the fact that no evolutionist has produced a plausible *guess*, much less a theory supported by evidence, to suggest how a purely natural process could have evolved from the mud, sand, mists and seas of the primeval planet the brain that conceived Beethoven's Ninth Symphony and the reactions to the beauty of music, of art, and of nature.

It seems that the argument against evolution is pure metaphysical brocade, artfully draped so as to obscure the cogent evidence of science. Evolution like everything else is not a certainty. But in the present state of knowledge, it must be regarded as proved beyond reasonable doubt. The consequences of the general acceptance of the doctrine of evolution were utterly typical of all such sophistical arguments when at last they fizzle out. With the collapse of explanation by unknowable unknowns, *scientific questions were asked that would not otherwise have been dreamed of*. The door swung open wide on a whole world of new and pressing problems of direct importance to biology: What is the mechanism of evolution? What forces shape the course of evolution? What does it all mean? Many of these questions are at the centers of actively raging, latter-day controversies, some between science and the regrouped forces of the supernaturalist legions.

We cannot explore here all the byways of evolutionary theory. This has been done masterfully by a leading student of the subject, Julian Huxley, in his book *Evolution: The Modern Synthesis.* Some of these subsidiary ideas will emerge in subsequent chapters. But because it is directly pertinent to our later discussions, let us dwell a moment on one vital concept which has crystallized from evolutionary thinking, the notion of *adaptation.*

Since men first began to think charitably about evolution, they have been impressed and awed by the conception of marvelously integrated men arising from lowly forms of life. To many, this signified that evolution was *creative* or possessed some sort of *orientation.* It was denied that evolutionary change was entirely random, for, if it was, how could one explain the magnificent interrelationship between structure, function, and environment as found, for example, in the protective coloration of butterflies or in the design of the human hand? Some insisted that the evolutionary process proceeded in straight lines, transformations building upon each other undeviatingly and inexorably. Thinkers of this persuasion (the concept has been called *orthogenesis*) usually point to the ancient, tiny eohippus who by gradual and stepwise change evolved into the modern horse.

G. G. Simpson presented a very instructive lesson on the psychological pitfalls in interpreting data in problems of this sort. He suggested a hypothetical case wherein a fossil collection had been assembled and some feature such as leg length was plotted on a graph against the time of origin of the fossil. The individual observations would look like this:*

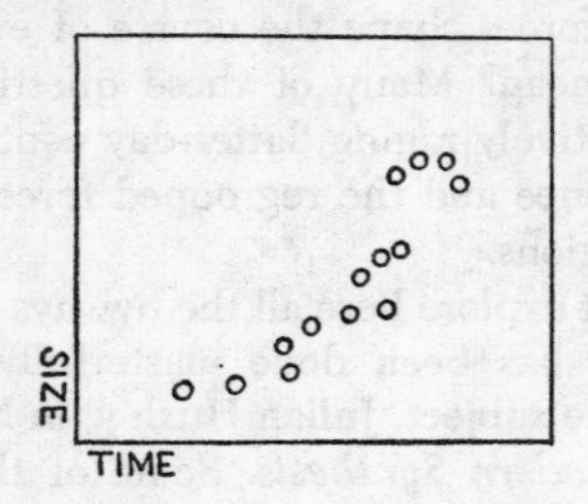

Student A, desiring to find evidence of separate orthogenetic series, might interpret these data in this way:

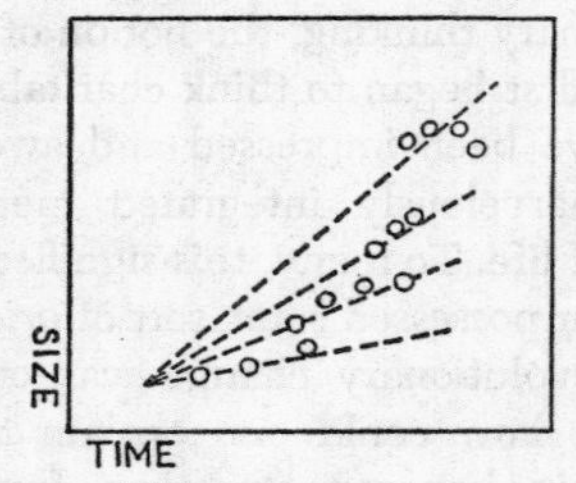

Student B, who basically believes that evolution occurs in a sequence of stages each arising by a major leap without passing through transition forms, will visualize the findings differently:

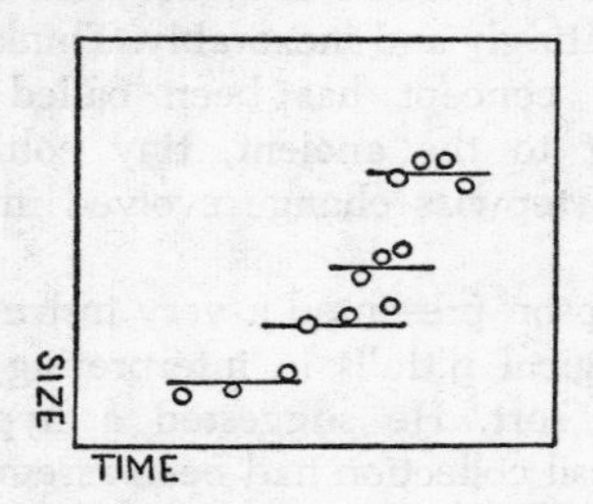

* Figures are redrawn from G. G. Simpson, *The Meaning of Evolution,* Yale University Press, 1949, by permission.

And, finally, Student C may see the findings as evidence for a single, continuous, *oriented,* but not necessarily orthogenetic, process:

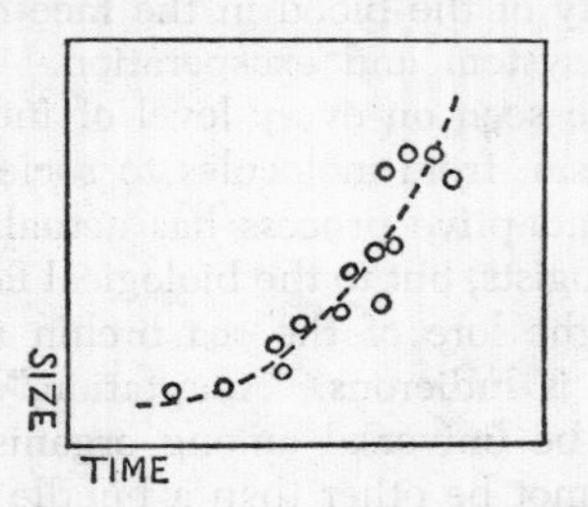

We must agree that evolution is not entirely random. The environment does, after all, impose some limitations. An organism has only a restricted number of available environments, and each imposes its own terms for survival. And yet it appears that the *direction of evolution* cannot be attributed solely to something within the evolving form. It is neither of these two alone but, instead, the relationship between them, the interplay of organism and environment, the complex process for which we use the term *adaptation.*

Adaptation is one of those words that must be handled very carefully. As an abstract term denoting a process which may or may not be wholly understood, it is directly in danger of meaning different things to different people. In addition, as was pointed out by Medawar, there are syntactical hazards in its use. Unlike the combinations "mutant and mutation," "concept and conception," "adaptation" is both gerund and substantive noun: "adaptation" is the process and "the adaptation" is the result of the process. What is true of adaptation used in the substantival sense may be quite false of adaptation used in its other sense.

The omnipresent process of adaptation has produced numberless instances of the harmonious fitting of the organism to its environment, some of the utmost delicacy, and many, no doubt, so subtle as to have so far escaped discovery. One could fill a book with examples: the parasite and the host, muscles and the skeleton, enzymes and substrates, the hummingbird and flowers, the stable, mild alkalinity of the blood in the face of varying diet, the nervous system and exasperation. A microcosm of fitness can be seen on every level of integration in the living organism, from molecules to societies. The existence of the adaptive process has actually been denied by some biologists, but to the biological fieldworker, long schooled in the lore of the sea urchin and the shrike, this position is ludicrous. "Adaptation," wrote Huxley, "cannot but be universal among organisms, and every organism cannot be other than a bundle of adaptations, more or less detailed and efficient, coordinated in greater or lesser degree."

A variety of themes has developed around the central idea of adaptation. *Preadaptation* refers to changes in an organism that do not necessarily suit him for his own environment but do fit him for some other environment available to him. Preadapted organisms who are near a new, and now suitable, niche are likely to immigrate into it and to do so successfully. Here further adaptation occurs and the original preadapted level of fitness is improved upon. Goldschmidt gives as an example of preadaptation the case of cave-dwelling animals, who have a highly developed sense of touch but lack eyes. They are eyeless not because they are in caves but, conversely, for one of two other reasons: (1) only animals who already prefer darkness will survive the ever-possible loss of eyes by chance variation (mutation), and (2) animals who by chance develop a superior tactile sense are then preadapted to enter caves where they can thrive despite the chance loss of eyes.

By such mechanisms, evolution has succeeded in filling with life every corner of the vast world. With the emergence of land animals, a whole category of new environments became available, waiting only for the process of adaptation to provide tenants: the soil, the branches of trees, the air, the caves, the deserts, and the sides of steep mountains. This process, called *adaptive radiation,* gets very complicated because before new environmental niches can be filled they must offer food. No animal could live on land until there were plants, and when herbivorous animals did become established there were now attractive prospects for carnivores and intestinal parasites.

Simpson quoted the analogy, first proposed by T. Huxley, for the filling of the earth with life.

> He likens it to the filling of a barrel with apples until they heap over the brim. Still there is space into which quantities of pebbles fit before they overflow. Again sand is added, and much of it packs down between the apples and the pebbles. The barrel is not yet full and quarts of water may be poured in before at last the barrel can hold no more.

There is a duality in the adaptedness of any organism to its environment. Since no two organisms experience exactly the same trials and tribulations, there is a limit to the consonance of evolutionary predesign. Weiss wrote: ". . . what an organism is prefitted for by its evolutionary endowment is merely a statistical norm of conditions, the standard range which is relatively constant, the individual manifestations of which, however, vary at random from case to case." Thus we find that evolution provides an approximate sort of fitness which is elaborated by mechanisms for on-the-spot adjustments elicited by random need. If one were never wounded, one's blood would never clot and yet one would always have in reserve the clotting mechanism. The same is true for innumerable mechanisms, neurological, skeletal, endocrine, which are available to restore tranquillity should the need arise. Of these, we shall hear more in later chapters.

It should be noted that evolutionary adaptations can be detrimental. Why, it might be asked, if adaptation brings specialization and successful adjustment, do races become extinct? The answer probably lies in the sluggishness that often accompanies prosperity. When a race has filled its environmental range and all opportunities have been seized, the ability to adapt diminishes. While better and better adaptations to the specific environment may be accumulating, the species becomes more and more inflexible to change in the environment. Should conditions suddenly be altered, a whole race of lazy, specialized organisms, whose avenues of possible change are limited, may be wiped out. Should environmental change come gradually, the group will wane and, as it grows smaller, reach a point where deleterious inbreeding occurs with consequent accentuation of undesirable family traits. The appearance of freakish, "inadapted" forms heralds extinction as it did with the dinosaurs. This seems to be the price of overspecialization and, no doubt, points a moral.

The world contains some species that seem immortal. The shark, the oyster, the opossum, are almost unchanged from their ancient ancestors low on the evolutionary ladder. These are perhaps best explained by their small size, modest requirements, and general lack of fastidiousness. The environment which permitted their early survival has never drastically changed and so they continue on—not an immortal species, because all life on earth will one day end, but close to it.

Occasionally, a species long believed to be extinct, turns up alive in a remote corner of the modern world and presents the evolutionary theorist with an indescribably valuable link with the past. Perhaps the most exciting example of this kind of discovery was the recent appearance of a coelacanth on a baited hook in the Indian Ocean off Madagascar. It was previously thought that a very early type of fish had, 350 million years ago, evolved into three different forms: the lungfish which still lives today; the amphibians, progenitors of today's land-living vertebrates; and the coelacanths which for some reason died out seventy-five million years ago. But in 1938, a living coelacanth was pulled out of the water off South Africa. The icthyologist J. L. B. Smith hurried to the scene, but, to his and biology's great disappointment, the creature had decayed and only its skeleton and occasional pieces of skin remained. The announcement of the find, however, stunned the scientific world.

Smith began the quest for a second specimen and systematically distributed thousands of leaflets to native fishermen asking their help. The campaign succeeded when in December 1952 a fisherman recognized a five-foot, 100-pound coelacanth in a Madagascan village market. Smith obtained a special aircraft from the prime minister of South Africa and flew 3,000 miles to the specimen. Though its odor was strong, its head slightly bashed in, and its body partially cut, the find was largely intact. It is said that Smith broke down and wept.

He excitedly reported his discovery in *Nature* and concluded preliminarily that the species is indeed alive though in 300 million years it has changed very little. The discovery was hailed as the "greatest of the century," and detailed researches on the grotesque carcass were launched immediately. Smith declared that the fish clearly represented a new genus which, in honor of the prime minister, he proposed be named *Malania*. Taxonomists—those gentlemen in the back room who must first be thoroughly convinced—have not yet adjudicated the proposed new genus. In the meantime, the channels of Mozambique have been watched for new specimens, and, according to recent word, nine living coelacanths have been captured, all in good condition. The discovery of these specimens has magnificently confirmed theoretical predictions made by the paleontologists about the origin of vertebrates from the indirect evidence of fossils. We now have a "living fossil," and it is an impressive testimonial to the sophistication of modern paleontological theory. For once, a deduction made from fossils has received confirmation.

Because this is not a textbook on evolution, I will not undertake to discuss some of the more technical questions in evolution, as, for example, the microevolution-macroevolution theory* which (in a word) distinguishes between the mechanism of evolutionary change within a species and that which, by large steps, creates new species and genera. The burden of this book is to throw light on the workings of living organisms, the fruit of millenniums of evolution and adaptation. Adaptation would be the leitmotiv behind everything one could say about organism. In considering organism, we are considering nothing more than "bundles of adaptations" each carried down as an historic response to the challenge of environment.

* The author of this controversial view is Goldschmidt, the distinguished professor of zoology at the University of California. He holds that "large mutations" give rise to "hopeful monsters" which may serve as the starting points for new evolutionary trends. This theory has been recently and effectively disputed by G. G. Simpson in his excellent book *The Major Features of Evolution.*

CHAPTER VIII

THE NATURE OF LIFE

The ass went seeking for horns and lost its ears.
—Proverb

Several months before the time of this writing, I was present at a meeting of one of the most distinguished of biochemistry departments. We were having tea. Members of the group were then following up a recent discovery made by one of them relating to the chemical mechanism by which the cell synthesized nucleic acid, the substance of which the genes are made. The discussion was interrupted by a message from a local philosophical society asking if the department would provide a speaker to participate in a forthcoming symposium on the nature of life. Everyone looked at each other in dismay. All assembled understood biochemistry and heredity and genes and enzymes, but no one felt he had anything to say about life. The request was politely declined.

One of the remarkable and frustrating aspects of modern biology is the fact that the roaring tide of specialization has left no one who feels qualified to hold forth on the problem of life itself. Biology has its taxonomists, botanists, bacteriologists, and biochemists, each an expert in his own domain, but no one wants to tackle the single overriding question common to all. Much has been written on the subject but, happily or unhappily, little by working biologists, who are chained to empiricism and not to speculation. The bulk of such literature has, therefore, appeared in philosophical journals and in books written for general readers.

Linus Pauling recently remarked on the difference in viewpoint between the working physicist and biologist: "The physicist says 'what can I say about the world that these data will not rule out?' while the biologist says 'what is it that these experiments force us to believe about nature?'" Unfortunately, nothing has been observed empirically that forces us to believe any one thing about the basic nature of life. Of the several hypotheses that have been offered, none has been capable of definite testing. We cannot yet do what we would like to do with a hypothesis: designate it true or false. At the moment, the most we can say of such notions is that they are useful or useless in leading us to new experiments. Actually, experimental data can at best contribute only indirectly to this problem. No one can enter a laboratory as Sigmund tried to do and undertake to study Life. We study examples of life, in specific areas of inquiry, by asking discrete questions of limited scope. The answers when taken together may provide a basis for generalization by whose reflected light we hope to illuminate the biggest question of them all.

In this chapter I will say something about the development of the point of view that most biologists now hold about the nature of life. It is a question which, in my opinion and in the light of what is now going on in science and philosophy of science, is capable of an answer right now. We will return to it later. It is not a very satisfying answer, for it suggests that the question is meaningless.

Living systems: Are they machines?

When men became aware that they were somehow different from sod, they began a polemical sword dance which is today not yet ended. A fatal fascination lay in the question of whether the riddle of life could be explained by sophisticated combinations of physical and chemical laws or, alternatively, by the workings of some extramaterial agency which alone gives life its anima. (It is, of course, fallacious to reason that this question admits of only two possible solutions. As Bertrand Russell has remarked, "When you meet a stranger, there are exactly two possibilities: on the one hand he may be called Ebenezer Wilkes Smith, on the other hand he may not.") From the Age of Greece to the Age of Biochemistry, the battle has shuffled back and forth across traditional disciplinary boundaries, into and out of biology, physics, and chemistry, back through theology, up and down the long, drafty corridors of metaphysics. Here, as perhaps in no other field of inquiry, can be seen the crazy quilt of frank speculation, honest application of scientific method, the paternity of wish to thought, the ceaseless kneading of modest but partial evidence into exorbitant theory. The old maxim "Who is to decide when doctors disagree?" did not here apply. All men seemed to have an answer to this question. And so, in true philosophical tradition, the issue comes richly garnished with a fretwork of "isms"—a little something for everyone. I have no intention of discussing all of these, but instead propose to sketch in briefly the past and present thinking on this question, take a tentative position, and then, because this is the central issue of theoretical biology, return to the problem in a later chapter.

It is obvious to all that living things are physical objects. They have weight and solidity and exist in a physical matrix. No one has reliably experienced disembodied life. The materials which make up the organism are known to every chemist. We know how some of these substances are put together but we are far from knowing all there is to know on the subject. We know also that all living things die and, after death, retain, at least momentarily, their same structure, weight, and physical continuity. These two general assertions are perhaps indisputable. The question is: What accounts for the difference between living and nonliving physical objects, between the animate body and its corpse?

The *something* that transforms matter into life has been many things to many men. To the ancients, it was the psyche, the life principle, or the soul. To Aristotle, it was three souls. To the early atomist Democritus, it was something made of atoms as were all things. Because soul atoms were conceded to be of a finer and more mobile texture than ordinary ones, this theory gave nourishment to the universal belief in ghosts, shades, wraiths, and other such discarnate post-mortem phenomena. But to the later atomists Epicurus and Lucretius, the particulate nature of the soul implied that the soul could not survive the death of the body, therefore death and ghosts were not to be feared. Descartes, early in the seventeenth century, made his famous distinction between mind and matter wherein a dualistic world was pictured whose material half was strictly mechanistic. Mind did not occupy space and was characterizable only by its function: it did the thinking. To Descartes, the nonmaterial part of the world was chiefly concerned with intellectual matters, thinking, reasoning, and feeling. And, though the "rational soul" did directly act upon the material body somewhere in the valve manifold of the pineal gland, the remainder of life's functions all had a material basis. Thus, Descartes gave such great impetus to mechanistic biology many began to urge that the soul was merely a superfluous hypothesis.

Biology, however, was not purged of animal spirits. Frank spookism did give way to more scientific-sounding concepts embodying the idea of *vital force,* a term which was perhaps less objectionable because it better passed the meaninglessness test. Obviously, it explained nothing, serving only as a verbal symbol of the answer still being sought. Vitalism became a diluted animism and today includes a whole catalogue of nonmaterialistic points of view.

Progressivism in the vitalist camp plus excessivism in materialist interpretation soon started the pendulum swinging convulsively. The entrance of rigid mechanical explanation into psychology and the resulting conclusion that human morals and judgment are merely the automatic products of mechanical processes almost by itself brought on a revolt against mechanism. Perhaps the most instructive case history was that of Thomas Huxley himself. According to McDougall,

> Huxley, the most effective champion of Darwinism . . . the most positive of the positivists, who had eloquently celebrated the iconoclastic thrusts of mechanistic biology, in his famous Romanes Lecture (*Evolution and Ethics*) delivered at Oxford near the end of his life, revoked the main feature of his earlier teaching and called upon mankind to defy the laws of mechanical nature which throughout his life he had so effectively expounded as all-sufficient. . . . Huxley seems to have been moved to his revulsion by pondering upon the intolerable implications for human life of the mechanical biology.

The turn of the twentieth century is remembered as an era of truculent debate and experimental derring-do. Prior to this period, discussion hinged chiefly on how best to interpret the everyday facts of life. Argument was more dialectical than scientific. How can one explain human action, development, and memory? The gifted and beguiling Henri Bergson, using a curious methodological combination of intuition and fragmentary (and selected) scientific evidence, argued that memory has no material basis. To the principle that does guide such functions, he gave the name *élan vital.* Again and again, science stubbed its toes on the point that organic evolution, especially as advocated by the extremist neo-Darwinians, had failed miserably to explain the enigma of human consciousness. Vitalist arguments of this type took on new weight with the emergence of seemingly corroborative *experimental data.* Wilhelm Roux dramatically reported in 1888 that he had taken a frog's egg, allowed it to undergo its first cell division, and then killed one of its two cells. The results were a half-embryo and an enthusiastic renaissance of the science of experimental morphology.

Because this experiment suggested that something invisible and very complex resided in the egg and controlled its future destiny, there was launched a whole string of audacious, if somewhat macabre, experimental manipulations of the growing embryo. The German biologist and philosopher Hans Driesch commenced the work which made him probably the greatest of all the champions of vitalism. He tried to repeat Roux's experiments using the sea urchin egg. After destroying half of a two-celled embryo, he obtained, not a half-embryo, but an embryo normal in every detail except size: it was half the normal size. Roux's findings in the frog were controverted in the sea urchin and it looked very much as though the first cell division of an egg did not result in two dissimilar halves. Driesch went on to produce perfect miniature embryos from partially destroyed larger embryos and from small bits removed from embryos. He demonstrated in newts the most astonishing restitutions of whole limbs following the amputation of a leg. From all of this, he concluded that life must be a "harmonious equipotential" system and in each organism must reside a vital *entelechy* which somehow keeps track of the blueprints for the whole adult form. (Driesch resurrected the term entelechy from Aristotle, who used it to mean a potentiality which has become an actuality.) He argued that no conception which views life as a machine, however far pushed, can account for the origin of a whole organism from a single cell. Something else must explain it, and this something *per exclusionem* is the entelechy.

In response to the challenging fire of Driesch and the experimental morphologists, men of biology dispersed themselves along a broad spectrum of opinion ranging from thoroughgoing, hard-boiled materialism on one end to idealistic metaphysics (which held that the world of matter is pure illusion) on the other. The dispute, while still fundamentally between mechanism and vitalism, took on a more subtle character as interpretations developed finer shadings. By hindsight, much of this conversation has a distinct flavor of carping, as men fought to introduce new names for old ideas.

The vitalist cause was carried forward into the new century by an impressive array of natural scientists. By knitting together the diverse threads that dangled from the separate fields of biology, philosophy, and psychology, these men were able to fabricate what could be called the doctrine of modern vitalism. We might quickly sift through these arguments and identify their advocates. They break down roughly into two categories of inexplicability: life and mind. We have already referred to the claims of nonmaterialists on the origin of life and to the jaw-breaking theories of Driesch, whose operating procedure, we recall, was first peering at a regenerating newt leg, failing utterly to understand it, and then concluding that this wonderful event can be explained only by the entelechy. A group led by E. S. Russell and W. E. Ritter emphasized that organisms depend for their autonomy on their *wholeness* and their marvelous integration. This position, sometimes called *organicism* or *holism*, is, in essence, not particularly unpalatable to materialists. To say that life depends upon the complex organization of its material parts is perfectly compatible with good mechanism, which will agree cheerfully that there are no pieces of living matter, but only living organisms. It is when certain organicists start talking of purpose and denying even the possibility of a physicochemical explanation of the integration of organism that mechanists politely demur. This more rigorously vitalistic faction of the organicist group included J. S. Haldane,* father of the resolutely materialistic J. B. S. Haldane, General Jan Smuts, the brilliant South African statesman and philosopher, and A. N. Whitehead, the profound and erudite philosopher of Cambridge. These men held firmly to teleological views and to theories that spoke of organismic "wholes" and which, paradoxically, often professed to be nonvitalistic. They merged imperceptibly with the views of the last vitalistic sect we will mention, the one which arose chiefly because of the apparent impossibility of accounting for psychic phenomena and religious experience. So much for vitalism.

As these positions were taken, mechanists did not remain silent. Lancelot Hogben, in his book *The Nature of Living Matter,* dismissed Bergson, Whitehead, and Haldane as introspective philosophers and stood strongly and squarely on the empiricist position claiming that nonverifiable ideas of vital forces were pure nonsense. The

* Haldane *père* provides us with a good example of conceptual myopia. When it was discovered how to measure the energy going into and out of an organism, mechanists pointed to the fact that *everything* that went in could be accounted for. No energy, they said, was converted into vital forces. Haldane replied that this was no argument at all against vitalism. "One might as well try to prove from measurement of the intake and output of energy by a locomotive that the driver does not exist." If the driver is intended to be analogous to the vital force, this is a poor analogy indeed. It ignores the fact that locomotive drivers also have energy requirements and, in this example, the driver is an integral part of the whole system. Of the energy put into the locomotive *system,* some would clearly go to the driver.

vitalistic psychologist McDougall angrily accused Hogben of conducting his case according to the good old legal maxim "When you have no case, abuse the other party's attorney."* Joseph Needham in 1936 published *Order and Life,* the Terry Lectures of that year and, as an experimental embryologist, spoke out for mechanism and against the views of Driesch. He closed the volume by saying:

> In conclusion, I would refer to the perplexities of Driesch, at the beginning of the century. . . . A great deal of water has flowed under the bridges since then. We no longer feel the necessity which we felt to place the "intensive manifoldness" of the egg outside space-time. In 1895 very little was known of the complexities of the colloidal state, next to nothing about molecular orientation at interfaces, and nothing at all about the biological significance of paracrystals. . . . The potentialities of the protein chain, and the phenomena of molecular deformability and contractility were unguessed at, and there was no hint of the exploration of solid bodies by x-ray analysis. These many and great advances give us every promise of a profounder insight into the nature of organic form. To abandon the quest at this stage would surely be the height of folly.

This argument might be made even more strongly today.

It would be pointless to try to give notice to all the leading spokesmen for the mechanistic view, now so widely held. Instead let us look into the merits of the case.

* McDougall also declared Hogben's position to be far to the right. "I say 'right' because, although Hogben no doubt considers himself to be far out on the left wing, that is, I think, only one more misunderstanding on his part."

Frogs, clocks, flames, and crystals

The fact of the matter is that extravagant and implausible vitalism of the variety of Hans Driesch is all but a dead issue in biology today. As we have already mentioned, vitalism leads to no progress since it addresses no questions to nature and, as a matter of course, receives no answers. Whatever happens, it is the principle at work, all-knowing and inscrutable. To the mechanist, all biological events require explanation in physical and chemical terms, and hence *everything* arouses surprise and interest. Probing questions are asked, nothing is taken for granted, and the result is progress. The vitalist is left in his armchair, contentedly pondering the occult.

Still, despite the fact that "flagrant" vitalism is dead, neither is strict and rigid mechanism universally accepted by biologists today. The organicists survive and hold on to the view that biology is irreducible to physics. To them, the biological structure and method is intrinsically autonomous. Were they maintaining merely that much of biology has *not yet* been reduced to physicochemical explanation, their position would be unassailable. But they say much more than this. They hold that *in principle* such explanation is not possible and that such explanation should not be the goal of biological research. How valid is this view?

In the first place, nothing so far discovered warrants the view that biological events will *never* be totally explained in physicochemical terms. That is only for further research to say. According to the philosopher Ernest Nagel (with whose position I agree entirely), there are two problems: *defining* biological laws in physicochemical terms and *deriving* biological laws from physical and chemical laws. Certainly the realization of the former is frequently possible (for example, the connection between the amount of blood ejected from the heart and the rate of the heartbeat) whereas the satisfaction of the latter is not as often possible (as, for example, the lack of a clear physicochemical explanation for cell division). But what is there to indicate that such explanation will not one day be possible? There is no reason to abandon this as our goal.

Organicists talk about the "wholeness" of organisms, their unifiedness, integrity, and oneness. They claim that we are dealing with a sum which is greater than the sum of its parts. From the complex integration of parts emerges something bigger and better than a mere sum—an organism! They decry the mechanist who studies the parts separately under the delusion that these results will in any way increase our understanding of the total organism. Nagel makes a vigorous and long overdue attack on the verbal reefs which surround the word "sum." He acknowledges the familiar use of "sum" in expressions such as "the sum of $2 + 2$" or the "sum of forces." But what is meant when someone says "the function of the kidney is more than the sum of the functions of its cells, blood vessels, tissues, etc."? The answer does or should depend on the body of theory underlying one's concepts. Using a purely mechanistic theory, the behavior of a clock is easily explained as the sum of the behavior of its cogs, wheels, and pendulums. But, says Nagel,

> Though the thermal behavior of solids is not the sum of its parts relative to the classical kinetic theory of matter, *it is such a sum relative to modern quantum mechanics.* To say, therefore, that the behavior of an organism is not the sum of the behavior of its parts, and that its total behavior cannot be understood adequately in physicochemical terms even though the behavior of each of its parts is explicable mechanistically, can only mean that *no body of general theory is now available* from which statements about the total behavior of the organism are derivable. The assertion, even if true, does *not* mean that it is *in principle* impossible to explain such total be-

havior mechanistically, and it supplies no competent evidence for such a claim!*

Organicists point to living *form* and *reproduction.* But does not the flame have form which restores itself after distortion by wind or motion? And cannot flame produce numberless other flames by mere contact? We can explain the flame mechanistically and do not postulate a "spirit of flame" or a flame principle—although, interestingly, ancient peoples did think flame was alive. Crystals reproduce and grow, and recent years have seen new machines with memories.

In defense of organicism, much has been said on the subject of the laboratory synthesis of life. The organicist pointedly claims that this can never come about. Perhaps this is true and perhaps it is not. Our materialistic account of life is still quite sketchy. Possibly, even in the future, such a synthesis might still elude us. But what bearing does this have on the issue? We can now give an adequate materialistic explanation of the solar system but the day is far away indeed when we will be able to make one.

For the practicing biologist, for the man who every day enters the laboratory to perform his experiments, organicism means little and contributes less. Thousands of biological scientists the world over, whether explicitly or not, have rejected this outlook and are proceeding upon mechanistic suppositions. The measure of their success is the growing profundity of their insight and the thickness of each year's periodical lists, both of which seem to be increasing exponentially.

With progress occurring at such an incredible rate, who is to say what will happen in another hundred or thousand years? What can justify the solemn pronouncement that this or that will never happen? The answer is nothing. This is not to argue that we will one day possess the "secret of life," whatever that phrase may mean.

* Italics mine.

Because of the indeterminateness of the small events which go to make up the big event, the organism, because of the probability aspect of all scientific propositions, because every new truth is joined indivisibly to its bête noire, new ignorance—for these reasons, we shall *probably* never know all there is to know about the living organism. But, decidedly, this is not the same as saying that an adequate explanation of life in the language of physics and chemistry is not possible. As we shall momentarily see, it may be close at hand.

PART THREE

TWENTIETH CENTURY, THE AGE OF ANALYSIS

CHAPTER IX

THE LATEST REVOLUTION

> We have found a strange footprint on the shores of the unknown. We have devised profound theories, one after another, to account for its origin. At last, we have succeeded in reconstructing the creature that made the footprint. And lo! it is our own.
>
> —A. S. Eddington

About 2,500 years ago, a Greek named Zeno confounded his contemporaries by proving that the fleet Achilles could not possibly overtake a tortoise who had been given a head start. The proof was elegantly simple: the pursuer must always come first to the point from which the pursued has just departed. When Achilles arrives at the tortoise's starting line, the tortoise will have moved a little way beyond this line to a new point of advantage. If Achilles takes any time at all to nullify this new lead, he gives the tortoise time to creep ahead to still another, if progressively smaller, advantage. Achilles thus can never defeat his rival.

This paradox of Zeno had a profound effect upon the history of logic and mathematics, for it instilled in the Greek mind a *horror infiniti*—which paralyzed the creative imaginations of the classical geniuses of mathematics. Yet the concept of infinity and the infinitesimal is the cornerstone of modern mathematics. By abhorring it, as Dantzig has observed, Greek mathematics stopped short of algebra in spite of a Diophantus, stopped short of an analytic geometry in spite of an Apollonius, and stopped short of an infinitesimal theory in spite of an Archimedes. Modern calculus is nothing more than a theory of infinite processes. But today we realize that in the very act of moving, Achilles is traversing a continuum and not an infinite set of discrete discontinuous points—or, in the words of Grünbaum, his motion is legato not staccato. His course, then, is more like a series of whole numbers than of points in space, since for every whole number, there exists a next number, but with any two points in a continuum, another point can always be squeezed between them. An infinite number of nonvanishing distances converging to zero can have a finite sum and can be traversed in a finite time. And so, in the view of modern science, Achilles could have overtaken the tortoise after all!

What is extraordinarily interesting, therefore, about the paradox of Zeno is the fact that Zeno always knew that Achilles could outrun a turtle. Everyone knows that. Yet, in the light of his proof, Zeno reached a metaphysical conclusion: that change and the testimony of the senses are illusory and that time is unreal. He could have chosen the alternative course by concluding that his proof might be faulty—but he did not, presumably because he didn't want to. The lesson of this parable is significant. It is at the heart of the great revolution that the twentieth century brought about in science and philosophy.

In the next four chapters, we will consider in outline some of the ideas brought forth in this era: ideas which, as we shall later show, have profoundly influenced the course of biological thought.

The decline and fall of the absolute

The issue at stake in this ideological revolution concerns the relationship between the real world itself (if such there be) and our knowledge of the world, as set forth in what we think of it and can meaningfully say about it. The point is nicely illustrated by the case history of Euclidean geometry. Although ancient geometry probably arose out of mere practical necessity, Euclid gave it its organization and rigorous deductive character. Through deductive logic, all of the theorems of geometry could be proved true, or at least as true as the few necessary basic axioms upon which every deductive system must rest. But these were easily available to the ancient Greeks. There were, everyone agreed, a number of self-evident truths that are so obvious they could be accepted without proof, for example, the statement that "only one straight line can be drawn between two points." Another such axiom was that "through a given point, one and only one straight line can be drawn parallel to another given line." This, too, seemed self-evident to Euclid as it also does to us.

Yet there was something disturbing about the "parallel postulate." Euclid himself must have thought so for he avoided using it in his first twenty-eight propositions. And other mathematicians disliked it, too, feeling uneasy about employing it as a basic axiom upon which the validity of the remainder of geometry would depend. For twenty centuries, unimaginably vast efforts were expended in an attempt to convert the axiom into a proved theorem derived from *other* axioms. All efforts had failed when, in the nineteenth century, a group of mathematicians almost simultaneously brought forth the same new idea. Although the geometry of Euclid clearly corresponds with our everyday world of moderate dimensions, what is there to indicate that Euclidean geometry remains valid in the vast expanses of celestial space? It is true that the sum of the three angles of a triangle is 180°. But this is a triangle small enough to be measured in our laboratory. What of a triangle in space at whose corners are the sun and the two most distant nebulae? Need the sum of *these* three angles equal 180°, and how could we verify our answer? It is clear that there exists no logical necessity for believing that Euclidean geometry is valid in the reaches of astronomical space, which, after all, may have bizarre properties affecting the measurement of size and distance. These considerations gave rise to a variety of *non-Euclidean* geometries in which the parallel postulate was arbitrarily denied. If this is done, geometries emerge which are perfectly consistent internally but which merely conflict with our "natural" and visualizable picture of the world. The question now arises, if there is a multiplicity of geometries, which one corresponds with physical reality—both in terrestrial and celestial space?

This was a dilemma that caused Newton no serious difficulty. In his time, the universe was a visualizable machine, whose geometry was Euclidean and whose space and time were absolute. Thus, Newton denied absolute motion, the movement of bodies which bore no relation to any external object. This concept is usually illustrated by picturing a laboratory aboard a moving train. As long as there is no acceleration, the passengers would have no way of discovering evidence of their motion by experiments done exclusively with equipment belonging to the laboratory. (Needless to say, the earth is such a vehicle.) Interestingly, as Mach has pointed out, Newton violated his own expressed intention to investigate only *facts* when he spoke of things like absolute space and absolute motion, for these are purely constructions of the mind that cannot be observed empirically.

It was another such construct of the Newtonian era that began to cause trouble. Although somewhat noncommittal in his views on the nature of light, Newton criticized the wave theory, whose founder had been Huygens. And the Newtonian school, interpreting the master's views perhaps more narrowly than he had intended, developed a corpuscular theory of light which pictured light as particles streaming from a luminous body. But the followers of Huygens insisted that light was a wavelike phenomenon. Moreover, it was argued, if light is a wave motion and the world is a material mechanism, light must do its waving in a material medium just as the waves of the sea exist in water. This function they assigned to an unobserved entity, a substance first described in detail by Descartes—the ether. It was a curious substance, imponderable, ubiquitous, space-filling, and capable of vibrating. The fact of the matter is that the ether was an elusive phantom which Newton himself sometimes referred to as a "spirit." Clearly, its main property was to serve as the carefully fabricated final piece in a huge jigsaw puzzle which fit because it was cut to fit. But, as the late Lord Salisbury put it, the ether amounted to little more than the "subject of the verb 'to undulate.'" Its saving grace was that the theory in which it played a part continued to be phenomenally successful in predicting many natural events.

The ether's days were numbered, however. Firstly, the ether had been visualized as an "elastic solid" for the simple reason that the properties assigned to it by the needs of theory were similar to the properties of ordinary elastic solids which were already understood and mathematically formulated. In other words, the unobservable entity whose invention was a theoretical necessity was thought of as something analogous to a well-understood observable entity. It did not take long for scientists to recognize the trap: merely because two separate physical phenomena are described by almost identical mathematical formulas, one cannot justifiably conclude that one of these phenomena is the ultimate reality in terms of which the other is to be explained. One might as well say that since gasoline flows like water, it may also be used to put out fires.

Secondly, there is a considerable difference between concocting a physically unobservable entity (such as the ether), which successfully enables us to predict the behavior of observables (such as light), and the question of whether such unobservables really exist. In 1881,

Michelson and Morley asked whether the ether really existed by performing an ingenious experiment, one that could not have been done earlier because of its reliance on the new skills of optical instrument makers. These workers reasoned that if the earth is careening through the stationary ether and if light is a wave motion that advances through the ether at a fixed rate, then it must follow that if a light beam is split by mirrors so that one half goes a certain distance and is reflected back again, while the other half is projected the same distance and back again but at right angles to the first beam, then the reunited rays should produce an interference pattern, since the two half-beams will now have been altered by the differences in their path lengths through the ether. It would be similar to what would occur if the path lengths were measured of two swimmers swimming equal distances in a swift current, one downstream and back and the other across and back. The experiment, repeated many times since, flatly contradicted the view that the earth is moving through a stationary ether. For if it is, the results of this experiment should have revealed it.

It was clear then that our ideas of space and time had been superficial, and the stage was now set for the work of Einstein. Einstein recognized that uncritical assumptions were being made in the merest act of measuring distance and time. To eliminate confusion, he postulated the radical-seeming view that things look different to different observers at different places and different times, while the velocity of light must appear the same to all observers no matter what their position or motion may be. To illustrate, length is usually measured by laying a measuring rod alongside the distance to be measured. We have measured an object and find it is one yard long. We wish to compare its length with another object in another city. We take our yardstick with us and perform the second measurement. They are the same. But how do we know that by moving the ruler we have not altered its length? One way to find out might be to use a second ruler to measure the first since length can be gauged only by the use of rulers. But the same question crops up again. In other words, we may *observe* that the two rods are equal and congruent when they are next to each other, but when they are apart, we cannot establish their equality by direct observation. Likewise, to establish the simultaneity of events in distantly separated places, we must rely on synchronous clocks, that is, clocks whose minute to minute intervals are the same in terms of time elapsed. But how can we establish that two distant clocks are synchronous? If the clocks are "stationary," one could send light signals from one to the other. If the light took the same number of seconds on the two clocks to traverse the same interval, we would say that time was being reckoned the same on both clocks. Now, however, let us compare several clocks located in various points in space, one of which is "stationary" while the others are all moving at the same rate of speed and in the same direction. We could easily synchronize the moving clocks with each other by the same method of light signals we used to synchronize two stationary clocks. But if the moving clocks are synchronized with respect to one another, they cannot be demonstrably synchronous with the stationary clock since the criterion of its synchronousness—the time it takes for a light signal sent by someone sitting on the traveling clock to reach an observer on the stationary clock—will be changing as the position of the moving clock changes. Thus, if we wish to establish the simultaneity of two events, one of which is occurring in the vicinity of the moving clock and the other near the stationary clock, the result of our determination depends entirely upon which clocks we employ as our standard.

We see then that *simultaneity* and *length* are relative concepts which depend upon the position and state of motion of an observer. It follows from this that we can make no more than a relative statement about whether the geometry of the universe is Euclidean or non-Euclidean. Just as the statement "MacDougall Street is to the left of Sixth Avenue" depends for its objective truth upon an additional statement telling whether we are looking north or south, all statements about which geometry corresponds to the physical world depend on a number of separate considerations. As Reichenbach has pointed out, we cannot say "the two rods located at different places *are* equal" but only "we will *call* them equal." In making such a statement, we are not stating a truth but a definition. By this definition, which implicitly accepts a solid rod as a standard, the world's geometry is plainly Euclidean. In a different part of the universe where we cannot use yardsticks, the geometry appears to be non-Euclidean. And thus we must qualify every statement and measurement with detailed addenda containing definitions and the positions of observers. The basic dilemma remains unresolved but we must agree that the realization of its unsolvability is a discovery of the first importance.

It would be difficult to exaggerate the importance of this discovery upon the philosophical basis of science and on all thought. The essence of Einstein's critique of classical mechanics, and this is the kernel of his brilliant insight, is the idea of construing scientific notions in terms of the actual operations or measurements upon which they rest. This concept, to which P. W. Bridgman has contributed so much, has been called *operational analysis*. We may illustrate it by quoting an example cited by Carl Hempel. How can we think meaningfully of the concept "harder than"? "This rock is harder than that one"—the answer is simple if we define "harder than" operationally. Rock A is harder than rock B if upon drawing a sharp point of A across B, a scratch appears in B. As a methodological precept, operationism has had a profound influence upon modern physics.

What kind of connection can there be then between human knowledge and the physical world now that Einstein has told us to beware of physical statements that contain no terms capable of operational application and to reconcile ourselves to the fact that in making theories we must first make apparently arbitrary decisions between alternative geometries, chronometries, and benevolence knows what else? With some exuberance, A. N. Whitehead wrote:

> The new situation in the thought of today arises from the fact that scientific theory is outrunning common sense. The settlement as inherited by the eighteenth century was a triumph of organized common sense. It grounded itself upon what every plain man could see with his own eyes, or with a microscope of moderate power. It measured the obvious things to be measured, and it generalized the obvious things to be generalized. The eighteenth century opened with the quiet confidence that at last nonsense had been got rid of. Today we are at the opposite pole of thought. Heaven knows what seeming nonsense may not tomorrow be demonstrated truth. The reason why we are on a higher imaginative level is not because we have finer imaginations, but because we have better instruments.

To the weary travelers of the centuries, these developments variously appeared. To the young in heart, the new tidings were joyous and exciting, and vigorous new movements in logic and philosophy promptly took shape. To the backward-looking and tender-minded, the new world view was nothing short of catastrophic. It meant that an opaque curtain had once and for all descended between science and philosophy, behind which neo-Thomists, neo-Kantians, and neo-Aristotelians could carry on their traditions in peace and quiet. To biologists, there appeared only an illegible scrawl on a dimly seen wall. And it should be noted, perhaps, that to most people the work of Einstein meant nothing.

Words, conceptions, models, and meanings

Of the suitable topics for long evenings of pleasant but inconclusive conversation, a perennial favorite is the question of whether progress in science follows after advances in philosophy or whether it is the philosophers who do the following, devising new views of the world when events force them to it. Did the political philosophy of Rousseau lead to the French Revolution or did the philosopher's insights follow upon the cataclysm? It is an intriguing question which historians still debate, and it is clear that there can be no simple answer. As we have already noted, science and progress are intimately involved with the beliefs, philosophical assumptions, and traditions of each age. I mention this here, however, to point up an instance about which there can be little doubt as to who followed whom, the scientist or the philosopher. For the potent province of modern analytic philosophy owes its existence to the Einsteinian revolution in physics. Only later did the sequence reverse. As we shall presently see, the precepts of today's philosophy have reached out to influence and unify all manner of intellectual currents. Not the least of these is our conception of the nature of life.

Einstein pointed out that the statement "two events some distance apart occur simultaneously" cannot be used to derive any observable fact. Here was the impetus to a new philosophy whose chief preoccupation has been with the meaning of language. Since all knowledge must be set forth in language, it is the meaning we give to language which confers upon knowledge its weight and ambiguity. What Einstein was saying was simply that if one wished to understand the Michelson-Morley experiment, one had to commit oneself to the view that the meaning of a statement is strictly related to its verifiability. This conception of the meaning of language had already been voiced by other physicists before Einstein, but it was the monumental work of Einstein that gave these gropings their vast significance for all thought.

Let us consider this question of meaning. I have already mentioned that the great difference between men and beasts is the power to use symbols. Language, of course, is a system of symbols, and it is language, both for its ability to represent ideas and to aid in their development, that largely accounts for the intellectual superiority of men over animals. What is curious is the fact that we look so seldom at the phenomenon of language, whose role in the world of affairs has no parallel. Fortunately, students of language are doing it for us, and what they have told us about this mighty commonplace is fascinating and disquieting.

For example, we recognize that our language is made up of a large number of individual words. Let us suppose that someone tried to improve the language by increasing its richness indefinitely, that is, by inventing a horde of new words to designate more and more subtle and complex concepts. From an alphabet of twenty-six letters, we could concoct, say, 8^{26} or about 300 sextillion eight-letter words, more than enough to replace each whole sentence that has ever been written by a different printed word, which could then serve to represent the meaning of the whole sentence. It is apparent that such enrichment of a language would destroy it, since nobody could remember so many words and since the manifestation of meaning for a word depends upon its repeated use. Thus, a child, having seen the word "naughty" used repeatedly, comes to associate it with a common and recurrent feature in a collection of otherwise differing situations. In other words, since nothing in the world is ever *exactly* repeated, our word carries with it a range of applicability which more or less determines how much variation can be tolerated before the word becomes inappropriate. The word then is a generalization which selects and labels a feature or class of features from the welter of irrelevant features.

If our language was so rich that each word would be used only rarely, words would lose their meanings, because the essential ingredient for a process of generalization, repetition, would disappear. This is evident in the difficulties experienced by children in learning a language. Their main trouble is that they have had too little experience with a word to have grasped that feature of experience which the word designates. That is why a two-year-old will point to a glowing street lamp and say "moon" or to an ape in the zoo and say "Daddy!"

Now the meanings of words are attached to them by human decisions. There is no physical or biological necessity that connects a word with the thing it denotes. These connections are definitions, and in the understanding of definitions lie some great issues. There are several ways of defining words. We may define them ostensively, that is, by saying the word and then pointing the finger. For example, "building" is defined:

But we cannot define every word by pointing; some we must define explicitly. Thus, "Profit is the excess of returns over expenditure." This is the meaning we decided to give to the word "profit." We could just as easily have said, "Profit is a place where limestone is quarried." But we didn't.

Part of the power of words lies in the fact that they aid us in recognizing instances of things for which a word exists. That is, we *use* definitions as diagnostic formulas for the recognition of phenomena or objects. Here is the kernel of a practical problem. It is our daily need for recognition criteria, our absolute dependence upon identification methods based on observed correspondences with our man-made criteria, the necessary preliminary act to drinking water, to selecting the toothpaste from the cabinet, to commenting on the weather, to everything we do. In most cases, we are caused little inconvenience by such problems. If we are asked for a dime, we have no difficulty selecting a coin from the many in our pocket that agrees with the definition of the word "dime." But the difficulties in this area can plague and frustrate the scientist. Sigmund wanted to elaborate the properties of an amoeba and someone handed him a small blob of jelly. Was it an amoeba? Did it possess those characteristics which by definition are designated by the word "amoeba"? He wanted some sodium chloride and someone handed him a bottle of white powder. Was it sodium chloride? It is apparent that in most cases of this kind, we tend to rely upon the label on the bottle for assurances as to what the bottle contains, thereby transferring to another the responsibility for having verified the correspondence between the contents and the properties attached to the word on the label. As every biochemist knows, however, there are too many bottles whose contents have nothing to do with the words on the label.

Even this problem is simple compared to the difficulties in establishing the applicability of those many words in our language which are vague in that there are borderline cases in which it is impossible to say whether the word should or should not be applied. I shall speak of this later, though the reader is correct in suspecting that I consider "life" to be such a word.

We have spoken so far only of words and their meanings. But language is more than mere words: it is also statements. Propositions or statements are the fundamental units of language which possess actual meaning and truth value. In this sense, an isolated word has no meaning, for the logicians point out that unless it stands for a sentence, a word by itself has no meaning. Thus, "table" has no meaning unless one points, physically or mentally, to a table indicating that he means "that is a table." The sentence has meaning. And, of course, meaning and truth value are confined to language and do not apply to the physical things themselves which are denoted by language.

The abstract truths of science are propositions containing the words and symbols of science. This is interesting to consider in view of the hectic rate of expansion of the scientific vocabulary. The truths that we seek today may find expression tomorrow in sentences containing words that are unknown today. Is not our seemingly limitless present vocabulary adequate to cope with any conceptual eventuality? I think the answer to this lies in the realization that the vocabulary of science represents a symbolization of the scientist's intellectual models, and as his models change, his vocabulary expands.

But what are models? This important and tantalizing concept demands our attention. We have already mentioned that science consists of a sequence of oscillations between abstraction and experiment. Good scientists are therefore constantly ambulating back and forth between armchair and laboratory. Experimental data suggest theories and theories suggest new experiments designed either to help confirm or effectively contradict theory. A well-confirmed abstraction thus becomes a highly probable parcel of knowledge.

Abstractions can exist at every level of complexity, as pointed out by Rosenblueth and Wiener and many others. Those low on the ladder of complexity are directly open to experimental verification. If I say the drug colchicine stops the division of cells in a growing onion root tip, I have only to test this experimentally to justify the abstraction (and give it a certain probability). If I next attempt to say that *all* drugs that generally resemble colchicine inhibit the division of *all* cells, the abstraction is of a much higher order of complexity and enormously more difficult to test experimentally.

Because of the complexity of higher abstractions and because of the desirability of establishing such higher generalizations, scientists are forced to devise *models* of nature, simplifications achieved by eliminating irrelevant detail, from which higher abstractions can be more easily derived. It happens that most attempts to explain the meaning of models break up in hopeless confusion, yet the idea is simplicity itself. To most of us, "model" suggests small airplanes or sailing ships inexplicably moored within whisky bottles. But in science, the word "model" means a construction, real or imaginary, in which something complex is rendered understandable—or, as is usually the case, simpler. Their purpose is only to help us formulate our ideas the better to evolve new ones.

The validity of this procedure is as good as the exactitude with which the crucial actuality of nature is embodied in the model, the best model of nature obviously being nature itself. The model is intended to incorporate in workable form the *essential* features of the natural system under examination. Models may be intellectual or material, the former being abstract statements in words or symbols of an idealized simplified situation. Their language may be informal, as, for example, "all stress stimulates the adrenal gland," or the statement may be formal, symbolic, and mathematical. Material models are simplified material representations of a complex system (such as electronic computer and brain) selected on the supposition that some essential aspect of the complex system may thereby be singled out for study.

Obviously, much of the inevitable uncertainty of science lurks in the question of the admissibility and appropriateness of the chosen model. Should my chosen model be too simple or actually irrelevant, I am predestined to failure. Many chosen models are, by hindsight, astonishingly unsuitable. Other dubious-seeming models have turned out to be the inspirations of genius.

Unfortunately, we cannot know the propriety of our models, intellectual or material, except from the retrospective vantage point of future success or failure. Recently, I heard a lecturer describe his researches in sociology in which he used as his model the ultimate particles of physics. Their clinging together as atoms and molecules suggested to him the essences of society and he termed the phenomenon *proto-society*. Here we will have to await confirmation or denial of our present skepticism about the suitability of the chosen model.

Clearly, there are dangers involved in using material models. The elastic-solid model of the "luminiferous ether" which we have discussed suffices to illustrate this danger. The error lurking in material models far different in size scale from that of nature is amply illustrated by the mechanical model of the universe propounded in the Newtonian era. This structure, embodying Euclidean geometry, seemed correct and logical because it was most easy to visualize conceptually. But the geometry of celestial and subatomic space turned out to be non-Euclidean, far more difficult to visualize mechanically in the mind's eye and hence untranslatable into handy material models. Here, contemporary models eventually retarded progress.

In biology, models of every level of complexity are used, and because of the nature of the scientific problem they can be helpful and treacherous. Some appear outwardly more "mechanical" than others. There has been great enthusiasm lately for "mathematization" in biology, and frequently this has had amusing consequences as pointed out by J. A. Rafferty. It leads sometimes to *circularism.*

> The biologist builds an elaborate and intricate theory in vernacular. The mathematician simplifies the theory and describes it in mathematical symbols. He then deduces consequences which are already evident from the verbal reasoning of the

biologist. He "puts into numbers what everybody knows in words". Or he arrives at consequences which are fictions of his simplifications in devising a neat mathematical model. The mathematician may have enjoyed his mathematical exercise, but science is none the better for it. Biomathematicians working *in biologica vacuo* are particularly susceptible to the insidious circularity of modeling by description.

Models in biology consist chiefly of substitutes for the total organism which are variably reduced in complexity. We may use a smaller animal to study psychology because this animal has a seemingly simpler social integration. We use fruit flies to study genetics because they enter a new generation every twelve days, a notable change in the time scale when it comes to comparisons with some other organisms. We use bacteria to study intermediary metabolism because they are single-celled organisms and can be grown on simple media of known composition. (Sigmund used amoebae.) We constantly compare the thermodynamics of the organism to that of the engine and teach our classes that metabolizing food is like burning coal. Purified enzymes are used to eliminate the complexities of cell membrane permeability and structural organization. Each of these models represents a different level of complexity. Each has only a limited contribution to make to the highest abstractions, those of universal applicability.

Thus we see the connection between a scientist's mental models and his vocabulary. In an essay called "Language and Science," Stanley Gerr clearly showed how scientific terms (and nonscientific terms for that matter) are evolved. They may arise from a crystallization of phrases and groups of words into fixed expressions which are used over and over again as symbols of an intellectual model. An example is "the specific dynamic action of proteins," an expression which refers to the observation that following a protein meal, the heat production of the body increases. This heat is essentially wasted and has been called, in another expression representing another abstract concept, "the cost of digestion." In using these terms, we seldom think of the intimate events of metabolism which are proceeding in blissful unawareness of our discursive ruminations. We don't even think of the scientist sitting by his calorimeter watching its dials. We think instead of the intellectual model embodied in the expression "cost of digestion." This functional sense of language is reflected also in terms like "spectrophotometric methods," "depolymerization," "electrify." These terms are the linguistic evidences of the progress of science.

In the early stages of knowledge of a subject, when little is known, our inadequate conceptions force us, as Gerr states, to use linguistic props, metaphors, crude similes, and elaborate descriptions which endow our first fragile models with structural rigidity. But as knowledge grows, language is formulated and entities and relations emerge as *conceptual units*. Thus concept and language are correlates. In the early days of biology, the basis of heredity was completely unknown. When Morgan postulated the gene as a particulate bearer of hereditary characteristics, an extremely useful model was elaborated. In recent years, more subtle and precise experiments have shown several possible shortcomings in the gene theory and our language is now changing to include words like "locus" which correspond to newer intellectual models.

And so it appears that the nature of truth is intimately bound up with semantics. The philosopher Tarski, in a brilliant analysis of this question, ended with the definition, "A sentence is true if it is satisfied by all objects and false otherwise." For example, "The sentence 'the snow is white' is true if, and only if, snow is white." The degrees of correspondence between abstract statement and model and model and nature are the degrees of truth of a scientific statement. In both areas, there is ample room for fallibility.

Modern logic has asked the question, "When is a proposition meaningful?" and after much polemical controversy has proposed as an answer the ***verifiability theory of meaning*** which, stated simply, holds that a proposition is meaningful only if it is, in principle, verifiable as true or false. (We would be more explicit if we said confirmable as more or less probable.) It should be kept in mind that meaning here refers to cognitive meaning. *Meaningless* means factually meaningless and has no reference to psychological, emotional, or esthetic meaning. Despite all that has been said for or against this view, it has given a powerful tool to science. One recalls the famous interchange of published remarks of C. I. Lewis and M. Schlick on the merits of this theory of meaning. Lewis argued, for example, that the concept of immortality is unverifiable and yet meaningful. Schlick answered that indirect phenomena may, *in principle,* justify a hypothesis of survival after death. To this verifiability, the hypothesis of immortality owes its meaning; beyond the possibility of verification it has no meaning. A sentence whose probability of truth cannot be determined or altered from possible observations then is meaningless: *here is a cornerstone of modern science.*

Schlick wrote:

> If we utter a sentence without meaning it is always our own fault. The tremendous philosophic importance of this remark will be realized when we consider that what we said about the meaning of assertions applies also to the meaning of questions. There are many questions which can never be answered by human beings. But the impossibility of finding the answer may be of two different kinds. . . . If it is due to chance circumstances to which our human existence is confined, there may be reason to lament our fate and the weakness of our

physical and mental powers, but the problem could never be said to be absolutely insoluble, and there would always be some hope, at least for future generations. . . . But what about those problems for which it is *logically* impossible to find an answer? Such problems would remain insoluble under all imaginable circumstances . . . this calamity would happen only if the question itself had no meaning. It would not be a genuine question at all, but a mere row of words with a question-mark at the end.

The history of science and particularly biology abounds with examples of meaningless questions or pseudo problems. How was matter generated from nothing? Do organisms contain vital forces? What was the cause of the universe? (If there were a first event in the universe, it could not have a cause.) What is the purpose of human life? What is the nature of nothing? And so on and so on. When we can set aside such questions as being outside the realm of possible empirical verification, we have arrived at the view that the logic of language determines the limits and structure of meaningful discourse.

Let it be said in ending this discussion that the problems of language are among the deepest questions that men have essayed to answer, and they are merely mentioned here, not delved into. Philosophers continue to debate the questions of meaning and language, and the quality of this dialogue remains vigorous, particularly since certain formulations of the verifiability criterion of meaning have turned out to have a number of unwelcome logical consequences. Although the empirical and analytic trend in philosophy represents a major turning point in the history of critical thought, no one need fear that speculative and intuitive philosophy has passed into the beyond. It remains alive and presumably always will as long as there are people whose views of the world are basically rooted in emotion, hope, and fear. Certainly, many a present-day philosopher still considers speculative philosophy worth doing. As might be expected, one of the problems in the growth and consolidation of logical empiricism seems to have been the overaggressive use of the theory of meaning by what Feigl has called "young iconoclasts." The temptation is strong to sweep aside difficult problems by declaring them meaningless, and this has happened too often. This criticism is easy to make, but it, too, is shaky because it implies the desirability of airtight criteria of meaningfulness against which we can measure whether young iconoclasts have indeed gone too far. Unfortunately, there are no such criteria, and here is where the question stands in the philosophy seminars of today.

Nevertheless, the analytic view has made monumental contributions to our thinking in science and biology. Before we discuss them, however, let us say a word about some of the other notions that have sprung up in the fertile soil of modern philosophy and science.

CHAPTER X

EXPLANATION IN SCIENCE

Shemin: I think ——'s theories are infantile.
Racker: We don't care if they're infantile, David, just as long as they're correct.
—Overheard at the Enzyme Club, 1956

At a recent international meeting of Nobel Prize winners in physics, something of a furor was created by statements made by two of the world's greatest nuclear physicists, Werner Heisenberg of Germany and Hideki Yukawa of Japan. What caused the excitement was a declaration of dissatisfaction with the two theories which are the keystones of contemporary thought in nuclear physics—the theory of relativity, which seeks to explain the universe at large, and the quantum theory, which deals with the forces within the atom. Science, they said, must now seek a new explanation for the structure and properties of the elementary particles of physics, for neither the relativity theory nor the quantum theory adequately explains some of the revolutionary discoveries that have been made in recent years.

Heisenberg said, "Existing theories at best serve to give a semiphenomenological explanation for the qualities of elementary particles, but they fail to explain their existence convincingly." And Yukawa said, "Granted that the existing theories have something essentially correct, our further step must be to have a deeper insight so that we can approach nearer to a unified theory of elementary particles."

We can learn much from this episode, for just as great dramas draw upon the emotions shared by all men, what we are witnessing here is a great scientific drama whose theme is a commonplace of everyday life: the search for explanations. The physicists are telling us that discoveries have been made which are not yet explainable. They now seek the answer to the question "why?" having already answered the question "what?" We recognize in this quest the essential purpose of all scientific inquiry, going beyond mere description by providing explanation. No one could reasonably disagree with this assertion. It is worth noting, therefore, that there is continuing and often hectic disagreement among philosophers about aspects of the nature of explanation. If we are to enter the catacomb of science—and particularly biology, where the gloom has been thickest—we should really look in on this wrangle. Some of it is uncommonly interesting.

The nature of explanation

Some have held that there is no real difference between *description* and *explanation*. Others have taken the position that all scientific explanation is *circular* and can ultimately be boiled down to statements like the famous one of Calvin Coolidge, "When many people are out of work, unemployment results" or "He takes eight baths a day because he is compulsive." We will recognize that if "compulsiveness" were diagnosed on the basis of the eight baths a day, the statement is circular and adds nothing to our understanding.

Still another conception holds that explanation consists in the systematic reduction of the unfamiliar to the familiar. But this view makes us uneasy: falling apples are familiar but what is familiar about the law of gravity?

Let us consider these points. There are, of course, differences between description and explanation. A descriptive generalization simply formulates in some manner the results of many observations. Usually, in the history of science, description precedes explanation and, in fact, makes it possible. Suppose, for example, we observe the motion of a particle, making observations at successive intervals and recording its position at those times. To answer the question "Where was the particle at such and such a time?" we have only to look at our descriptive table. Even if we find it possible to express the motion of the particle in a simple mathematical formula, we have still done no more than describe its movement.

Similarly, to invent a biological example, suppose we are concerned with the color of animal fur. We might set up a table in which we list down in one column the names of various animals with their coat colors in another column. If now we list the predominant color of the customary habitat and then declare that animals tend to have the coloration of their environment, have we achieved an explanation? No, because the generalization is still purely descriptive. It is "what" and not "why."

Turning to the circular view of explanation, here is treacherous terrain. We know where we stand in the simple case of the physician who says, "You have a headache because you have cephalalgia." Although this type of explanation is common in medicine, it consists of nothing more than translation into Greek. But in the history of biology, a number of crucial developments have rested solely upon such flimsy supports. An example occurs to me which I have not seen discussed previously. It will be recalled that one of the widely applauded developments of nineteenth-century biology was the theory that *protoplasm* is the universal stuff of life. This theory is still being taught as a fundamental principle of biology. Yet in reading the literature of that period, an odd thought arises about the theory and its status as a scientific generalization, for it contains a paradox, and I believe one can show that the discovery of protoplasm both aided and hindered the cause of science. When it emerged, "the brotherhood of protoplasm" seemed to be a potent concept that threw new light on a variety of scientific questions. But the protoplasm idea had another aspect: it was logically empty and colossally vague. The ground stuff of life? What does it mean?

Let's take a moment to analyze this point briefly. Formal logic tells us that a statement is a tautology that is empty of empirical content and necessarily true. The facts of the world can never falsify it. The statement "If my mistress were named Penelope, her name would start with 'P'" is true whether or not my mistress's name is, in fact, Penelope, and, happily, nothing in the sentence informs us what her name might actually be. As a source of empirical truth, the sentence is empty; that is why logical relations are empty or tautological. Science is filled with unchallengeable tautologies. But when the same statements are phrased in terms open to empirical verification they may be true and they may be false. Thus, if "east" is defined as that point on the horizon which is 90° to the right as one faces north, the statement "The sun rises in the east" may or may not be true and can easily be tested experimentally. Here, the word "east" had a meaning before we brought the sun into it. But, if we define "east" as the place where the sun rises, the same statement becomes a tautology, empty of empirical meaning. Under these circumstances, the sun can rise nowhere else.

The question then becomes: Did "protoplasm" have a meaning before the theorists decided that all living substance is made of it? From the evidence I have seen, the answer is no. Certainly, it was not a new word in the nineteenth century. According to Cameron, the phrase "*De parentis protoplasti*" appeared in a sixth-century hymn that was sung during Passiontide. Purkinje, before 1840, used the word protoplasm to refer to the living substance of plant and animal cells—what he said was that cells *consist of* protoplasm—but I see no indication that he defined it by any special physical, chemical, or biological properties. If he had and *then* it was pronounced the universal substance of life, the "protoplasm theory" would be an induction based on experimental data. What happened, I think, was the exact reverse. The theory was stated as a tautology, "All life is protoplasm," which inescapably means "That which lives we shall call protoplasm." *Then,* in time its physical properties *were* gradually defined, and the word took on a new significance in the light of later empirical experience. In any case, we eventually found that what we have known as protoplasm is an elaborate organization which is dissectable into a hierarchy of parts. Although one is never justified in criticizing the technics of discovery—an important discovery would remain important though its discoverer stumbled over it in a dark alley—this concept, by its nature and its era, could only have been an intuitive decision on an essentially verbal level.

I raise the point about the protoplasm theory, because, suspecting it of being a tautological definition, I further suspect it of being a definition that implied different things to different people. Did it mean a physical entity or a class of entities? One is reminded of the beginning of Woodger's tale of the land Naamba.

> Once upon a time, long long ago, there dwelt in a village which later was called Naamba (the precise geographical location of which need not detain us) a people endowed with the power of recognition and speech but, to begin with, a very limited vocabulary. They had demonstrative pronouns and made great use of gestures. But they had no proper names, nouns, or adjectives. The results of acts of recognition they expressed in the form "here is another of those." Finding this highly inconvenient one of these people—a man of great originality—

> invented proper names. This man, whenever he recognized his pet dog, said, "here is Fido again," and whenever he recognized another object which was more like Fido than anything else, but at the same time obviously *not* Fido again he said, "here is *another* Fido." But this also proved to be inconvenient and insufficient, because another inhabitant, copying the first, had decided to call his dog "Dido." So instead of one saying "here is another Fido" and the other saying "here is another Dido" they agreed each to keep his own name for his pet, but both to say, "here is another bobo," when they recognized Fido-like *or* Dido-like objects.

In other words, the question was: Is protoplasm a Fido, Dido, or bobo? If we mean it as a class of objects rather than an object of the class and merely explain away its almost infinite variations with the old saying, "All flesh is not the same flesh for there is one kind of flesh of men and another of beasts," then we are again opening the door to conceptual trouble. Empiricists most willing to subordinate hypothesis to fact hardly knew where to go to "confirm" the theory of protoplasmic universality. But to some of the metaphysically inclined (and this raises another point), protoplasm was just their dish: it had wonderful overtones of mystical music of the spheres and conveyed poetic images of quivering disembodied life, flowing and swirling in a cloud of unknown unknowables. For those who wished to see it that way, I suspect that the protoplasm theory may have heaped extra fuel on the fires of vitalism by implying anew a degree of complexity that only vitalism could account for while simultaneously arousing fervent opposition to this new outrage of materialistic science.

I only suspect that the first happened, but I know that the second did. In a pungent essay written by Thomas Henry Huxley in 1871, one finds the following passage referring to his earlier lecture *On the Physical Basis of Life:*

> In it there was nothing new; and, as I hope, nothing that the present state of knowledge does not justify us in believing to be true. Under these circumstances, my surprise may be imagined, when I found, that the mere statement of facts and of views, long familiar to me as part of the common scientific property of Continental workers, raised a sort of storm in this country, not only by exciting the wrath of unscientific persons whose pet prejudices they seemed to touch, but by giving rise to quite superfluous explosions on the part of some who should have been better informed.
>
> Dr. Stirling, for example, made my essay the subject of a special critical lecture, which I have read with much interest, though, I confess, the meaning of much of it remains as dark to me as does the "Secret of Hegel" after Dr. Stirling's elaborate revelation of it. . . . A most amusing example of this fashion of dealing with scientific statements is furnished by Dr. Stirling's remarks upon my account of the protoplasm of the nettle hair. That account was drawn up from careful and often-repeated observations of the facts. Dr. Stirling thinks he is offering a valid criticism, when he says that my valued friend Professor Stricker gives a somewhat different statement about protoplasm. But why in the world did not this distinguished Hegelian look at a nettle hair for himself, before venturing to speak about the matter at all? Why trouble himself about what either Stricker or I say, when any tyro can see the facts for himself, if he is provided with those not rare articles, a nettle and a microscope? But I suppose this would have been *"Aufklarung"*—a recurrence to the base common-sense philosophy of the eighteenth century, which liked

to see before it believed, and to understand before it criticised. Dr. Stirling winds up his paper with the following: "In short, the whole position of Mr. Huxley, (1) that all organisms consist alike of the same life-matter, (2) which life-matter is, for its part, due only to chemistry, must be pronounced untenable—nor less untenable (3) the materialism he would found on it."

In the furnace glare of today's biology, the word protoplasm has a somewhat old-fashioned look. The analytical movement has bitten deep into the complexities of living substance and has yielded a more concrete, if not "ultimate," vocabulary. Today, we speak of protoplasm in its latter-day context, wherein it is defined in chemical, physical, and biological terms. We *now* have enough empirical evidence to agree enthusiastically that there *is* fundamental similarity between the protoplasm of all living things and that, no doubt, protoplasm is "the ground stuff of life." This, however, is a very different thing, in fact the very opposite, of stating as a principle that protoplasm is the substance of life because that which lives is protoplasm.

In other words, we achieve explanation when we relate our specific observations to a separate verifiable generalization or law which is outside of them and from which they could potentially have been predicted. We did not explain our moving particle merely by describing its motion mathematically, but we would explain it if we showed that the motion is under the influence of a nearby magnet, for the law of magnetic fields would permit us in principle to predict the particle's movement. Similarly, we did not explain the color of animal fur merely by pointing out its resemblance to the background. It is by connecting coat color with the idea of visibility and the concept of protection from predatory animals that permits us to say the polar bear is white because white fur enhances his chances of survival. By going behind what is observable, we have explained his color. And likewise, if "compulsiveness" were an independently ascertainable empirical quality, we could use it to explain the behavior of a man who took eight baths a day.

We do *not* achieve explanation when we refer our observations to an analogy or to some appealing metaphor—as, for example, the attempt to clarify biological parasitism on the basis of what we know of human political systems. Just such an explanatory view was recently set forth in the scientific literature by H. W. Stunkard, who, among other things, wrote that the honeybee is *in reality* ". . . a most pathetic little creature . . . a martyr, and a victim of the 'welfare state.'" The hazards of such an analogy need no comment. It clearly does not bring together a set of observations with a general law under which they may be subsumed. It, therefore, is not a valid explanation.

I regret to say that the very laws upon which explanations must rest are themselves the subject of fretful discussion. We all understand intuitively what a law is: it is a generalization about the world for which considerable evidence has been gathered. But philosophers are troubled by the borderline cases in which it is difficult to say whether a statement is a law or something else. These are intricate questions of logic and we will not presume to enter them here. It does not seem to me that great importance attaches to the precise limits which are set to the application of the word "law." For our discussion, our rough definition should suffice.

Interestingly, Haldane has even complained about the use of the word "law" in this context. He prefers to speak of the "uniformities of nature" and do away with the possible implication of a law giver or a legislative body of atoms. "If a piece of matter does not obey a law of nature it is not punished. On the contrary, we say that the law has been incorrectly stated. It is quite probable that every law of Nature so far stated has been stated incorrectly." Several views have been held on the nature of these laws. There is the older view that laws are absolute, and the extreme, recent positivistic view that we can only say that phenomena occur *as if* certain laws held. The British physicist Jeffreys wrote, "A well-verified hypothesis will probably continue to lead to correct inferences even if it is wrong." He comments that "laws" which ultimately turn out to be inexact have often been remarkably more exact than the data on which they were first formulated.* "When Einstein's modification [of the law of gravitation] was adopted, the agreement of observation with Newton's law was three hundred times as good as Newton ever knew." There appears to be no reason for saying there are no regularities in nature to which our statements of natural law correspond. "One might as well say," wrote Haldane, "that because no maps of England give its shape exactly, it has no shape."

When all is said and done there seems to be evidence that even the "laws of nature" are changing. Modern physics suggests the possibility that changes are taking place in the speed of light and the rates of chemical reactions. In other words, the universe is changing, and it becomes hazardous to attempt calculations concern-

* We have recently witnessed a dramatic instance of a law of physics—one which had successfully predicted natural phenomena since its innovation thirty years ago—abruptly shattering before our eyes. The so-called law of parity held that two sets of phenomena, one of which is a mirror image of the other, behave in an identical fashion except for the mirror image effect. According to this law, were we in communication with beings on another planet, we would have no way of telling whether they meant the same thing by "right" and "left" as we do. But in early 1957, brilliantly conceived experiments were reported that invalidate the law of parity, for they proved that among the particles of physics right-handedness of spin is crucially and discernibly different from left-handedness, thus permitting an absolute identification of right and left in all possible worlds. It would be difficult to overestimate the importance of this discovery.

ing the very remote past and future. It appears that eternal natural stability is as improbable as its psychological corollary, eternal truth. This should worry no one except the seeker of eternal certainty. It may turn out that fundamental change and uncertainty are the nearest things we have to eternal principles.

Frequently, we seem to content ourselves with descriptive generalizations without seeking to reach the explanatory plane. Worse, sometimes we confuse the two. The error is serious simply because descriptive generalizations preclude reliable predictions. Of course, we do often predict on this basis, but with scanty justification. Without an outside connection, we have little real basis to assume that A5 will necessarily follow A1, A2, A3, A4. If the series is not explained, we do not understand the thread connecting the terms and we can never know when the series is long enough to permit valid prediction. For example, would 4 or 12 be more likely to come next in the series 18, 57, 42, 91, 72, . . . ? Only after it is recognized that when the numbers are written out as words (eighteen, fifty-seven, forty-two, ninety-one, seventy-two) they are arranged alphabetically as in a dictionary, is the series explained. The answer is obviously "twelve."

There are a number of things that we as authors of biological explanation aspire to and take for granted but rarely discuss. For one thing, we assume that there is order in the universe and that nature is intelligible. We assume that inductive reasoning is safe. We also tend to stick close to the "simplicity postulate," a rule of cerebral economy that can be traced back to the medieval thinker William of Occam. His rule, often called Occam's razor, read *Entia non sunt multiplicanda praeter necessitatem*—entities shall not be multiplied beyond necessity—a sane preachment that has greatly influenced thought. Restated by Bertrand Russell, it says that "if everything in some science can be interpreted without assuming this or that hypothetical entity, there is no ground for assuming it." We are, thereby, admonished against inventing unnecessary entities, dominions, powers, rules, causes, and connections. What we must bear in mind, however, is that there is no proven necessity for this rule of thought, for though logic may tell us not to invent unnecessary symbols, logic cannot tell us not to multiply entities. As we have seen, the course of biological science raises substantial doubts as to the equivalence of simplicity and validity. As Woodger has aptly written: "The biologist especially, faced with the unutterable complexity of living things, cannot but feel that the apparent successes of the simplicity postulate are liable to be achieved by throwing some of the main cargo overboard under the mistaken impression that it is merely ballast." This warning presumably goes to young and old iconoclasts alike.

Looking backward for causes and forward for goals

The story is told that a citizen of the town in which Democritus lived was killed one day by a tortoise that fell from the sky upon his head. The people were shocked and wondered what explanation there could be for such an extraordinary event. Suddenly someone recalled that an eagle had been observed circling around directly above the scene of the tragedy. Things then began to make sense. The eagle was the bird of Zeus and it had dropped the tortoise on the victim's head. Why would Zeus have sponsored such an occurrence? There could be only one reason—to punish a man who must have been guilty of some grave crime. And, with this, the people began to probe into the man's past for the scandal they knew they would find.

Democritus watched these events and shrugged. If they find their scandal, he thought, they will think they have proved the operation of divine vengeance. But why need these events have occurred to serve a purpose? And so Democritus confronted his neighbors with some irrefutable facts. True, eagles are fond of tortoise meat. It is also true, they agreed, that in order to break the hard shell of the tortoise, the eagle must drop the tortoise from a goodly height onto a suitable rock. "Therefore," said Democritus pointing to the victim's bald head, "why can't we simply assume that the eagle mistook this shining pate for a rock fit to break a tortoise on?" And the people conceded that it was just as reasonable to imagine a nearsighted eagle as an impetuous and wrathful king of the gods.

We have spoken of explanation but have said nothing of causality. Yet in ordinary life, the usual method of explaining an event is to state its cause. I was sick because I ate a green apple. The stock market collapsed because the President was sick. Poliomyelitis is disappearing because of a powerful new vaccine. There is the cause, then the effect—what could be simpler? Unfortunately, almost anything could be simpler, for the concept of causality has long been a troublesome one. A large part of this difficulty is traceable to the ineradicable idea that everything that happens happens for a purpose.

Man is a vain creature. All through history he has enthroned himself at the center of the universe, indisputable emperor of all he surveys. He has traditionally ignored or uneasily repressed the conclusions of geology and astronomy, that man is but a brief interlude, having existed during less than a hundredth of a per cent of the history of a tiny speck of cosmic dust, the earth. Instead, he has often seen himself as the object and goal of the whole cosmic enterprise.

Philosophers call this attitude *anthropomorphism:* it has led people to grave and often fatal error. Historically, this point of view has taken many forms: the a priori assumption that the sun rotates around the earth, the ancient and modern gods who look like men and share their foibles, the reluctance to believe that man descended from apes, the strident contention that living and nonliving matter are necessarily fundamentally different, the attribution to evolution of some great and awesome purpose.

That the world has purpose, the view called *teleological,* is believed by a large number of people. The teleologist's arguments are many. He says that the world has a pattern and must therefore have a purpose, that man is too intricate and complex to have just happened. He points to evolution (now that he has been forced to swallow the fact of evolution) as a cogent argument for world purpose: life is becoming more complex and it is evolving toward a goal of perfection. Furthermore, argues the teleologist, if the world had no purpose, why else would it have been created? Humans can have purpose, why can't the world have it? Most people believe in it, and it says so in the Bible.

If we are to discuss the living organism, this issue requires some consideration. Refutation of most of these arguments is not difficult; a few, however, do not yield so easily. Furthermore, refuting an opponent's case is not the same as establishing your own. Modern philosophy, moving both in the avant-garde and in the rear encampments of modern science, has given careful attention to the debate between explainers-by-cause and explainers-by-purpose, and it presents us with a parcel of rejoinders whose conspicuous unwrapping would be most instructive. As we shall see, the modern view of causality—which has profound significance for biology—is still another outgrowth of the new physics.

As was evident in the town of Democritus, the attitudes of the ancient Greeks toward physical occurrences were somewhat divided. The early discoverers of mathematical regularities in the movement of the stars believed that a strict and inexorable order characterized these events: they were attributable to blind, causal laws, or to what is called *causal determinism.* All the events of the world were the results of other events; nothing was arbitrary or accidental. But for the majority of the ancients, the apparatus of causation was viewed through anthropomorphic glasses. *Fatalism* was the accepted basis of natural events. Just as men controlled physical objects, the gods controlled men, each of whom was impelled toward his inescapable destiny according to a heavenly plan.

But the success of mathematical formulation could not be ignored. Using mathematical relationships, a Galileo could predict the outcome of a physical event, such as the position and velocity at any given moment of a ball rolling down an inclined plane. The unequivocal success of such predictions soon spread to the domains of light, heat, and electricity. With complete knowledge of the initial state of a system, mathematical analysis permitted rigorous prediction of the future state of the system. Of course, in most cases, one was unable to determine the *exact* state of affairs in a physical system but this was one's own fault. Human imperfection, it was generally agreed, would eventually be gotten around when better instruments of observation became available.

Causal determinism was given its most trenchant affirmation by the brilliant mathematician Laplace, who declared that were there a superhuman intelligence capable of knowing the position and momentum of every atom in the universe and of solving all the mathematical equations, it could, with precision, state the minutest detail of every event whether it be thousands of years in the future or as remote in the past. This strict view of physical determinism was the direct outgrowth of Newtonian physics which viewed the world as a huge machine whose mode of operation would be completely described if our knowledge of physics were perfect. Nor was its universal acceptance to be wondered at. Not only was its power of prediction demonstrably uncanny but there was the captivating spectacle of progressively improving agreement between observation and equation following directly upon every refinement in technical accuracy.

Causal determinism is distinctly different from fate. "It

is blind," wrote Reichenbach, "not planning; it does not favor or hate men; it is a determinism not in terms of future aims but of past facts, a determinism not in terms of a supernatural command but of a physical law. But it is as strict and exceptionless as the determinism of fate. It makes the physical world comparable to a wound clock that goes automatically through its stages."

But the mid-nineteenth century discovery of the laws of gas behavior hinted that all was not well with rigidly interpreted causal determinism. Gases are swirling collections of *individual* molecules whose agitated movements appear completely random, senseless, and, of course, quite unpredictable. And yet the gases themselves, in the whole, nicely follow the mathematical laws of pressure and temperature and conform admirably to classical deterministic science. Thus, the experimenter was confronted with a *large and rigorously predictable* event which was the resultant of an enormous number of *small and totally unpredictable* events! This is not to say that the movement of each tiny particle is not governed completely by the laws of classical mechanics. It well may be. The unpredictability of its path means that, for one reason or another, *no human observer* could make the prediction. Recognition of this paradox forced him to the conclusion that the seemingly predictable behavior of gases was, in fact, nothing more than the very high probability that the average result of many small seemingly random events would be something corresponding to mathematical expectation, the replacement, really, of causal law by probability law.

The question remained whether or not determinism was operating on the micro-level. Does not causal law determine the zigzag path of each individual particle? It soon became apparent that there simply was no way of knowing by observation the behavior of the individual particles, especially those particles which make up the atom. And there would be no way until the unlikely day when measuring instruments could be made which approached in size and energy the particles being measured, for these are particles which are joggled around merely by being looked at. Although many wished to believe that the tiny elusive particles moved deterministically and there was no absolute proof that this was not the case, *there was no experimental evidence for believing that it was* and no reason or need for continuing to do so except habit. We seem to be living in a world which looks, and for practical purposes is, deterministic and yet which deeper down contains a shadow world of cryptically indeterminate micro-events whose causal basis, quantum theory tells us, is fundamentally and intrinsically undemonstrable.

Such notions are familiars of daily life. In America each year about 40,000 people are killed in automobile accidents. This number is so remarkably constant it is predictable, that is, it is predictable with a high probability of accuracy. And yet, despite the intransigent protests of modern-day fatalists, each individual accident is clearly the result of a certain constellation of circumstances: error, weather, position, and so forth. Even though each individual accident is casually determined, we as observers lack the means to predict these circumstances with enough accuracy to enable us to predict which individual will have a fatal accident in a given year. As far as we are concerned, his fate is indeterminate, but in a population of 160 million individuals, the prediction of the number of accident victims can be made within a few per cent. This, then, is not true determinism, but statistical probability. It is not impossible that some year, under identical conditions (newfangled crash preventers would disqualify the argument), this number will be much smaller or perhaps larger. It is highly unlikely, however.

Probability operates in another way in this situation. It could be argued convincingly, I think, that there is nothing in principle that prevents us from improving our prediction of the annual accident rate to the point of almost absolute accuracy. What would be necessary would be complete information on the weather throughout the country, the detailed driving plans of each individual, the mechanical condition of every automobile at every minute, and so forth. This information is only technically unattainable; in theory it could be obtained. We then could sit down and by massive calculation and analysis successfully predict the occurrence of accidents. Why then would this not give us *absolute* accuracy? For if it does, we have a causal law that is strictly deterministic. The answer is: because we have forgotten to obtain complete data on the position of meteors, since it is clearly possible that one of them could upset our predictions by landing on someone's car. With this possibility accounted for, who can say what others may have been overlooked? We begin to see that we can never formulate absolute laws. Our laws are high probability statements, and this is true also of the laws of classical physics which deal not with gases and particles but the simple mechanics of the inclined plane. If they were not probability statements, laws would have to contain the phrase, "This law will operate successfully as long as nothing happens to prevent it from working." If laws were written that way, they would lose their meaning.

Since we have said that explaining an event consists in relating it to some outside law, what do we mean when we explain it by pointing to its cause? The answer to this lies in the fact that *causes* are events which are connected by little causal laws to other events. Here we encounter one of the most crucial questions in science. We all speak of causes and we know what we mean when we say "A causes B." But it is often overlooked that no one ever observed the phenomenon of anything causing anything else: *what is observed is a temporal sequence of spatially contiguous events, not causation.* One can observe that B follows A. When one observes that *whenever A occurs, B occurs,* he may be in a position to declare that he has found the cause of B. The repetition of the observation is essential, because we are surrounded by a stream of miscellaneous events occurring in temporal sequence, one after the other. But because these are not regular occurrences, we do not infer causality. If they were regular occurrences, we would assume causality, or, in more precise language, we would say, "If A occurs, it is highly probable that B will occur." This, in fact, is a causal law. And it is a law to say, "If I eat a green apple, I will get sick," for this is the law by which I explain my sickness, and eating a green apple is its cause.

There is one further question about causality. A regularly preceding causal event may be difficult to identify. Is the five o'clock whistle, which is regularly followed by an exodus of workmen from the factory, the cause of their departure? If A, in a black mood, calls B a numbskull, and B takes a gun and shoots A dead, what is *the cause* of A's extinction? Is it the bullet? Is it the hole in A's head? Is it A's ill temper or perhaps an event in his childhood? Is it B's volatile nature, or does it have to do with some chemical occurrence in his hindbrain? It is apparent that danger lurks in using the word *cause* in its substantival sense—*the cause* of something. In a dynamic stream of events occurring in space and in time, it may be impossible to pin down *a cause*. We must fall back on the intuition of the scientist and hope, with Woodger, that he does not "sharpen his demands too much and unconsciously turn his causal postulate into an absolute metaphysical principle."

The theory of evolution burst forth in an era when causal determinism was at its zenith. The process of evolution was readily assumed to be subject, like other natural phenomena, to absolute laws. Biologists, as we have seen, were, as usual, divided into two camps: the *mechanists,* who, as we recall, see no difference between living and nonliving matter and who assume that both are subject to the same laws of physics and chemistry, and the *vitalists,* who believe that life is a singularity not open to final analysis in physicochemical terms. Many vitalists are *finalists,* holding the teleological view that the universe is purposeful, evolution has a goal, and that all life has been a means to some end, persuasions which are clearly on the fringes of theology. Interestingly, as was pointed out by Simpson, there was a curious reversing of roles by vitalists and mechanists on the subject of evolutionary determinism. In physics, materialism or mechanism was traditionally associated with strict adherence to causal determinism. But in evolutionary theory, we find the staunch advocates of a material basis of evolution gravitating toward the view that randomness and apparent indeterminism characterize the over-all process, while the vitalists, conversely, were strongly deterministic.

It should be noted that determinism in evolution can have gradations of meaning. The strict Laplacian view that all evolution is implicit in some event of the remote past represents an extreme position. Conceivably, the course of evolution could be determined by material means and yet not be destined by fate or any other external influence to follow a set course.

Darwin and the so-called neo-Darwinians (known to some as the "muscular" Darwinians) stressed as all-important the role of hereditary variation (mutation) which many assumed to be *wholly random* and thus beyond the pale of a mechanistic observer. The lineal descendants of Buffon and Lamarck, the early evolutionary vitalists, deny a final material basis for life but nevertheless invoke a theory of predetermination to explain the supposed tendency of evolution to follow straight and fixed pathways toward some finalist goal. Actually, no one denies that there is direction in evolution. The question is: Why need direction involve purpose? Anything going anywhere has direction but need this be called purposiveness?

Simpson, the brilliant American paleontologist, holds that evolution is in part demonstrably deterministic and aptly points out that evolutionary sequence is historical in nature.

> In any truly historical process, the determining conditions are far from simple and are not immediate or repetitive. Historical cause embraces the *totality* of preceding events. Such a cause can never be repeated, and it changes from instant to instant. Repetition of some factors still would not be repetition of historical causation.

This view, it seems to me, best accords with the facts as we know them. We cannot infer even apparent causal laws because we are not in a position to observe repeatedly the clear and unentangled process of temporal sequence as it occurs in evolution. The situation is always too complex to be repeatable and our evidence is necessarily indirect. In other words, we are unable to carry out *experiments* on the process about which we are making hypotheses.* If determinism does, to a limited extent, play a part in evolution, it is far from predictive and, by every predilection of science and logic, totally devoid of purpose.

The arguments against teleology seem decisive. One who infers a master purposeful design from the complexity of life should remember that complexity is a relative term. In a world with almost infinite time and material at its disposal, the number and complexity of possible combinations is almost infinite. If complexity presupposes purpose, then it must presuppose complexity of purpose. Surely this is an unnecessary burden on one's already overstrained wits. To the argument that as long as mechanistic determinism is unprovable, teleology is reasonable, there is the obvious and equally inconclusive retort that as long as teleology is unprovable, mechanistic determinism is much more reasonable. Some contend

* Though an exception to this statement will be mentioned in Chapter XIII. It has recently been possible to simulate bacterial evolution in the laboratory.

that because "the world has a design"—a hideously vague statement—like a watch it must have a designer. To this Bahm answered, "The argument from purposiveness of parts of the world to purposiveness of the whole world involves what logicians call the 'fallacy of composition.' The fallacy in the argument, 'This is a bunch of large apples, therefore this is a large bunch of apples,' and the fallacy in the argument, 'This world is made up of purposive beings, therefore this world is purposively made up,' is the same."

Harold Blum suggested what I think is a very good argument by analogy. He recalled the striking evolution in French cathedral architecture which occurred within a few medieval centuries. "Starting with the round-arched Romanesque style, which could only build stone vaults over small squarish areas, developing through the Norman, was reached the Gothic, which flung its stone vaults high into the air to the joy of men's hearts and the greater glory of Mary the Virgin." Although by hindsight it looks very much as though the ultimate goal of this evolution was the vaulting with stone of areas large enough to accommodate large hordes of worshipers, can it be argued that the early architects foresaw this achievement or the means of its accomplishment? Clearly they did not and clearly the analogous position with regard to evolution is untenable.

The decline of "either" and the fall of "or"

From time to time in these pages, we have had a harsh word for that habit of thought which contentedly reduces all questions down to a tidy set of alternatives: pleasure-pain, scientist-humanist, mechanism-vitalism, animate-inanimate. Undeniably, such a pattern of thinking arises naturally, for we are surrounded by clear-cut examples of dichotomies at work. A light switch is either on or off. A doorbell is either ringing or silent. A problem in long division is solved correctly or incorrectly. In these clear cases, we have opposites standing in absolute conflict with one another. There is no overlap; the middle ground is excluded.

The trouble begins when we set up our alternatives in areas that either need not or cannot be so treated. Order and chaos; hot and cold—these are not opposites but relative positions on a continuous scale of values. There is a middle ground that is thoroughly respectable, for it is as much on the scale as the more remote positions. Another kind of difficulty occurs which can be illustrated with an example. Suppose we examined ten thousand houses in succession and found that half were made of wood and half were made of stone. We would then conclude, with some justification, that the next house we see will quite probably be stone or wood. And if we are correct and our experience continues to show no exceptions, we may begin to believe that houses are made of stone or wood, that they *can be* only stone or wood. If someone then told us of a house that wasn't stone, we would logically conclude that it then must be made of wood. Here is a different kind of dichotomy. We haven't said that wood is the opposite of stone, nor that wood and stone are at different ends of a spectrum of values. Neither is the statement "houses are wood or stone" the same as the statement "houses are wood or not wood," for the latter is necessarily true and would not require us to have examined ten thousand houses.

The point of these remarks is simply this. Biology, as perhaps no other field, is rooted in an apparent antithesis: life versus nonlife. And dangling from its branches are hordes of similar conceptions that through the years have been supposed to facilitate thinking: body and mind, structure and function, organism and environment. In view of the fact that the great "antitheses of biology" and their use in explanation have had such a hoary tradition, it is quite necessary to say a brief word about them, for I believe we have here another kind of trap in need of being closed.

We have spoken of four kinds of antitheses: the on-off kind, the hot-cold kind, the stone-wood kind, and the structure-function kind. The first is, implicitly, a yes-no situation. An event occurs or it does not occur. There is the thing and its negation, and, in most cases, we have contributed little to the advance of knowledge if we declare that something either will or won't happen. We are necessarily right about such predictions. Our chief concern should be to restrict such statements to those situations that are open to a yes or no interpretation. When we do, we can then relax for we know that to accept A is to reject B and that nowhere in the universe is there a third possibility.

Hot-cold, as was pointed out, is not a yes-no dichotomy, but a pair of positions on a scale. We must never forget the in-between positions. As for stone and wood, these are not opposites at all, though they are in danger of appearing to be, since our experience seems to tell us that they are the only available alternatives. The hazard here is a psychological one against which we must guard ourselves. The next house may be made of gingerbread.

We come then to structure and function, perhaps the most puzzling of the four. It need hardly be pointed out that these are not antitheses, contrasts, or gradations. They are two aspects of a thing, two ways of looking at it, which have no business appearing in the guise of an antithesis. Their equivalents in society are anatomists and physiologists, and though they are often found quarreling, they are not the antithesis of each other.

With the ultimate recognition of the needless confusion in such usages, some interesting ideas emerged about different ways of looking at things. When confronted with the fact that certain physical phenomena could be equally well explained by postulating a particle or a wave, and no possible way of determining experimentally which was the case, Niels Bohr developed what was called the *principle of complementarity,* according to which both interpretations were accepted as two ways of looking at the same thing. They are complementary, not contradictory, and we are urged to accept the fact that two different mutually exclusive but equally truthful observations may be made of the same phenomenon.

This notion, which has the appearance of good sense, spread rapidly into other areas that had long been knotted up in similar dilemmas. In studying the brain, for example, should one employ the method of psychology, which considers the mind, or the method of biochemistry and physiology, which studies neural transmission and metabolism? Complementarity says both are necessary aspects of the picture, though they are operationally mutually exclusive, for no one can manipulate a brain in a test tube and interview it at the same time.

From here, the great leap was easy. The discoveries of science and the dogma of religion were quickly set forth as complementary descriptions of the world. Here we must be skeptical. Religion and science are not competing descriptions of the world with an equal claim on truth. For religion, *by definition,* is inaccessible to science, and the facts and "evidence" upon which it rests are unacceptable to science. And because skepticism seems wise here, one feels like taking another look at the principle of complementarity in its original physical context. It does, in fact, do nothing to resolve the impasse, but substitutes instead a different word for the Heisenberg principle of indeterminacy. It conceals the fact without helping us to understand that we are trying to say *both* that the two descriptions—religious-scientific, mental-mechanical, wave-particle—are about the same thing *and* that they are about different things. This would, it seems to me, discourage further inquiry into difficult problems by generating an illusion. All is well, all is explained; "complementarity" is at work and will take care of us. The word reminds one, however, of "conservative liberalism."

The key question then is: What sort of a pair is life and nonlife? On the face of it, the question is one that could scarcely be answered without observational data. What do biologists, the collectors of data, have to say on the subject? Regrettably, it is rather difficult to find out.

In 1937, N. W. Pirie published an essay called "The Meaninglessness of the Terms Life and Living," and in 1953 in an article called "The Origin of Life" he said essentially the same thing. Pirie is an excellent English writer and the arguments were convincing. He pointed out that "life" and "living" are words that the scientist has borrowed from the layman who has always regarded life as a metaphysical entity. But now we have entered a zone where these words serve us no longer.

There is little point in entering all the evidence on this question. The matter comes down to this: whatever quality one would like to consider as a minimal requirement or a diagnostic trait of life, that quality can be found present in objects that we all agree are not living and absent in objects that everyone knows are living. This is true of movement, reproduction, metabolism, and so on, although authors have insisted at various times that one or another of these traits, self-replication or autoregulation, was the *sine qua non* of life.

I tend to agree with Pirie though not with everything he says, and, interestingly, I find neither does he. One of the difficulties is the circular conflict: "This definition of life is no good because it includes some non-living things." Clearly, the statement implies a prior accepted definition of life. Pirie, too, despite his rigorous style and aggressive technic of scientific debate, discusses the "origin of life" and, while stating, "Life is not a thing or philosophical entity: it is an attitude of mind toward what is being observed," simultaneously he uses the term he denies, *e.g.*, "No other place and time seem more suitable for the appearance of life than here and now."

In addition, he stands in a variety of combative postures upon a stage whose very boards are the presupposition that "life" has a meaning. For example, there is his published comment concerning the views of his physicist friend J. D. Bernal, "He does not know enough to contribute usefully. This criticism may be looked on as a simple example of the old injunction to the cobbler to stick to his last." One feels like asking Professor Pirie exactly what last a cobbler would have to be familiar with to be qualified to discuss the origin of life. Physics? No, Pirie seems to say: Bernal is a physicist. Furthermore, we are interested in life, not matter (though at other times we deem the distinction meaningless). Biology? No, we are dealing with a phenomenon of inanimate molecules. At the witching hour of the "origin" are we to trot out the physicists and trot in the biologists? Who precisely is qualified to consider and speculate upon the origin of life? As far as I am concerned, until we have learned very much more, the answer is *everyone,* including the feuding luminaries, Pirie and Bernal.

This sort of doublethink is not easily avoided. Most of us feel we know the difference between life and nonlife and life and death. With some self-discipline we can accept the view that there is no rigid boundary between the two, but only a zone, a spectrum shading from the obvious to the obvious. In this area so far, we can only describe, and we gain little from pontificating on whether an object lives or lives not. We realize, in candor, that nothing is added to our understanding if to accommodate the entity we mold our definition.

But let us not forget that if a zone of ambiguity exists, it exists where we put it. We control the verbal stratum of our science, and I see no reason why the zone of ambiguity could not exist elsewhere, say between plants and animals. Though absurd by our present conceptions (whether or not they are explicit), is there any compelling reason why our "instinctive recognition" of life should not fade into uncertainty at the point where movement ceases? There is none. To argue that there is, one must maintain that plants *are* living though they don't move, and to do this, one must have already formulated a definition of life which includes plants. As perceptual objects, plants are plants whether we call them living or not: "life" is a conceptual object. In other words, Pirie is correct: "life" is beyond rigorous definition—but he, I, we will speak of life because we all know what it means in the large area of nonambiguity. The errors to be avoided are compulsive rigidity and failure to be happy in the company of uncertainty. When asked what viruses are and what they do, we can answer. When asked, what is life, we must reply with no more or no less than an enigmatic smile.

At the moment, I am having difficulty thinking of any use to which a definition of life could be put—*other* than to the everyday problem of recognizing death. When a scientist manipulates a living system, it is occasionally useful to him to know if it has died. If the system is a horse, there would seem to be few problems. But we quickly discover that the ambiguity of "life" affects "death" in reverse. If it is a bacterium, a seed, or a spore, the problems may be insurmountable, and in practice we usually establish an arbitrary end point at which death, by decision, is recognized to have occurred. Quiescence and death can look very much alike and their distinction brings us straight back to the bar of verbal decisions.

I think we will agree, a chapter or two hence, when we have seen some of the recent evidence and the direction it is taking, that "life" and "nonlife" are words like "hot" and "cold." They are ends of a spectrum whose graded quantity is complexity: life is on the complex end, nonlife on the simple. Between the two is a middle ground which is neither one nor the other. It is, one might say, what it is. . . .

CHAPTER XI

INSTRUMENTATION, INFORMATION, AND LONG DISTANCE

> Writing is practiced either by means of the common alphabet . . . or of a secret and private one, agreed upon betwixt particular persons, and called by the name of cipher.
>
> —Francis Bacon (1605)

Let us imagine that we are scientists working in a laboratory where we have at our disposal all of the technics and measuring instruments of physics and chemistry. We can measure physical dimensions such as weight and length with enormous precision and can analyze the chemical composition of an unknown object down to the last impurity. We have the conviction that under these circumstances we could completely characterize any physical object and, with accuracy, state whether two given objects are the same or different.

A skeptical friend decides to put us to the test. He arrives with two bundles and requests us to say in concrete terms whether their contents are the same or different, and, if different, what the differences are. We open the package and find that one contains the Sunday edition of the New York *Times* and the other contains an equal weight of blank newsprint in the middle of which is a large, messy blot of printer's ink. We start to work. Both specimens contain the same weight of paper and the same number of particles of whatever it is ink is made of.

Both have the same musty odor. Both serve equally well as seat pads in Lewisohn Stadium. We know there must be a difference since the circulation of the *Times* is extremely large, but would no doubt be nil if people found on their doorsteps only paper containing an ink blot. With our backs to the wall we concede that the only *physical* difference is in the *spatial arrangement* of the ink with respect to the paper. In one case, the ink is arrayed in neat rows of discrete curlycues and lines; in the other, the ink is in one large puddle. The difference, then, is a question of the *order* and *arrangement* of particles of matter.

Here is another of those conceptions which, we suddenly recognize, has an absolute significance for every phase of our existence. The idea of order! Let us examine this notion, for it is a pillar of contemporary thought and only recently have men awakened to it.

The true nature of noise, dirt, stuttering, and poison

Let us consider a more familiar situation. A man is sitting at home waiting for an important telephone call. His children are in the next room re-enacting the French and Indian War, down to the last screams of the dying. The phone rings but, in the din of battle, our man does not hear it and he misses his call.

The phone bell in our little story was a signal which was being sought and, in the presence of a high noise level, the signal was lost. What could have been done to prevent this loss? If the man moved out into the garden to escape the noise, he would also have eluded the signal. If he put on a hearing aid to amplify the signal, he simultaneously would have amplified the noise. Thus, the *signal-to-noise ratio* was too unfavorable and unless it could be changed—by selectively amplifying the signal, slugging the children, or both—the difficulty would continue.

The same would be true if one were searching for a

house number from the front seat of an automobile. All would be well in the clear light of day. But, in a fog, the light rays passing from the sign to the eye would be chaotically scattered by droplets of water in the air. The result would be a blurring of the physical shapes being sought, which, if severe enough, would prevent their detection. These situations are commonplace. In everything we do, there is a background of distracting phenomena which becomes disturbing whenever its intensity level is high enough. The static on the radio, the light seeping into a sealed packet of film, the commercial advertisements we must endure on television—in each of these cases, we must successfully minimize the unwanted background if we are to receive the signal with clarity.

Aside from their simple appropriateness, there is another good reason why we use the terms "signal" and "noise" in this general way. Although the crucial importance of the signal-to-noise ratio has long been understood intuitively, its formal analysis and introduction into the world of great ideas were the achievements of communication engineers working in the Bell Telephone Laboratories. (And here, in my opinion, is a magnificent illustration of the power of abstract thinking.) These workers became concerned with the following practical problem: An individual wishes to send the message "I love you" to an acquaintance in a distant city. He is aware that there are several technical systems for sending such a message, all of which are essentially mechanisms designed to reproduce this sequence of words at a distance. The sender is of a pedantic turn of mind and has determined that his message shall go forth via the quickest, cheapest, and most accurate of the available communication systems. He will, of course, be dissatisfied if his message becomes scrambled, whether into something incomprehensible like "T kolg yom" or into something comprehensible but different in meaning like "A live cow." The communication engineer, on the other hand, has the job of satisfying his customer while making his service economically competitive against all others.

Assume that a new telegraph company decides to bid for the contract. How should it transmit the message? It might, for example, devise a code wherein a telegraph key is held down one second for the letter "a," two seconds for "b," and so on, with one-second waits between each letter. By this method, it would take 131 seconds to transmit the message. The wastefulness of this is apparent, and because of it the Morse code was invented. In this system, three signals appear in different combinations: a long pulse, a short pulse, and a short silence. By arranging the code so as to give those letters most frequently used the briefest code symbols (the letter "e" is a short pulse or dot, the letter "t" a long pulse or dash), our message now can go forth in 67 seconds. Even this isn't very good, and the next obvious step is the invention of short code units for whole words or common phrases. But when we start doing this, some new problems arise. For one thing, the saving in transmission time should not be squandered in accuracy, for it is obvious that economy in time can often be achieved by permitting some deterioration in the final replication of the message. Communication engineers have intentionally promoted a certain amount of deterioration because they have recognized that the English language contains many redundancies. The letter "u" after "q" is always redundant, the "h" after "w" often is, and many double letters are too. By cutting these out in their coding practice—so that any transmitted message is already "deteriorated"—a moderate increase in efficiency can be made.

But a major problem arises when deterioration occurs unintentionally. Since the message is transmitted by physical means, via electrical impulses in a wire, it is subject to the distortion inherent in all such processes which originates from the constant random motion of all molecules, the so-called thermal noise. The behavior of the electrical circuit is always the statistical average of the behavior of innumerable individual electrons. If the noise level goes up, the signal may become garbled. Likewise, if the code becomes too efficient (say, one very brief dot means "I love you"), the signal, in effect, becomes weak, and the message may again be lost in the noise. To offset this a certain amount of redundancy in the form of repetition may be desirable. That is why telegraph companies always repeat numbers and names in sending telegrams. But if the code is so subtle or the signal so weak, no amount of repetition will guarantee that each feeble blip is not just part of the noise. Such subtlety becomes secrecy.

The implications of this are very great indeed, for our message has two aspects to it. It is first a set of words selected out of all others, to convey some information, and it is second a physical phenomenon in a wire that can be interpreted as an orderly orientation of electrons in contrast to a thoroughly random arrangement, which incidentally conveys no information. From here, it is an easy step to the realization that the degree of order is a measurable quantity with a profound meaning. The relative rarity of the ordered arrangement of the code symbols when compared to the number of possible arrangements gives a measure of the information in the message. This is not as difficult as it sounds. If our wire could transmit no more than 1,000 different arrangements of code symbols, the ones that were used most infrequently would contain the most information. Their rarity implies their improbability and unexpectedness. When they finally do occur they convey much information. Thus, the combination of three letters "the" would be used frequently, would be never unexpected, and would add little to the total of information. The three letters "SOS" are a much rarer combination and convey a great deal of highly specific information. A printed page of the New York *Times* is obviously a rare arrangement of ink marks compared to all the possible ways of applying ink to the paper. The *Times*, then, contains a much higher level of information than a random collection of letters or an ink blot.

The concept of information content applies in many situations. Suppose the busy desk clerk of a large hotel was handed an unmarked key by a mysterious stranger who would say only that a valuable necklace was hidden in a room that this key would open. He could extract the desired information—which room should be searched for the necklace—without too much difficulty, *if* the key contained that much information. In other words, if the key's structure was unusual enough to open only one door, the correct one, he should have to search only that room. The information would reside in the rarity of the pattern of grooves and notches. If, however, it was a master key capable of opening all the doors, it would contain no information, and he would then have to search all of the rooms. The same considerations apply to the use of fingerprints.

What is so interesting is the fact that the mathematical expression for the content of information in a system is precisely the same as that for the *negative entropy* of a system. As we may or may not recall, the second law of thermodynamics states that the negative entropy of a system, which is, among other things, a measure of its degree of molecular order, is always moving in the direction of chaos, and, in any self-contained corner of the universe, order may be restored only by putting energy into the system. To anyone with a formal garden, these physical terms are unnecessary. If the garden is planted in a highly ordered arrangement of rows and designs, energy must be expended constantly to prevent a drift toward disorder in the form of weeds, ragged growth, and desiccation. Likewise, energy in the form of thinking, writing, and linotype-operating must be expended to create the ordered rows of ink that are the New York *Times*. It is just as unlikely that the *Times* would appear if the ink were just thrown at the paper as that the garden would maintain itself through the summer if untouched by gardener's hands.

The significance of these concepts for biology is fundamental. As we shall presently see, the organism is a highly unlikely arrangement for a group of molecules to find themselves in. Yet this almost incredible complexity is all provided for in a blueprint carried within a single fertilized egg cell. The hereditary code is carried in the genes, structures almost too small to be seen in the microscope. This is extraordinary! When biologists realized that the gene's enormous information content must reside in a highly specific arrangement of the matter within it, as in a key or phonograph record, the greatest biological question of them all was joined. It is the problem of determining how physical aggregations of matter become twisted and bent into complex arrangements in space, whose information content is so phenomenally high they become little oligarchies capable of directing their own reproduction, of accumulating other matter into their orbit, and of occasionally coming up with something like the Theory of Relativity. In Chapter XIII, I shall elaborate on what biologists now believe is going on here. But first, a bit more information.

Scientific instruments and their limitations

I should like to say a brief word about scientific instruments, the very symbols by which modern science is known. And well they might be symbolic of science, for progress in instrumentation is a necessary condition for the progress of science. The instruments and machines of science are essentially devices for extending the limited powers of our own bodies. Our telescopes, microscopes, and spectrophotometers are strong new eyes; electric motors and nuclear reactors are extra muscles; and the UNIVACS, MANIACS, and assorted other -ACS are our extra intelligences. We will speak of "electronic brains" in a later chapter. Here I want only to make the point that the laboratory instruments we use in our experiments are basically communication systems for the transfer of information. And, as a message can "deteriorate" in a telegraph wire, it can surely do the same in a laboratory instrument, no matter how elegant its control panel. If the results of an experiment depend on a reliable message, here is a place to tread carefully. The importance of instrumental accuracy in hypothesis construction is perfectly illustrated by the story of the fat lady who tried to weigh herself on a defective penny scale. A passing inebriate, noticing that the dial read twenty pounds, muttered, "She mush be hollow!"

In Chapter V, it was observed that the essential feature of a scientific experiment is an intentional interaction with the object under study that can be controlled and manipulated by the experimenter. It is the purpose of such interactions to produce some *signal* discernible to the senses. Where the scientist is interested only in establishing the existence or nonexistence of some entity or occurrence, he will be satisfied merely to note the presence or absence of the signal resulting from his intervention. This would be a *qualitative* experiment involving a "yes-no decision." For example, if we wished to know if a test tube contains iron, the simple addition of a substance which interacts with iron to produce a blue color would provide this information.

Experiments become *quantitative* when a measurement is made of the extent of the perceived interaction. Measurement implies comparison with some appropriate yardstick. The yardstick here would be a similar chemical reaction, but one conducted with accurately known quantities. The measurement consists in comparing the extent of the reaction of the unknown with that of the known. Thus, if we wish to learn how much iron is in the tube, the blue color must be compared with blue colors produced with carefully weighed amounts of pure iron. If the color is found to be identical with the color obtained with one milligram of pure iron, we conclude that the unknown contains one milligram of iron. This is measurement. Measurement is comparison.

All quantitative measurements in science are conducted in this way. The establishment of a measuring scale by alignment with known standards is called *calibration.* If someone is presented with a kitchen scale which for some reason lacks a dial, his predicament is not entirely absurd. He has only to obtain a good set of weights (which were themselves carefully calibrated with other weights) and, one at a time, place them on the scale, marking the dial where the needle comes to rest. Actually only two points need to be marked, since Hooke's law states that the deflection of a spring is proportional to its load. Thus, one could establish the one-pound mark and the ten-pound mark with weights; the locations of all intervening marks could be simply computed. Presumably, the manufacturer of a scale which comes equipped with its dial has already gone through these maneuvers. Often, however, he has done so with only one scale and has copied the dial face onto all the other similar scales. The error of this practice may be of little consequence in the case of scales used in fish markets. Clearly, the weighing instruments intended for delicate scientific measurement must be accurately and individually calibrated.

In many instances, measuring instruments are easily calibrated against certain natural "constants" instead of other calibrated standards. In these situations the unit of measure may be defined by the natural phenomenon. For example, 0° Centigrade is defined as the freezing point of water under certain conditions; 100° C. is the boiling point. Given a blank thermometer we can calibrate it either by immersing it in freezing water, marking the mercury level, then boiling water, marking it again, and dividing the space between the two marks into a hundred equal intervals (each a degree) *or* we can place it in contact with an already calibrated thermometer, transfer the reading onto the unknown scale, change the temperature and do it again. Then by simple arithmetic the interval of a single degree can be computed and scratched carefully into the glass.

There is a strong inclination among physicists to define as many units of measurement as possible in terms of accurately reproducible natural constants. The advantages of such standards are obvious. The meter unit of length was devised in 1790 to represent one ten-millionth of the earth's quadrant (the distance from the North Pole to the equator). Speculation arose as to whether the meter could be reproduced if the earth were changed, say by collision with a comet, and so a natural standard independent of terrestrial form was sought. Various proposals were made but it now appears that the ultimate standard of length has been found in a wave length of radiation emitted by mercury-198, an isotope transmuted from gold by neutron bombardment. The spectacular accuracy, reproducibility, and presumed immutability of this standard of length will, no doubt, survive world catastrophes and planetary collisions. This should be comforting to all who make measurements.

So much for the measuring scale of the instruments. The uncertainties of calibration contribute importantly to the danger of message deterioration. But they are not the only danger source. First the instrument acts as a detector. Its photocell "sees" the ultraviolet light we cannot see, its sensitive antennas "hear" the distant radio stars we cannot hear. Then with the message plucked out of the universe, the instrument communicates it to its other side. It now is an indicator. A dial registers, a column of fluid rises, a moving pen makes a tracing on the long roll of graph paper being driven past it by a clock motor. The length and intricacy of this pathway of communication is often incredible—from the phenomenon to the detector to the communication circuit to the indicator to the eye and then the mind of the observer. It is a long dangerous journey and, at every step of the way, including the last one, the noise must be kept down and the signal up. When that is done, and the calibration is reasonably good, an instrument can sometimes be used with profit.

CHAPTER XII

THE TECHNIC OF DISCOVERY

Seated one day at the Organ,
I was weary and ill at ease,
And my fingers wandered idly
Over the noisy keys.

I do not know what I was playing,
Or what I was dreaming then;
But I struck one chord of music,
Like the sound of a great Amen.
—Adelaide Anne Procter

Having explored the nature of language, the scientific method, and truth, having purged ourselves of the taint of nonempirical, nonlogical, nonacceptable thinking, we come to that enigmatic something which, to me, gives science its riotous excitement and rugged, romantic beauty—those nonutilitarian qualities for which adequate allowance is never made in the syllabus of method. It is the *mind of the scientist*, the meat that gives body to the meal and the cognac that makes it memorable.

Most of what we have said on the principles of logic and the analysis of language tells us only how scientific truth may be defended. But we have learned nothing of the mechanisms of its discovery. We lightly repeat in discussions of this sort that knowledge derives from the sequence: experiment, hypothesis, deduction, test experiments, inductive generalization. But the ground that must be crossed in order to move through these stages is mountainous, misty, and unmapped, as only those who have dared it can know.

We have done our experiment and recorded its results

in a black notebook. We recognize the uncertainties built in to the data but can only estimate their extent. *What do we do now?* The book says invent a hypothesis that will "explain" the results. We have come face to face with the mystique of the creative mind.

The creative act

I have thought about the nature of the creative process and have reached a somewhat aberrant conclusion. I don't understand it and I don't think anyone else does either. From what has been written, the main approach to the problem seems to have come from introspective psychology, the autobiographical accounts of great creative thinkers which try to tell how they did it. In a recent book, one finds such statements by thirty-eight individuals,* ranging from Einstein to Mozart, Spencer to Spender, and though the material is extremely interesting, it is clear beyond all doubt that no man has the capacity alone to raise to the surface all the underwater currents and rip tides of his own consciousness.

In any event, all tell different stories, often in wonderfully vague phrases. For example, the poet Spender spoke of "a dim cloud of an idea which I feel must be condensed into a shower of words"; Whitehead: "the state of imaginative muddled suspense which precedes successful inductive generalization"; Chekov: "If an artist boasted to me of having written a story without a previously settled design, but by inspiration, I should call him a lunatic"; and Poincaré, whose statements on this problem are classical: "Ideas rose in crowds; I felt them collide until pairs interlocked, so to speak, making a stable combination. By the next morning I had established the existence of [new truth]." The only obvious common prescriptions are hard work, self-discipline, and thorough educational preparation. And all seem to agree that the moment of achievement is a moment of delight

* B. Ghiselin's book *The Creative Process.*

and satisfaction reminiscent of Spinoza's definition of pleasure: "the passion by which the mind passes to a higher state of perfection." In the words of Agnes Arber, "This emotional element in discovery is perhaps the factor which makes it so elusive, and so refractory to organized control." Machines cannot control it, "Marches of Dimes" will not promote it, and we, apparently, cannot explain it.

The reason is, I think, that the creative process is so closely tied in with the emotional structure of an individual, it is a poor subject for generalization. All sorts of factors are at work and no analysis can avoid oversimplification. Ideas come by day, by night, by chance, by work, and by play. They come in dreams, in hallucinations, in seminars and saloons. Most are quite bad and are seldom voiced, suppressed by their authors' critical faculties. Some are good; a few are brilliant. Since we seem not to know how they arise, we might reasonably inquire from whence they arise.

Professor Boring of Harvard has recently offered an impressive answer to this question. He points out that "in each age there are covert influences that make up what has been called the climate of opinion, and by Goethe the *Zeitgeist*—the conventions of thought and the unquestioned assumptions that are implicit in the culture in general and science in particular. . . . They constrain originality and reinforce tradition, as well as limiting the irresponsibility of the cranks who, excelling in originality, are deficient in critical wisdom." Apparently, we all feed on the *Zeitgeist*, unconsciously directing our interests to the issues of the day, formulating our thoughts in the linguistic clichés of the day, employing the established technics of the day. The result is eternal frustration for the historian of science who would trace out the "influences" acting upon any given scientist. Did Newton's teachers shape his development or was it the *Zeitgeist* of his century? Who knows? Wrote Boring, "Again and again scientific progress halts because the correct next step contravenes some firmly rooted theory or belief." How true this is we have already seen in some of our historical reflections.

We must recognize, therefore, what Bacon and Descartes failed to recognize. Science is a truly creative enterprise. Though the logic of its method can be described with rigor, the successful *use* of the method requires an act of intuition by the creative mind. Science, then, is an art. For the method of the artist is also well understood. All he does is dip his brush in paint and apply it to the canvas in the proper places. It is knowing which are the proper places, however, that distinguishes a Cézanne.

The beast within: its nature and nurture

All of which brings up a matter too rarely discussed. What about the scientist as a creature of emotion and human fallibility? The temper of our times has generated widening gulfs of alienation and distrust between scientists and other people and, in the spirit of scientific inquiry, those of us who are dedicated to it begin looking at ourselves to learn what we are and if the blame is ours. We see some interesting things.

At first glance, scientists may appear to be different. A well-done study of the outstanding young men of American science was recently published in *Fortune* magazine (and, in my opinion, its subjects were indeed outstanding). The survey clearly showed them to be mavericks, differing from the majority of society in endowment, desire, and belief. Among other things, most were well aware of their so-called alienation from society, were politically liberal, and, interestingly, were hardheaded hedonists who found pleasure in the thrill of discovery and generally doubted the view that scientists tended to be nervous wrecks.

But these were the *successful* men of their generation and, though many seek it, not all gain success. What of the rest of us? Here we encounter the disturbing conclusions of Lawrence Kubie, who has delved into the emotional problems connected with the scientific career. His argument is based on psychoanalytic experience with individuals, but no scientist reading it will fail to discern in part the outlines of his own reflection. Kubie tells us that the young scientist often reaches maturity after the abnormal childhood of precocity—overly bookish, unathletic, socially withdrawn, sexually immature. He may choose a career in science under the influence of highly complex and unnoticed symbolisms, as, for example, the aspiration to medical careers by those filled with guilt-laden curiosity about the body. Since no youth can know in advance the joys and sorrows of his chosen field, his choice must be based upon outward appearances, dramatizations, and fantasies.

Each successive step in the method of science calls forth a greater emotional investment and adds to the difficulties of remaining objective. When the ego is involved, self-criticism may come hard. (Who ever heard of two scientists battling to prove the other right?) One has always a vested interest in the successful outcome and, whether we enjoy admitting it or not, each of us feels the pressure to succeed, to blaze "new trails" perhaps before we have mastered the old, to remain productive and therefore admired, to embark obsessively (as did Sigmund) upon a romantic crusade toward epic truth. It is apparent, therefore, how latent neurotic tendencies may impinge upon and distort the clear mandates of scientific method and may generate error, unrealistic values, anxiety, and—let's face it, since science is done behind closed doors—dishonesty. Because scientists are human and science is not, as in all fields the thin thread of integrity is sometimes strained to break.

The idea of dishonesty in science is a hard one to swallow, for it is as difficult to understand as it is shocking. Yet the history of science is studded with tales of fraud and grand larceny, some of which have an ill-boding Old Testament flavor. For example, a recent note in *Science* recalled the case of one of biology's more notorious mountebanks, Paul Kammerer, a Viennese zoologist, who claimed in 1924 to have proved that acquired characters are inherited with experiments done on spotted salamanders. The great William Bateson challenged Kammerer, and the acrimonious debate that followed found many eminent biologists on both sides of the argument. Bateson demanded to see Kammerer's specimens but Kammerer demurred. No matter where Bateson went in pursuit, Kammerer always managed to elude him. The chase finally ended in 1926 with the examination of the specimens by G. K. Noble of the American Museum of Natural History and Hans Przibram, director of the institute where Kammerer worked. The sensational findings were promptly reported in *Nature*. The genetically transmitted salamander spots turned out to be made of India ink. A short time later, Kammerer committed suicide.

What dishonesty exists among scientists is rarely on such a grand scale. It is subtle and, no doubt, frequently unconscious behavior. The experiments that "work" are reported with no mention of those that failed. The data that support the hypothesis are seized upon; the rest are explained away or forgotten. In today's hectic world of publicity and promotion, the spreading practice of granting academic advancement to those who have made "important" scientific contributions has added fuel to many a latent fire. In a highly complex field, published scientific work cannot be quickly confirmed or denied, nor do most scientists care to spend their time verifying or challenging what other scientists have claimed. In any case, university trustees are not likely to go to the laboratory for guidance in making staff promotions.

Many scientists, similarly, find themselves in a breathless race for priority—for the glory of being first to make some discovery and report it. While there is nothing dishonest about that, its effect can be disturbing upon sociological conditions within the scientific community.

Moreover, it breeds dishonesty, for in its wake comes the disingenuous doubletalk we normally associate with advertising and politics. Perhaps such competitiveness has one useful function: it is an inexhaustible source of reliable lunchroom conversation, for the gossip of scientists is eternally concerned with the latest bulletins on who is "scooping" whom. I'm reminded, however, of the plight of a former colleague who, at the proud completion of a job of scientific work, found that he'd been scooped in 1891.

The balancing factor in this situation is the honesty, wisdom, and intuitive good sense of the large majority of scientists and scientific editors. Dubious work should not be published, but dishonest work often has the appearance of solidity. And yet, when it reaches a journal, as often as not, it meets a proper skepticism—partly because the work somehow does not "sound right," and partly because every scientist knows in his heart that this sort of thing goes on in the world. It's uncommon, it's difficult to talk about, it's sad, but it's true. It is equally true that honest work may not "sound right" for reasons of novelty. Scientists realize this too: that is why their darkest suspicions are practically never made audible.

Kubie gives us some haunting case histories: a scientist so anxious to bolster an already proved theory, he falsified data; a sarcastic professor perennially vituperating against his colleagues from the security of the lectern; an acclaimed scientist who finds no joy in success. The portraits are familiar and the conclusions sobering. One thinks of these things on his daily rounds, as he views the contemporary scene, as he reads statements to the effect that scientists should not enter debates upon morality, art, and politics (those areas beyond the ken of scientific inquiry)—and depending on his fiber, one may feel naked, perplexed, resentful, or gratified that these insights are at last being achieved.

The conceptions of Kubie are not an indictment of scientists: they are descriptions and attempted explanations of some of them (and, in saying this, I wish to disavow any sense of mysticism I may have invoked about the scientific mind. At the moment, it seems mysterious, but I do not doubt that it is, in principle, explainable.). No more do these ideas detract from the status of science than did Darwin's dyspepsia from the greatness of his thought. Whether or not they are valid, only time will tell. But we cannot deny that we have made progress if we recognize with Kubie that "the idyllic picture of the innocent, child-like scientist who lives a life of simple, secure, peaceful, dignified contemplation has become unreal fantasy." We see that science is not a thing apart and there should be no moat of isolation. This viewpoint, it seems to me, enlivens the spectacle of modern science and endows it a little with some of those universals that are the essences of great literature and drama.

Regrettably, then, we have had nothing to say on the technic of making discoveries.

PART FOUR

CONTEMPORARY BIOLOGY, ITS PROBLEMS AND PROSPECTS

CHAPTER XIII

THE LIVING ORGANISM TODAY

Life is not a tale told by an idiot, because no idiot is sufficiently irrational to think up such a tale.

—Herman Betz

In the preceding four chapters, we took notice of certain recent intellectual currents that, together, may be loosely referred to as the analytical movement in thought. It is the turning upon itself of the quest for knowledge, wherein every instrument of thought is held up to the light. Language, logic, models, meaning, information, intuition—each has been put to the test and all have emerged as creatures of human dimensions. We have seen that, to a large extent, the spearhead of this intellectual dragonnade was the great new revolution in physics. We now turn our attention to the arena of biology. How has modern thought influenced our inquiry into the nature of organism—if indeed it has influenced it at all? What is the condition of biology today?

In 1929, a book was published called *The Science of Life*. Its eminent authors were H. G. Wells, Julian Huxley, and G. P. Wells. It was a massive treatise over 1,500 pages long, purporting to set before a general audience a summary of the state of biology at the time of writing. We would be unfair were we to regard it as the definitive word on this subject, for the book was not intended as a scholar's encyclopedia. Yet, we may consider it a reasonable statement of the biologist's frame of mind a short generation ago—despite the occasional reviewer or two who complained at the invasion by Wells and Huxley into territories not technically their own. As we turn through its pages, we find discussions of the various forms of life from flatworms to sea serpents, the theory of evolution, blood and breathing, heredity, vitamins, disease, emotions, and very much more. What is missing, however, in this meadow of material is a sense of structure or direction, a clearly defined center of intellectual gravity, around which all other ideas may be balanced. This is no criticism of the skill of the authors, for they accurately divined the temper of their subject. That was the condition of biology then. Needless to remark, each of the topics mentioned is of exceedingly great importance. Later work has expanded these areas into even larger, more impressive domains, no one of which may be overlooked.

But a discourse on the fundamental nature of bricks need not linger long over houses and walls. The intervening years have clearly revealed that there is one question in biology that transcends all others—a question that science needed insight to ask and that now it may soon be ready to answer. It is the question of the gene.

What is a gene?

Living organisms *reproduce* themselves and *regulate* themselves. All of their other properties—growth, motion, adaptation, irritability, metabolism—are but specifications of these two broad functions. Autoregulation, the self-perpetuation of functional stability and structural integrity, confers upon an otherwise highly unprepossessing blob of jelly and its gritty little inclusions of solid matter the ability to maintain itself in the face of a universe of destructive forces. But the property of self-duplication is more mysterious still.

To say that a cell reproduces itself is to say a very great deal. It implies that every one of its whirling atoms and molecules, every biochemical system and self-regulating mechanism, every ingredient we have yet to discover is somehow reduplicated in ultimate detail. It implies that the cell will be of the species of its parent: an amoeba will not produce a paramecium. This is an astonishing state of affairs. Given the particles of life, the proteins and sugars, the enzymes and small organoids that must float in the protoplasm, the surface membranes and nucleus, how would one arrange them, if one had to, so that they would do this for themselves? The question recalls the image of Sisyphus.

Deep within the flux of cellular reproduction lies the dominion of heredity, where time past and time future are joined in physical dimensions. Because all living systems, from microbes to men, are born of their kind and bear their kind in perpetuating the breed, they must somehow transmit to their offspring their own distinctive traits. Stating it another way, they pass on to the next generation its membership in the species—which, we may recall, is roughly defined as a distinctive, interbreeding, constellation of traits and characters. Clearly, the number of individual *traits* that a living organism can possess is limited only by the number we can make out. Men have always distinguished each other by skin color and physiognomy, but who would have imagined a century ago that humans could be classified by blood groups? Yet blood groups were found to be heritable according to strict laws once they were discovered, and the same is true for countless other traits which in contrast to structure and outward appearance are equally less conspicuous. As technics of observation improve, the list of observable traits grows larger. Hence, we cannot yet classify an organism *completely* because we have yet to discover its every trait.

All traits are not heritable anyway. Many of the characteristics of an organism belong to it alone and are not transmitted to the offspring. When it goes, the traits go. Goldschmidt makes clear the difference between hereditary and nonhereditary traits in his instructive example of the beans. If an experienced bean farmer finds he has three seed varieties which reliably give good harvests of small, medium, and large beans (say ten, fifteen, and twenty millimeters in diameter), we would assume that he has three hereditarily different strains. (Beans are useful for this example because they breed by self-fertilization. Interbreeding thus will not confuse the argument.)

If 1,000 beans are harvested from the crop of each strain, it is readily seen that within each harvest the beans are not all identical. We find in each group a certain number of beans above and below the average size. The crop, laid out in rows, looks like this:*

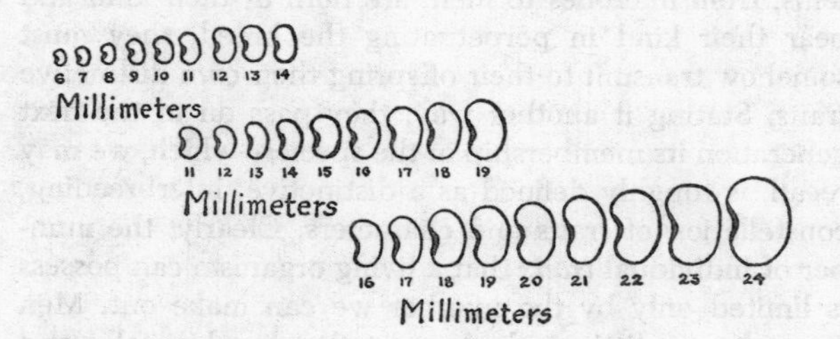

It would seem that the pure strain does not yield pure offspring but that individual differences still exist. These are called *variations* and they represent chance deviations from the "pure" trait, which, strictly speaking, is the recurring average trait of large numbers of progeny in many generations. From this it is clear that unless we were told its plot of origin, there would be no way of telling whether a randomly selected thirteen-millimeter

* Figure is redrawn from R. Goldschmidt, *Understanding Heredity*, Wiley, N. Y., 1952, by permission.

bean was in fact a large ten-millimeter bean or a small fifteen-millimeter bean—so that the bean's size, even though easily observable, would not necessarily reveal its hereditary constitution.

How then do we distinguish the hereditary strain? Goldschmidt's farmer plants his unknown thirteen-millimeter beans and at harvest time brings in a crop of beans varying from six to fourteen millimeters in length but averaging ten millimeters. The origin of the unknown parent bean is now clear. Heredity has delivered a generation whose *average* size equals the perennial average, although the parent was a variant which in its own generation contributed to the normal average. Geneticists call this kind of analysis the test of progeny.

To be valid, the test requires a constant environment. If two fifteen-millimeter beans of the same strain were planted, but one received more than enough sun, food, and water, one might yield an eighteen- to twenty-two-millimeter crop averaging twenty millimeters and the other a four- to twelve-millimeter crop averaging eight millimeters. It is seen that the "hereditary size" of fifteen millimeters is meaningful only if the environmental circumstances are carefully specified. Thus from the parable of the beans, we can deduce two great facts about heredity: 1) differences in *actual hereditary type* (which are called genotypes) can be masked by the appearance of the visible externals, and 2) the progeny of a single hereditary constitution are importantly influenced by environment so that the outwardly visible traits (phenotype) of offspring result both from heredity and environment or, as is often said, from nature and nurture. Thus a moderate-sized organism might actually be one of three things: a moderate-sized genotype in a normal or average environment, a hereditarily large genotype whose growth is stunted, or a hereditarily small genotype which is overly well-nourished. If either of the last two, the trait has been acquired and will not breed into the next generation.

We know this from everyday life. One sees the tall, healthy American-born children of foreign immigrants, who physically and mentally have come to resemble other American children, acquiring the language and culture of their environment. Despite the familiarity of such phenomena, exceedingly strange circumstances surrounded the development of our understanding of heredity. Even though science was a going concern in the mid-nineteenth century and there existed great contemporary interest in biology, when the portals were at last opened to an understanding of heredity by the Moravian monk Gregor Mendel, it took almost half a century for his work to be "discovered," though it had been duly published before the scientific community. In seeking to explain this major riddle of scientific history, Bentley Glass suggested that, in Mendel's time, thought had been so obsessed by the question of origin of species, that is, with hybridization *between* species, it had no interest in crosses *within* species. Glass recalls how tantalizingly close some contemporary writers seemed to come to understanding Mendel's work. In his book on hybridization, Focke referred to Mendel's work fifteen times and even quoted him, but with no understanding. The great theoretical biologist Nägeli corresponded actively with Mendel for years, exchanging reprints and experimental plant material, but because of Nägeli's preoccupation with his own theories on the nature of life, he failed completely to comprehend the work of Mendel. In time, says Glass, he came to despise it. H. J. Muller says of Mendel's neglect, he was "ahead of his time," uniquely perceiving both the nature of the problem of hereditary mechanism and the means by which it might be solved. Perhaps this is so, though it is ironic that this catachresis of history found the Genetics Society of America celebrating in 1950 not the eighty-fifth anniversary of Mendel's discoveries, but the fiftieth anniversary of the discovery of Mendel! This was entirely appropriate because genetics, the science of hereditary mechanisms, did not get into gear and drive away until Mendel's work had been disinterred.

Like all great scientific theories, Mendel's work knitted together in one magnificent idea an enormous collection of "useless" facts. First Mendel made the simple observation that sometimes a plant or animal has variations which differ in some characteristic such as color or size. But if an animal arises from a single sperm and a single ovum—as does a plant from a single pollen grain and ovum—does the appearance of two kinds of offspring mean that there are two kinds of germ cells? This was a question for nature to answer. Mendel went to his garden and selected some pea plants—a species whose pollen can fertilize its own egg cells—and after demonstrating in the chosen plants that, self-pollinated, they breed true for many generations with no diversity in the character of the offspring, he crossed two varieties which differed in size. The seeds that resulted, of course, had to be planted before the consequences of the cross could be known. And the new generation, as it unexpectedly turned out, were all the same, resembling one parent. In this case, tall plants crossed with dwarfs gave only tall offspring.

Now Mendel self-fertilized these offspring—their own pollen with their own eggs. In the next generation, however, there were talls *and* dwarfs, a result likely to turn men of lesser stature to other pursuits. How could this be explained? Mendel then did the simple thing which made him immortal. He *counted* the percentages of talls and dwarfs in this generation, perhaps the first use of a mathematical approach in the history of biology. The results were impressive: in a large number of trials, this generation contained three talls for every one dwarf. In subsequent breedings, the dwarfs breeded true, yielding only dwarfs. But the talls continued to yield mixed populations. Such results, Mendel concluded, point to a separateness or "atomicity" of the heritable traits and suggests the following hypothesis: hereditary characteristics are due to something that *determines* these traits; this something is actually transmitted from parent to offspring; these hereditary determinants must be *physical particles* which retain their identity and integrity during the process of fertilization. The fact that in the first mixed generation, the trait of dwarfness disappears altogether while it reappears in the next generation *in a definite quantitative proportion* proves that it was "there" all the time. In the course of its assortment (or recombination as it is called), it had merely been masked in one generation by the factor for tallness. And although these plants were outwardly, or phenotypically, tall, their true nature or genotype was hybrid as shown by the test of progeny. In brief, then, the core of the theory is the notion that heredity depends on a mosaic of separate and discrete physical particles with a continuing existence in time. The great Danish botanist Wilhelm Johannsen christened them *genes* in 1909.

The theory was soon brilliantly confirmed with only minor modifications in other plants and certain insects. It became clear, through evidence we cannot enter into here, that the hypothetical genes were arrayed in a linear arrangement along the stringy little structures called chromosomes that microscopists had long been observing in the cell nucleus. Textbook writers promptly seized upon the obvious model: the chromosome was a string and the genes were beads. And many microscopists looking at the chromosomes, or more precisely their stained, formaldehyde-treated remains, felt sure they could see little bulges along the edges of the chromosome. These, they wrongly concluded, must be the genes.

We cannot here follow the details of the work that soon poured forth. Suffice it to say that the idea of a *physical* basis for heredity galvanized the field of biology. There were great difficulties, of course. No one could examine a naked gene, for its properties were assayable only by genetic analysis of the progeny. It itself remained an inferred entity and a thoroughly remarkable one, for its small size and durability suggested that its material construction must be startlingly complex in detail. If a single gene were made of many small molecules, it was reasoned, it would be difficult to imagine how such structural complexity could be maintained since in these circumstances its properties would depend on the average behavior of many small molecules. The alternative view, according to theorists like Schrödinger and Delbrück, would be to picture the substance that makes up the gene, whatever it might be, as an enormous single molecule rather than a collection of small molecules. In this way, its stability, order, and permanence would be uniquely determined. They would not then be the consequences of statistical laws.

But how to get at the gene? If an experiment requires that we tamper with our object, how are we to experiment with the gene other than by simple crossbreeding? The answer to this question was provided in the late 1920's by H. J. Muller. Mendel's theory viewed the genes of each strain and species as permanent and unvarying. But this concept fails to explain how different strains and species arose in the first place. The theory of evolution, of course, rests squarely on the proposition that species somehow do vary—although Darwin knew nothing of Mendel, and his cautious and confused attempts to explain variation in the *Origin of Species* revealed a lingering faith in the heritability of acquired characteristics. How, then, can genic permanence and biological variation be reconciled? The answer is *mutation,* the occasional alteration of the gene itself.

When a gene mutates it is permanently altered. The offspring receive the mutant gene and transmit it to all subsequent generations. The three main reasons why the incidence of mutations might appear to be lower than it actually is are, first, that many mutations are lethal in that they prevent reproduction and, thus, extinguish themselves; second, many mutant genes are recessive and, hence, do not express themselves phenotypically; and, third, the visible results of many nonlethal mutations are so subtle they are lost in the welter of nonhereditary variations. Nevertheless, they do occur and studies on the genetics of corn showed that each gene has its own characteristic frequency of spontaneous mutation. This means that in every 100,000 seeds, for example, there will be one in which a given gene has mutated. Muller's contribution was the discovery that the incidence of mutations can be artificially increased by exposing the egg cells or spermatozoa to x-ray irradiation; the higher the dose the greater the frequency of induced mutations. Here was the tool genetics was waiting for! It was now possible to tinker with the gene on a wholesale basis.

One of the consequences of this work was the ultimate realization that it is the rare spontaneous mutation—whose cause is probably a stray bolt of the background radiation that is always present in the physical environment—which is the operating factor in evolution. This can be demonstrated in a nice experiment which, incidentally, also demonstrates the role that bacteria have come to play in modern theoretical biology. In bacteria, we can now observe evolution. We spoke of the burden that the historical nature of evolution places on the theorist. If evolution happened, it happened only once. With natural evolution, we can observe and cerebrate but not experiment, because evolution proceeds too slowly. We now recognize that a laboratory bacterium can pass through more generations in two years than has man in a million years. Bacterial evolution, therefore, can be studied by subjecting a pure culture of organisms to drastically unfavorable environmental conditions. As in the evolution of all life, only the fittest survive. In the experiments, "nature selects" only those individuals who may be resistant to such adversity. If, for example, an antibiotic is added to a culture plate, most (or all) of the organisms will be killed. Should survivors remain, they will grow and reproduce on fresh plates containing the antibiotic, revealing that the property of resistance is heritable. By such experiments, calculations can be made of the frequency with which the bacterial "antibiotic-resistance gene" spontaneously appears.

Although the antibiotic experiment could not have been described by Wells and Huxley—because antibiotics had not yet been discovered—they could have, in 1929, pointed to a similar experiment in radiated fruit flies subjected to unfavorable environments (they could have but they didn't). In any case, we have drawn even with the understanding of their decade. In broad outline, we see the gene as a hypothetical physical particle whose ordinarily stable complex organization can be disrupted by x-irradiation and whose properties can be known only by the consequences of its actions. As did Wells and Huxley, let us leave the gene here. We will rejoin it momentarily, but first let us enter another domain and speak of viruses. As we shall see, they will lead us back to the gene, though we may have trouble recognizing it this time around.

How the virus makes the cell make virus

What are viruses and what do they have to tell us about the nature of life?

Having argued that spontaneous generation had to be unequivocally demonstrated to be believed, Pasteur must have needed courage to declare that certain human diseases were caused by microbes which he could neither see in the microscope nor grow in the culture plate. But in those diseases that are caused by viruses, this is the case, and several of these engaged the attention of the great Pasteur. Several clear-cut facts were then known concerning ordinary pathogenic bacteria: they were microscopically visible, they could be cultivated on lifeless laboratory media, and they caused certain recognizable diseases. Pasteur knew only that he could neither see nor grow a causative agent in rabies. For a time, he suspected that these agents must be smaller than bacteria.

Pasteur's recognition of the role of viruses in infection strikes me as one of the larger scientific insights of all time. To appreciate it fully, we must recall the contemporary state of knowledge. The germ theory of disease was very new and still on shaky ground. To the medical mind, the whole abhorrent idea had long seemed ridiculous. But its successes could not be ignored, and by 1875 the theory enjoyed fairly wide acceptance. Germs caused disease, and the scientist's problem boiled down to proving that an individual organism caused an individual disease. It was a simple matter to find bacteria in the diseased body: the difficult part was to prove causation. The brilliant Robert Koch attacked this problem in 1876 while studying anthrax, a vexing disease of farm animals. As a result of his experiments, he proposed a set of criteria to aid in the establishment of a bacterial cause for a specific disease. These are the famous "postulates of Koch," which state 1) a specific organism must always be associated with a disease, 2) it must be isolated in pure culture, 3) when inoculated into a healthy susceptible animal it must always produce the disease, and 4) it must again be obtained in pure culture from the test animal. These rigid standards codified the problem of causal proof and guided the massive researches of the next few decades. The dawn of "pathogenic bacteriology" can perhaps be dated back to these classic studies on anthrax.

The germ theory, therefore, rested fairly securely at this point. Biologists had wrestled with the concept of bacterial life and, by struggle and creative genius, had established that the "infinitely small" play an "infinitely great" role in the economy of nature. It had been "proved" that spontaneous generation does not occur and that microbes arise only from parent organisms. It was established that bacterial species are real and stable, each dependable in its mode of action. Yet these theories were new, freshly conceived, and barely tested, when Pasteur failed utterly to isolate a visible organism from a rabid dog.

It was known that rabies was transmitted to man by the bite of a rabid dog, and Pasteur had little difficulty demonstrating that the saliva of an infected child when injected into a rabbit produced a fatal disease, readily transmissible from rabbit to rabbit. But repeated attempts to culture saliva failed to reveal the cause of rabies. At this point, the germ theory was clearly at the crossroads.

It is something of a cliché to say that Pasteur was a great scientist. For those who may have wondered why, here is one of the reasons. Believing that rabies was an infectious disease, yet confronted with the frustrating failure of the cultures (a technic with whose success he must certainly have been involved emotionally), Pasteur probed the deep canyons of his mind and came up with an exciting new idea. He abandoned the culture technic and conceived the notion of using the susceptible tissues of experimental animals to cultivate the causative agent instead of sterile nutrient broths. By inoculating a patient's saliva directly into the brain of a healthy dog, it became possible to induce rabies in the dog after an incubation period of fourteen days. As Dubos wrote:

> Thus was discovered a technic for the cultivation of an unknown infectious agent in the receptive tissues of a susceptible animal. This technic has permitted the study of those agents of disease which are not cultivable in lifeless media, and has brought them within the fold of the germ theory of disease. The Koch postulates in their original form could not be applied to the study of filtrable viruses and it is one of the most telling examples of Pasteur's genius that he did not hesitate to free himself of their requirements as soon as they proved unadapted to the solution of his problem. For him, doctrines and

technics were tools to be used only as long as they lent themselves to the formulation and performance of meaningful experiments.

It was soon recognized that bacteria have one other property not shared by viruses. Bacteria were too large to pass through the small pores of the porcelain filter, but in 1892, Ivanowski, a Russian botanist, showed that the agent responsible for mosaic disease of tobacco *would* pass through the same filters. What came through those pores were the "filtrable viruses." They were also the dragon seeds of a great new enigma. Actually, Ivanowski did not realize the importance of his experiment. Doubting his own data, he still believed mosaic disease to be bacterial in origin, and the world had to wait seven years until Beijerinck rediscovered the phenomenon and enunciated the theory of "living infectious fluid" (*contagium vivum fluidum*). In short order, a viral cause was established for a large number of animal and plant diseases, including many a plague of ancient infamy.

The demonstration that invisible viruses could be cultivated as readily as bacteria *if grown in the animal body* had enormous theoretical implications for biology. If the virus was a living unit, why could it survive only within a living cell? If it can survive only inside a living cell, we are compelled, whether we enjoy it or not, to ask, "Is virus a living organism?" Not even a halfhearted attempt could be made to answer these questions for many decades following the initial discovery of virus and its curious, rather dimly comprehended properties. The concept of virus emerged in a single context and no other, the power to produce disease. It was quickly recognized that different viruses can infect cells of all types, be they animal, plant, or bacterial. By residing in them they came to destroy them (and for our discussion this will pass as a definition of disease). This remained the only property which labeled the virus and hence the only means of its identification. This is, as a matter of fact, still true today.

For years, the question of whether viruses are living units has been begged by a variety of verbal devices. Since they were too small to be seen, it was not possible to say whether they had a nucleus or some other interior organization. In recognition of the single behavioral trait by which we can recognize viruses, they have (or it has) been referred to as "a factor" or "an agent" in careful stead of "an organism." To appreciate the scientific drudgery connected with any investigation of this question, it must be understood how severely the scientist was handicapped by the technical difficulties involved in merely deciding when he did and when he didn't have a virus before him. Each virus is absurdly fastidious and will grow only in a specific cell, frequently of only a single species. To survive, it must have its own kind of cell. The virus of rabies, for example, flourishes only in certain cells of the brain, that of mosaic disease of tobacco plants will live only in their leaves and no other. What this means is that the virologist confronted with a tube containing a drop of turbid fluid, which may or may not contain tobacco mosaic virus, must rub some fluid onto the leaves of the tobacco plant growing in his window box and then wait patiently. The appearance or nonappearance of the pathological symptoms of mosaic disease tells him yes or no. Actually, this isn't too bad. What of the encephalitis virus? These demand the brain cells of humans or near-humans, and encephalitis is fatal. Using one's laboratory assistants for such identification tests would only revive that antiscientific slogan of another decade, "They would boil their mothers in oil just to see what temperatures they died at"—so it became laboriously and tediously necessary to inject unknown samples into susceptible monkeys. If, in a month, the wretched beasts developed encephalitis, without first biting the investigator or coming down with something else, it would appear that the tube had contained virus—

that is, if the anthropoid hadn't already been incubating a case of encephalitis on his own initiative.

The inconvenience and expense of such technics requires no comment. For these reasons, certain areas of virus research could be explored only in the larger, better equipped laboratories of the world, to the great detriment of rapid progress. And for the same reasons, it is clear why much of the fundamental work on the nature of virus—as contrasted to the medical or applied problems—has been done on the viral enemies of plants and bacteria: they are simply easier to recognize.

Scientists did in time pull themselves together and, resignedly using these technics, began to cut their way through the underbrush. If a porcelain filter passes the virus, will a filter with smaller holes exclude it? In other words, does the word "filtrable" imply an absolute or relative characteristic? Collodion membranes of graded porosity answered this question by showing that viruses are particles of widely differing sizes, ranging from three hundred down to ten millimicrons. (A millimicron is a millionth of a millimeter.) The difficulties in measuring the virus by the size of the hole which will just fail to pass it are obvious. (It is also obvious that the term "filtrable" became obsolete when smaller filters were used.) Any inference of size from filter methods presupposes that the virus is a spherical particle. If it were a rod, passage through the pores would be much more difficult because of jamming and blocking of the type that occurs among logs floating down a narrow stream. Another great technical problem was the preparation of collodion membranes whose pore size was both uniform and reliably known. This was no easy matter. Not until 1927 was it possible for Elford to prepare collodion membranes with graded pore sizes such that the ratio of the largest pore diameter to the average pore diameter was no more than two. Elford's ingenious membranes greatly lowered the error inherent in such measurements but far from eradicated it. A third difficulty—

one which we will better appreciate later—was simply the migrainous necessity of having to assume that a particle only ten millimicrons in diameter, smaller in fact than certain protein molecules, could possess attributes of life such as reproduction.

The collodion membrane work which in 1930 disclosed the diminutiveness of viruses was the first departure of virology away from the classical narrows of medicine and clinically oriented immunology, the first look at *virus* as contrasted with *virus disease*. The reward was a first-class conundrum which a generation of biologists has been trying to solve.

Interestingly, an entirely different approach to the question of size took form during the 1930's with the invention of the ultracentrifuge. The great centrifugal force developed by the instrument threw down the viral particles in their spinning tube at a rate mathematically related to their size. All one had to do was follow a moving boundary by suitable optical devices. Unfortunately, here there were difficulties too. The mathematical laws governing sedimentation behavior required an accurate foreknowledge of the density of the settling particles. Such data are extremely difficult to obtain in viruses. Also, since virus is usually available in only meager quantities, it was often impossible to see the moving boundary of the virus column. Its position would then have to be located by tedious exploratory measurements of "infectivity" at various levels in the tube, to the great detriment of experimental accuracy.

Because virus particles are in a size range too small for microscopic visualization and too large for chemical investigation, a number of years passed before the picture of virus came into sharper focus. In time, a variety of increasingly sophisticated physicochemical technics converged on the problem of shape and size. The rod or sphere hypothesis received support from x-ray diffraction studies, and when the electron microscope finally crossed the barrier of optical microscopy, it became possible for the first time to measure viruses directly. Viruses were at last *visible*—little rods or spheres amazingly similar in size and shape to the models inferred from indirect measurements. To look at viruses in the electron microscope is pure fascination. There they are: shadowy and opaque, uniform and cleanly sculptured, inscrutably devoid of internal structure. One instantly feels the great appeal of such visual evidence and must warily guard against it. At the 1953 Cold Spring Harbor virus meeting, Robley Williams was moved to remark:

> The very directness of such evidence brings with it considerable hazard of misinterpretation, inasmuch as the temptation to accept visual evidence is great indeed, particularly when this evidence is in conformity with previously established notion. Lately, however, there has come a realization that the appearance of viruses, as discerned directly through the electron microscope, almost without exception fails to portray the shape and size of the virus particles as they exist in aqueous suspensions. It now appears that many of our morphological notions, derived from electron microscopy, are due for considerable revision.

The future of this problem is difficult to foresee. One gazes at these structures and recalls a prickly fact: they reproduce themselves *but only inside certain living cells*—and to each his own! What does it mean? The question may be asked two ways: What does virus reproduction mean and what does "virus reproduction" mean? We have already defined "virus," but what about "reproduction"? Here one must be careful. Since we recognize virus only by its infectivity, observing virus reproduction actually means observing an increase in virus activity *together with* an increase in the number of certain particles in the field of the electron microscope. The question arises again as to how one might be certain that the particles before one's eyes are the virulent agents causing the observable lesions in the host organism. It is the question that Koch tried to answer for bacteria, and to this day we must be satisfied with partial evidence yielding a measure of probability to the identity of physical particle and biological agent. For example, we can show that they have similar chemical and physical properties (but this clearly does not prove their identity); we can show that formaldehyde combines with virus substance *and* alters virus activity (but we can also show that other substances combine with virus particles without altering virus activity and still others destroy virus activity without combining in a manner accessible to chemical analysis). Uncertainty remains, though in many circumstances it has shrunken small. It is hard to doubt the identity of a particle under study to the bearer of virus activity when the particle sediments in the ultracentrifuge at exactly the same rate as the infectious principle, the particle migrates in an electric field at the same rate as the principle, and the particle has the same diffusion constant and filtration end point as the infectious principle.

Luria has emphasized the importance of recognizing the difference between *reproduction* and *replication*. The point is subtle but keenly important. When we think of reproduction, we think of an organism growing in size and then dividing. Let us remember that this sequence of events *must* be a mere outward manifestation—an epiphenomenon, if you like—of some critical event in the inner workings of reproduction in which *some elementary structure responsible for transmitting the hereditary code* from generation to generation is duplicated or replicated point by point. This inner event happens—replication occurs—and *then* reproduction can take place. The existence of this time sequence would seem to be a matter of logical necessity. If the reader finds the logic muddy, will he mentally tread water until we return to this crucial thought in another context?

Saying it in another way, 1) cells grow and divide,

2) cell growth and division is controlled by some inner mechanism carrying coded information, therefore 3) this mechanism must somehow be duplicated, and *duplication* may have nothing to do with *division.* In the rigorous language of Luria, "all growth and reproduction should ultimately be traceable to *replication of specific chemical configurations by an essentially discontinuous appearance of discrete replicas.*" It is an abstraction of gigantic power. As we shall see, the study of virus reproduction is one of the most rewarding approaches to bridging the gap between growth and replication.

What apparently happens is this: the virus attaches itself to the surface of a cell of its choice; it (or part of it) enters the cell and literally disappears; the virologist looks and sees no trace of the virus; if he grinds up the cell, he fails to liberate a demonstrably infective agent; he watches; twenty-four minutes later the cell bursts releasing two hundred new fully formed virus particles ready to infect new cells; the host cell is dead, drained, and broken. Since these are the things we observe, we are clearly unjustified in stating that viruses grow and reproduce; we know only that they replicate. The burning question which is baking today's best brains is simply: What happens inside the host cell during those twenty-four minutes?

Considerably more information has been gathered on this question from the study of bacterial viruses than plant or animal viruses. It is interesting to note that the students of each of the three kinds of virus were for long years quite remote from each other. Thoroughly preoccupied with the practical problems resulting from virus activity, they communicated little on general questions concerning the nature of virus and inevitably they built up large semantic and methodological barriers between themselves. Only since 1950 have the three groups begun talking to each other earnestly and constructively. Books are now appearing on "general virology" and cross-fertilization between fields is slowly commencing. It is reasonable to guard against the a priori assumption that what is true for one virus is true for another; but it is unreasonable to contend that each virus is a distinct entity and that nothing learned on one is valid for another. The bacterial viruses more or less gained the upper hand for obvious reasons. These viruses cause bacterial dissolution or lysis. "There are few biological phenomena," wrote Evans, "that are as dramatic as this. When one adds a small amount of bacterial virus to a vigorously growing bacterial culture, nothing occurs immediately. Then, suddenly, the suspension begins to foam, as materials inside the bacterial cell are liberated into the medium, and within a short time the heavy mass of growing bacteria has been replaced by floating shreds of debris that settle slowly to the bottom of the containing vessel. The clear bluish supernatant liquid now contains a hundred fold multiplication of the original virus inoculum."

Thus, bacterial viruses have the technical advantage of easy detectability. They can be found simply by looking for clearing spots in a bacterial culture plate. It was the chance observation of such a clear zone that led to the original discovery of bacterial viruses. The early workers hoped that bacterial viruses (which they named bacteriophage or "phage" in laboratory jargon) would kill the bacteria in infectious diseases and thus prove useful therapeutically. There is hardly a bacteria known for which there is not a corresponding bacteriophage. Such hopes were overly optimistic, however, because phages like all other viruses turned out to be too narrowly specific in their attack on bacteria. Phage resistance would result from the first mutation toward resistance in a susceptible bacterial strain. Phage made its contribution in another way. It became the fruit fly of virology, the great model system that almost alone integrated virology into a unified science.

Actually, plant viruses, particularly the tobacco mosaic virus (known in the trade as TMV), had held the center of the stage for over twenty years in all matters of physicochemical characterization. The difficulties in their bioassay unfortunately make them not inaccurate but quite inefficient study systems. In recent years, a number of technical developments have emerged which may have greatly simplified the propagation and assayability of certain animal viruses. It is now possible to cultivate the poliomyelitis virus in living chick embryos rather than in the central nervous systems of apes and men, and it has been discovered that certain viruses such as the influenza virus cause red blood cells to clump together, the degree of clumping being proportional to the amount of virus present. A basis for an assay procedure is readily apparent. Interestingly, this phenomenon has provided an important theoretical clue to the mechanism by which a virus makes contact with the cell it is going to infect. The red blood cell is not penetrated by the influenza virus but its surface seems to have the same mosaic of chemical components as the cells lining the nasal passages. The red cell may prove to be an excellent model for the study of virus-cell interaction.

Faced with a bewildering array of viruses, each possibly unique and maddeningly fastidious, biologists made a decision calculated to expedite work, facilitate communication, and save wasted effort. A single strain of a common bacterium was elected—*E. coli,* strain B—an organism known to extend its hospitality to seven distinct bacteriophages. These were separated, characterized and named T1, T2, T3, T4, T5, T6, and T7. The plan was to concentrate study on these seven "coliphages," five of which turned out to look like tiny tadpoles in the electron microscope. T3 and T7 were small spheres. A large number of other traits of each of the seven phages were delineated, for example, their individual sedimentation behavior, diffusion rates, immunological specificity, etc. (Here again are traits whose recognition had to await technological developments. In the age when virus was no more than an invisible infectious agent, one might reasonably have wondered what traits a virus could have!) I emphasize the matter of coliphage traits in order to point out a series of hugely exciting discoveries made possible by their recognition. For one thing, when a bacterial cell is simultaneously infected by two closely related but different phage types, the progeny include both types in proportions similar to the infecting mixture. This may not sound especially startling but it could not, of course, have been predicted. During the "eclipse" referred to above, the period between the disappearance of the infecting particles and the appearance of new ones, particles and infective activity are both temporarily out of sight. Presumably the substance of virus becomes mixed in with the substance of host cell. In a double infection, however, everything seems to straighten itself out before the deadline and from temporary "disorder" reappears high order. A mixed infection with unrelated types yields a pure brood of one type only. The infecting particle of the other type is lost.

But when certain pairs of phages are used to produce a mixed infection in a host bacterium, a startling thing happens. The offspring include *new* types resulting from a recombination of the traits of the parental types. This fundamental result means that genetic mechanisms, genetic recombination, occurs in viruses! As is true in the genetic processes of higher living forms, recombination of parental traits in the offspring requires the formal conclusion that somewhere, somehow there must exist a number of *discrete recombinable genetic units,* vehicles by which a parent contributes its share to the traits of the offspring. These would be genes. We dimly sense that behind the twenty-four-minute eclipse lies an ancient and utter secret, perhaps the broad design by which life emerged in a frigid, star-pocked universe.

We know that virus replication occurs only if the metabolism of the host cell is proceeding actively—and if the environment provides adequate nutrition. It is clear that virus reproduction depends upon the metabolic machinery and food supply of the *host cell,* the virus particle apparently taking charge and turning all cell processes to its own purposes. What confronts us then is the supremely challenging spectacle of two separate viruses—structures not only lacking chromosomes but themselves far smaller than chromosomes in many cases—entering a host cell, fading from view for a brief interval during which the cell is forced to make new viruses according to instructions it has never seen before, and, finally, the emergence from the broken host cell of a large litter of new viruses, some of which bear the traits of both parent particles. This is mating and genetic recombination among otherwise inert particles! Before inquiring what significance this startling fact may hold for our concept of the gene, let us consider some observations that are even more astonishing.

The meeting of virus, gene, information, and chemistry

At the time that *The Science of Life* was written, one could truthfully say that the problem of heredity had been solved. It was known how the genes were sorted out to the offspring, and the concept of spontaneous mutation was firmly established. As far as the fact of heredity was concerned, it was explained by these mechanisms. What was not known, however, was *how* the gene does its work, how it influences the new organism to develop this or that trait. If the gene is pictured as a blueprint, how does it communicate with the builder? Some new approaches would now be timely.

The ingenious work of the California investigators Beadle and Tatum soon provided an important clue. To pea plants, fruit flies, and bacteriophages, these workers added a red mold of bread as a classical object of genetic investigation. So that we can clearly understand their experiment, let us consider some preliminary facts. Once the living organism has been conceived and its future traits determined, it becomes essentially a metabolic machine whose primary activity is the chemical conversion of nutrient materials to other compounds needed by the organism as structural elements or energy sources. We may illustrate the essential character of metabolism quite simply:

$$A \rightarrow B \rightarrow C \rightarrow D \rightarrow E \rightarrow F$$

A is an ingredient of the diet; F is a compound that the organism needs. The intermediate compounds are merely products and precursors in an orderly sequence of stepwise chemical reactions, each of which is made possible by a specific *enzyme* within the cell. Catalyzing and controlling these reactions is the only function of enzymes and, as we recall, enzymes are specialized protein molecules. For almost every one of the huge number of chemical reactions in the organism, there is one enzyme "in charge" of it. Without its specific enzyme, the corresponding reaction would not occur. There is evidence indicating that the high specificity of each enzyme is the result of the unique and intricate structure of its surface. It will, in fact, "fit" only one reaction. From information theory, however, we might have predicted such a physical basis for specificity.

We may, therefore, regard all biological traits as visible results of the functioning of one or another such sequence of enzymatic reactions. For example, brown eyes are brown because a brown compound has been chemically synthesized by a collection of enzymes in the cells of the iris, starting from some simpler compound obtained from the diet. Red hair, too, is a consequence of the enzyme-directed synthesis of a red pigment in hair. The same is true of height, blood group, shape, and all other traits. In other words, the presence or absence of specific enzymes determines the appearances which we call traits. Here we may have achieved a simplification, since it is surely easier to imagine a palpable relationship between a gene and an enzyme than between a gene and a pair of brown eyes.

Beadle and Tatum took a sample of mold that could successfully make F from A. (F could be any number of essential compounds such as tryptophan or pantothenic acid, but for the sake of clarity, let us stick with the letters.) The mold needed F for growth and reproduction, but if grown on a medium containing only A, it flourished since it possessed the enzymatic machinery to convert A to F. They found then that if they irradiated the mold, many offspring appeared which could no longer grow on a medium containing only A, but could grow if F were added to the culture. In other words, the F requirement for growth was unchanged, but the mold had lost the ability to convert A to F. By closer analysis, they could demonstrate that this radiation-induced loss occurred in just *one* of the steps, that is, the organism could not now convert C to D (for example), while the other steps remained intact. This could be shown in two ways: by demonstrating normal growth on a medium containing only D (proving that D → E → F is intact); and by showing a large pile-up of C when the medium contains only A (showing that A is still going to C, although C is not being removed). These results suggest that x-irradiation of the mold caused its offspring to lose a single enzyme. When an actual search was made for the "C → D enzyme," it was indeed found missing. Furthermore, if the mold was sustained by artificially providing it with the product of the missing reaction, it reproduced normally, and all subsequent generations were without the same enzyme and, hence, in need of a special diet of D.

The implications of this classical experiment are evident. A mutation, induced by radiation, results in a new strain lacking one enzyme. Beadle and Tatum, therefore, postulated that for each enzyme, there is one gene—the "one gene-one enzyme hypothesis." If the enzyme is a workman, in this view, it has its own gene as a personal executive.

This work, in addition, clarifies several outstanding

mysteries. For example, the red mold uses vitamin B_1 just as we do; but *it* can make B_1 from simpler compounds and we cannot. When Beadle and Tatum produced a mutant that could no longer make its own B_1, the compound—or an immediate precursor—had to be provided artificially. Since we must have our B_1 ready made, B_1 is a vitamin for us, because by definition a vitamin is a necessary substance that the organism cannot make for itself. That is why it is essential in the diet. To the normal mold, B_1 is not a vitamin. We may reasonably speculate that in the course of evolution, our ancestors once could make B_1 but through a mutation such as Beadle inflicted on his molds the enzymatic machinery necessary for its synthesis was lost forever. Had there been no creatures in our environment who could make it for us, like the bread mold, wheat plant, or whatever else passes under the name of "food," we might have perished then and there.

The question now comes down to the nature of the relationship between the gene and those protein molecules which are enzymes. Conceivably, the gene is some kind of master pattern which is copied physically in the manufacture of specific enzyme molecules. Since such high specificity is conveyed from the gene to the enzyme, we cannot avoid visualizing some sort of physical relationship such as occurs in printing. Thus, the gene might be an intricate template for stamping the specificity into its enzyme. If the gene were physically damaged, the resulting enzyme would be imperfect—and since an enzyme will not function at all even if only slightly imperfect, the consequence of mutation may not necessarily be a missing enzyme but an imperfect one which, lacking the ability to function, might just as well be missing.

This "printing" or "stamping" motion is compelling because it is a physical model, and it is clear that we are being pressed toward an examination of the physical nature of what biologists have been calling the gene.

Some method had to be devised to permit such a frontal assault, for the analysis of the gene through its genetic consequences had now entered turbulent, dilemma-infested waters. The geneticists were reaching that inevitable point in their science where suddenly old and trusted words began defaulting. For example, it was discovered in a number of cases that certain factors outside of the nucleus (which we will not dwell on here) can affect heredity. Since an alteration in a gene can be recognized only by its genetic effects, how can one distinguish between the effects of mutation and those of extranuclear hereditary determinants? This must mean that those observable genetic phenomena which we normally called mutations should not be so readily labeled, since the word "mutation" implies a specific mechanism for the phenomenon. In other words, geneticists awoke to the fact that they were trying to argue that x-rays produce a gene mutation because the mutants induced satisfy the accepted criteria for gene mutations, and that these mutants were due to an alteration in a specific gene because that is what we mean by gene mutation!

Likewise, it was pointed out that the fundamental idea of gene stability rests on experimental evidence obtained in "good" genes that behave "properly." A flock of elaborate explanations are available to account for the bad genes that behave improperly, but the fundamental problem remains. Genes, in fact, may always be stable and the explanations may, therefore, be unnecessary. Thus, we have another instance of data interpreted so as to insure conformity with a prevailing idea. This agonizing reappraisal within the field of genetics is quite analogous to that which occurred in physics with the theory of relativity. For we are here forced into a completely operational point of view. We must not only prevent ourselves from assuming any properties for the gene that are beyond verification, we must, in fact, define the gene in terms of the actual operations that are performed in dealing with it. Operationally, then, we can now say no more about the gene than that it is the smallest segment in the string of genetic material that can regularly be associated with some genetic effect. As we consider this meager statement, we again feel the necessity of tearing into the gene's substance. What is this stuff anyhow? Is it a thing? Is it a molecule? Is it a phantom?

The new approach began as a simple question: What is the gene made of chemically—or, more precisely, what is the chromosome made of, since genes are worrisome postulations and chromosomes are visible structures? It had been known for years that a peculiar substance could be extracted from the cell nucleus which, being acidic, was ingeniously named *nucleic acid.* It was then discovered that there are two kinds of nucleic acid which differ slightly in chemical composition and source: the kind that was found only in the nucleus was desoxyribonucleic acid or DNA and the kind that may be outside the nucleus, ribonucleic acid or RNA. The molecules of nucleic acid were found to be extraordinarily large, especially that of DNA. They were long thin chainlike structures made up of a large number, possibly thousands, of smaller units called *nucleotides.* These were the links in the chain. The nucleotides themselves were quite complicated, each containing four different kinds of substances called nitrogenous bases. For convenience, we may refer to these as 1, 2, 3, and 4. Thus, chemically speaking, DNA appeared to be a long chain of repeating units, each of which contained the same four bases, more or less like this:

. . . —(1-2-3-4)—(1-2-3-4)—(1-2-3-4)—(1-2-3-4)—. . .

No one knew, of course, whether the chain was as shown or of a random configuration such as this:

. . .—(3-2-1-4)—(1-4-3-2)—(2-4-1-3)—(4-3-1-2)—. . .

And for many years, no one much cared. The tedious chemical facts we have recited were eked out in the early part of this century and, shortly thereafter, nucleic acid was placed on the shelf to gather dust, a curious, gummy sort of white powder of unknown significance. Wells and Huxley didn't even mention it, for if it belonged to anyone in 1929 it was to the biochemists, not the biologists.

In the course of time, however, nucleic acid reappeared on the scene in several unexpected places. Wendell Stanley, for example, showed that the tobacco mosaic virus contained nothing but RNA and protein; and later workers found that the bacteriophages consisted entirely of a particle of DNA surrounded by a protein coating. When the virus workers managed to incorporate radioactive "labels" into the protein and DNA, they found to their surprise that when a virus enters a cell, the protein remains outside while the nucleic acid enters—as though the protein were a syringe which gave the cell an injection of nucleic acid. This was a stirring observation, for it suggested that it is nucleic acid alone—the same material biochemists had long ago put into bottles—which inside the host cell stimulates the production of two hundred replicas of itself plus, of course, two hundred protein overcoats like the one left outside. According to these results the power of virus reproduction resides somehow within the virus's nucleic acid. Since it alone can instruct a cell to begin turning out new viruses, it alone must carry the hereditary information which guarantees that the new virus will be a replica of its parent.

While biology was trying to swallow this fundamental development, still another emerged from the bacteriology laboratories. The following simple phenomenon was observed: Two cultures of the same species of bacteria were grown up which differed only in that one had trait *x* while the other did not. (We are using *x* for convenience. It could be any one of several hereditary traits—penicillin resistance, for example. Thus, *x* bacteria would be penicillin resistant; non-*x* bacteria penicillin sensitive.) An extract of the *x* bacteria was prepared which was demonstrably free of whole bacteria, particles, or other debris. The extract was then added to the growing culture of non-*x* bacteria. The results were quite startling, for the treated culture developed many colonies of *x* bacteria as a result of having been exposed to a mere fluid extract of the *x* bacteria. Moreover, the new *x* bugs bred true, showing that their newly acquired trait was hereditary. This phenomenon was called *transformation,* and the active ingredient in the extract was called the *transforming principle* or TP. As the reader has undoubtedly predicted, it was promptly shown that TP was, in fact, the DNA of the *x* bacteria. And again, DNA turns up as a carrier of genetic information.

An avalanche of questions followed these discoveries. Is DNA the substance of which genes are made? If so, is "a gene" one molecule of DNA or several—or, conversely, is a single molecule of DNA one gene or several? Where does DNA fit into the chromosome? Does DNA carry the information of heredity? If so, how, since no *chemical* difference can be detected between the constituents of the DNA of horses and bacteria? If a cell makes its own DNA in the course of reproducing itself, what insures that the new DNA will carry forward the hereditary code? How, for that matter, does a *molecule* duplicate itself? The only thing that could not be questioned was the dramatic fact that, at last, the fateful meeting had occurred between biology, chemistry, and physics. For DNA is a *chemical* compound carrying *genetic* information somewhere within its *physical* structure. The die was now cast for a unified attack on one of the greatest enigmas of science.

We cannot, of course, enter into the details of this work. Nor would it be possible to, since these are the questions that science is investigating in the hour of this writing. It is worth noting perhaps that almost all of the great developments mentioned above have taken place since 1950. And today, 1950 seems like the Middle Ages, for the situation is moving more rapidly than ever. Tantalizing developments are literally tumbling from the laboratories, in a manner which clearly suggests that possessing knowledge is not half as much fun as discovering it.

Thus, for example, in 1953 Watson and Crick examined a preparation of isolated DNA by the method of x-ray diffraction, a technic so brilliantly applied by Linus Pauling to the study of the structure of proteins and other giant molecules. It was found that the long DNA molecule is not a mere string of nucleotides but a highly organized structure shaped like a spring, or helix. The exciting part of their discovery, however, was that the winding of the spring involved two strands, not one. In other words, two parallel nucleotide chains were together wound around an empty cylindrical space. It was also concluded that any given order of nitrogenous bases in one strand determined the order in the other strand, since the limited space available in the tightly joined structure meant that only certain pairs of bases could exist side by side.

Here then was a picture of the DNA molecule which could explain a great deal. The presence of a double set of strands at once suggests a self-duplicating mechanism. The two chains could separate, then each could serve as a template for the formation of its partner strand, particularly since each base in the chain would attract the correct complementary base. The daughter DNA would then be similarly double-stranded while the order of the bases would be kept undisturbed. The preservation of the *order* of the bases is a crucial feature of this discovery, for every finger points to this order as the code in which all of heredity is written. Theorists were quick to point out that if the DNA chain contained only one hundred nucleotides with four bases each (it actually contains thousands), the number of possible arrangement of these bases would be 4^{100}, a number one thousand times larger than the number of atoms in the solar system. Here would be more than enough room for specificity in the synthesis of enzyme proteins, and one can imagine these bases in the act of assembling the different amino acids which make up protein in a *specific order*. Since all of the many varieties of enzymes contain the same kinds of amino acids, their specificity too lies in the order of their subunits.

In the current view, DNA does not directly preside over protein synthesis of specific enzyme proteins. This scheme would be analogous to the manufacture of phonograph records for commercial distribution. First, the artist makes a master. In order to duplicate the master, a negative pressing is made, and this in turn may be used repeatedly to press out new positives. Here the master is the DNA, the negative which transfers the information is the RNA, and the soft shellac which is stamped with a specific high-fidelity pattern is the protein or its precursor which becomes an enzyme. Or, as it was phrased at a recent scientific meeting, DNA is the Father, RNA the Son, and protein the Holy Ghost.

The two most recent developments in this field must be mentioned, for they typify the experimentalists' efforts to give meaning to the implications of the Watson-Crick hypothesis. In 1955, a bacterial enzyme was discovered in the laboratory of Severo Ochoa which, when placed in a test tube with some free nucleotides, links them together to form a giant molecule chemically indistinguishable from RNA. A similar enzyme for "synthetic" DNA was discovered a year later by Arthur Kornberg. And, in 1956, Schramm, in Tübingen, and Fraenkel-Conrat, working in Berkeley, discovered that free RNA, isolated from tobacco mosaic virus, could alone infect tobacco leaves, showing that the protein component of the virus was not essential for replication. Now capable of synthesizing an RNA-like molecule which lacks only a specific base order and is thus noninfective, the biochemist stands ready to join the virologist, whose specific RNA-replicating system provides a means of testing the success of attempts to bring order into the present disorder of the synthetic nucleotide chain. Although the random arrangement of bases in synthetic nucleic acid appears disordered to a tobacco leaf cell which rejects its instructions, one might reasonably suppose that some cell in the living world, past, present, or future, might find this arrangement the precisely correct one to effect its own duplication *in that cell.* This can be illustrated by supposing that we have drawn thirteen cards from an ordinary deck which, for the game of contract bridge, constitutes a miserable hand. We can, however, imagine the existence of another game of cards in which this same hand would be a winner. Thus, the "disordered" synthetic RNA may actually be a hopeful virus in search of a willing host cell. Unfortunately, the biochemist hasn't the time to test his product for infectivity in every existing cell type, for this would take an eternity. Rather, he will attempt somehow to achieve the specific order necessary for reproduction within a given cell. He will play contract bridge and try for a good hand, instead of taking any hand and searching for a game he can win with it. In the summer of this writing, such experiments are in progress.

One might call this an attempt to create life, but such a statement adds very little to our understanding of what has been done and what remains to be done. These are physical phenomena entirely accessible to our comprehension and, in this light, the word "life" has an anemic appearance. As for the gene, it, too, remains nebulous. At the moment, it is a property of a portion of a molecule and not a "thing" at all.

Current views on the origin of life

Having cut down the problem of the nature of life to molecular dimensions, having considered the question of how a collection of atoms might arrange themselves into a self-duplicating key, we are in as good a position as we will ever be to inquire how life began in the first place. It must have had a beginning since we know that the earth did not once exist. It is now well established that the earth was born of the sun. Modern theory concerning what Gamow calls "the blessed event" holds that very long ago, probably three to five billion years ago, the incredibly large mass of flaming matter which is our sun threw off portions of itself—possibly under the gravitational influence of a passing star. The solar tidal wave of hot gas cast off into space and broke up into separate portions which arrayed themselves in orbits about the sun, trapped by its gravitational field. Soon these gas balls began to cool and solidify, until hard crusts had formed. It was upon the outer crust of one of these planets that life, like a thin film of rust, eventually appeared.

There is an intriguing aspect to the history of scientific interest in this question. As we have already observed, the problem needed no answer as long as men believed that life could arise spontaneously on every side. Only when Pasteur showed that life must come from life did the problem of life's origin loom into view. And at the other end of the story, the most recent phase, it is abundantly clear that, during the years since Pasteur, speculation on the problem was almost doomed to meaninglessness by the lack of understanding of the nature of genetic material and the physical basis for the self-duplication of nucleic acid. Only the recent insights into information theory, specificity, and order, and the new work on nucleic acid and virus have brought perspective into this inquiry.

Thus, in the thinking of a decade ago, there seemed to be a logically reasonable way of picturing the origin of life. But it quickly ran into trouble. In this view, simple chemical molecules by a process of evolution gradually became more complex until finally, by chance or whatever, a combination occurred which, like DNA, could effect its own reduplication. The trouble with this is that DNA, as we know it today, can duplicate itself only when the catalytic machinery of a fully formed cell is available to provide the building blocks for the daughter DNA. The first DNA-like molecule would have no such servants, since enzymes and cells are of biological origin and we are speaking here of the *first* organism. Let us see how current thinking is attempting to "get rid" of this difficulty.

First of all, it is generally agreed that the events we are talking about took place between one and two billion years ago! Among other things, this means 1) that we do not know for certain what the earth was like at that time, 2) that we are constructing hypotheses that cannot be directly verified, 3) that their chief claim to truth must rest on their reasonableness, and 4) there is a great difference between stating what might have happened and what did happen. For in these "simple difficulties" begin the perennial arguments such as the one between Pirie and Bernal. According to Bernal, Pirie is saying we must remain silent until everything is known, and, according to Pirie, Bernal rushes into print with dangerous oversimplifications every time an astronomer or geochemist offers a new description of the infant earth. These are the occupational hazards that surround this question. In an attempt to avoid them, let us quickly try to outline the area of agreement.

The earth *was* created, and as the process of cooling took place, great quantities of heat were given off. But soon the earth's surface reached a temperature that was largely determined by the sunlight that fell upon it. During the early millenniums of the cooling period, rain began to fall—steaming, warm, drenching rain. It fell ceaselessly and formed at last the seas of the earth.

In the beginning of terrestrial time, the waters of the vast oceans were fresh, containing no salt. The salinity of the sea resulted from the steady erosion of land by "fresh water" rivers which poured endlessly into the sea. Over the long stretches of geological time, billions and billions of tons of salt and other minerals have been carried into the oceans so that the sea water of the modern world has a salt content of about three per cent.

It is fascinating to try to imagine what the world must have been like on its one-millionth birthday. We must visualize a scene of incredible desolation, no living thing, no trees, no fish in the sea, no sounds except the sounds of the waves and the wind. The land masses were surfaced with jagged, unweathered rocks and had no true soil, since soil is largely a by-product of bacterial activity. It is almost impossible to comprehend the amount of time that passed while the earth held no life.

Of this era, science has little specific knowledge. The strata, rocks and sediments of this period in the earth's history, the period known as pre-Cambrian, which are the usual types of geological evidence, are deeply buried, hidden by the crushing weight of later volcanic ages, continental periods, and glacial revolutions. A few exceptional sectors of today's earth have been discovered which are the result of very early geological transformation. One of these, the Laurentian mountain range of eastern Canada, is the remnant of probably the first extensive crumbling of the earth's crust, the so-called Laurentian revolution. But the main clues upon which geologists have had to rely have been indirect. What we know of the early world was learned with difficulty, by ingeniously gathered evidence and shrewd deduction.

In the great pre-Cambrian seas, where life did not exist, a different sort of evolution was taking place, the evolution of chemical molecules. We can say with some assurance that the infant world had its full complement of elements, its hydrogen, its phosphorus, its carbon, all the substances which are now so intricately woven into the fabric of life. But these elements, we must assume, then existed in a simple form. In considering the situation of that time, one naturally conjures up a model, a huge watery solution of chemical substances floating about and interacting. We have at our disposal a body of modern theory, both in thermodynamics and chemical kinetics, which gives us strong hints as to the probable mechanisms by which simple molecules evolved into complex ones. Suffice it to say that in a chemical system such as the one of our model, the events and interactions that take place are not governed *purely* by chance, but by chance functioning within the laws of chemical reactions, equilibriums, entropy, and free energy. We find that certain chemical substances such as carbon, which is so important to the living organism, have properties which predispose them to form long, complex molecular chains, especially when exposed to the powerful energy of sunlight. As Beutner aptly remarked, "Life is just one of the countless properties of carbon."

We have now arrived at the point where most arguments begin. The advance of chemical evolution has produced oceans of what Haldane has happily called "dilute warm soup," and we may reasonably suppose that in this soup is a large variety of randomly distributed chemical compounds, continuously building up and breaking down. We must now produce a hypothesis which will explain how a pattern of order could emerge from this disorder. Many suggestions have been made: molecules collected at air-water interfaces, on clay surfaces, in the oceanic depths, and gradually there developed a molecular chain whose growth and splitting was catalyzed by itself or by simpler molecules in the vicinity. It now appears that there is no logical necessity for assuming that protein catalysts are *essential* for the assembly of a replicating chain: they are only the best, not the only, way of doing it.

The difficulties caused by the assumption that enzymes had to assist in the origin of life call to mind the contention of a century ago that inorganic compounds differed from organic in that the latter could be made only by living organisms. This distinction appeared to break down when Wöhler artificially synthesized urea. However, as George Wald remarked, ". . . it showed nothing of the kind. Organic chemists are alive; Wöhler merely showed that they can make organic compounds externally as well as internally. It is still true that with almost negligible exceptions all the organic matter is the product of living organism." But it is the exceptions that interest us, because the origin of life was an exceptional occurrence.

The most recent theory to explain the spontaneous appearance of molecular order is that of Melvin Calvin. He points out that certain kinds of organic substances combine together by "piling up face to face or plane to plane," not as true crystallization, which would require concentrated warm soup, but as a kind of incipient crystallization that could occur in dilute warm soup. Calvin points out that DNA is precisely the kind of molecule that might form this way. And once formed, its ordered structure would influence the order in which a neighboring collection of molecules would orient themselves.

If such events led to the first nucleic acid, it is evident that there was no specific moment when life began. Had we been present as observers at that time, we could have wasted a great deal of time waiting for the first amoeba, for it is doubtful if one could have recognized the origin of life while it was taking place. In this view, we are relieved of the notion that life began in a cataclysmic instant as a result of a chance collision of the "right" molecules. This concept has always been hard to swallow. When one reflects on the stupendous complexity of the living organism, it is entirely reasonable to doubt that it could have arisen as the result of a chance event completely physical in character. And this has been the argument of writers like Du Noüy who interpret the extreme improbability of this event to mean that life was created by some extraphysical agency. One is not forced to this conclusion, however. While the probability is very low, particularly as viewed by the scale and context of human experience, it is not zero, and if the probability of an event is not zero, it can be expected that in a period of a few billion years, in a milieu as vast as the primeval oceans, the event may have occurred at least once and probably more than once. When the time scale is long enough, the improbable becomes the inevitable. But we need not postulate an event as unlikely as a cataclysmic collision. No individual element of a theory such as Calvin's is improbable; the measure of the improbability of all the elements occurring in proper sequence is the billion years or two it took to happen. That is why one should doubt—to quote Calvin—"that we will ever be able to put all the chemicals in a pot and place it in a radiation field and go away and leave it for a while and come back and find nucleic acids."

One of the problems in deciphering the origin of life is simply this: if chance could make a living system could not chance destroy it? Were not the forces of dissolution which surround all living systems powerful enough to destroy the first feeble slime of life? The answer lies in understanding the ultimate nature of the destructive forces of the environment. Essentially, they are two: oxidation and decay. We find, however, that chemical attack by oxygen could not have occurred to the first organism because the earth's atmosphere at the time contained no oxygen. It was not oxidative but reducing. It was, in fact, the organisms of the earth that themselves placed the oxygen in its atmosphere and produced its oxidative character. With the evolution of plant chlorophyll, photosynthesis commenced and the plant kingdom flourished, sucking in sunlight and dumping out oxygen. Today it is estimated that every molecule of oxygen in the earth's atmosphere has arisen from a plant at some time in the last two thousand years.

As for decay, we must recall that decay depends upon bacterial action and bacteria did not exist in the desolate world of the first citizen. Though a weakling, he was unthreatened; though easy prey, he met no enemy. For all we know, life is originating anew in our own times, but *today* it is quickly eaten by those creatures who, unknowing, are preparing themselves to be eaten. Such is the world of life.

One might make some deductions as to *when* life originated. Since life as we know it can exist only in a cool, solid-liquid world, the origin of life must have been delayed till the earth had a cool crust. Some actual evidence is available on the approximate time of the origin of life. Fossils have been found that can be dated back to the Cambrian period some five hundred million years ago, but these were already advanced in evolution, including the basic invertebrate animals and the beginnings of vertebrates. The fossil record before the Cambrian record is very unsatisfactory. The world's oldest sedimentary rocks do not contain fossils because the earliest living forms did not have the skeletons or hard bodies necessary for fossil formation. There have been some reports of algae fossils, "worms" and sponges in late pre-Cambrian rocks, but, according to various authorities, these are open to question. Recent studies on the dating of rocks by their isotope and radioactivity content have permitted geologists to establish that certain early pre-Cambrian rocks are two billion years old. Some of these contained materials that could possibly be organic in origin, so that life's beginning must be placed between the origin of the Earth, three billion years ago, and the oldest known sedimentary rocks of two billion years ago. It is clear that this still leaves enough time for some highly improbable goings on.

It is often asked whether life does or could exist on other planets. There is surely nothing to suggest a priori that our planet stands uniquely alone in the universe. Wald says, "Life is a cosmic event . . . it has come many times, in many places—places closed off from us by impenetrable distances, probably never to be crossed even with a signal." Urey believes that other planets, such as Mars and Venus, have histories similar to that of Earth with similar transformations of the atmosphere induced by the energy of solar radiation. But because of the lower gravitational field of Mars, its oxygen probably escaped completely from its atmosphere much as helium in time escaped from the atmosphere of Earth. The atmosphere of Venus is almost pure carbon dioxide with a total absence of water. Saturn apparently still has an atmosphere of hydrogen and methane, suggesting that it is a fossil planet. If, indeed, ultraviolet solar radiation is responsible for the oxidizing character of the atmosphere, it is easy to understand the situation on Saturn, which is so far from the sun it receives only one per cent as much solar radiation as the Earth. It appears that conditions satisfactory for life as it exists on Earth probably do not occur on the other planets of our system. This is not to say that some other sort of organism could not be thriving under these seemingly alien conditions. It just seems unlikely. And, of course, we are not speaking of numberless other solar systems.

One entertaining theory of the origin of life had it that life was seeded on the earth by little living particles brought through space from other planets. Arrhenius believed that these particles were propelled by radiation energy, literally by the power of starlight. We now know that the ultraviolet light of stars is destructive to life, and, for the purpose of our discussion, the pushing of the problem to another planet does not help us answer the question as to how life began. The event, say, on Pluto, inaccessible though it is, would still have to be explained.

In considering these problems, it is quite likely that we are ignorant of the extent of our ignorance. Further progress in this area must await a solidification of our ideas in other areas, from geochemistry to biochemistry, from genetics to physics. But we have a start and, as Bernal has said, "After all, biochemical evolution cannot be more complex than the organic evolution to which it gave rise."

Organism: the elusive hierarchy

Living organisms are *not* nucleic acid, however, and we must make a real effort to bear this in mind. Though we have spoken chiefly of the gene and the enzyme, it is the organism that lives in the world, that walks and grows and writes books on biology. What is the nature of this complexity that knows so many forms, but fails to hide their brotherhood? What is there about the organism that has made poets sing and scientists despair?

The essence of organism is at once subtle and irresistibly fascinating. The secret is in its name. The organism is an *organization* of materials and functions that are dedicated to the preservation of itself and its species. The allure of this concept, however, stems from the intricate system of *levels* of organization, a pattern which characterizes all living things. Thus, the cell is an organized entity at one level of complexity. It lives in a community of other cells, joining them in certain projects, competing with them for food, and either dying or dividing to form new offspring. Yet these cells may be part of a higher organization, the brain, which is a whole made up of the sum of its parts. Here is a structure on a more complex level of organization, existing and interacting in a community of other organs, not cells. Likewise, the whole man is still higher on the scale of organization, and men talk to other men, not brains or cells. We may also start with the cell and go down the ladder, for within the cell are self-concerned substructures, like the nucleus, the particles within the nucleus, and the particles within those particles—until we reach the level of the molecule and atom. It is this rising table of organization that is characteristic of organism, the elusive hierarchy that makes of thin voices mighty antiphonal choirs.

It is in the organism, the creature wrapped round the genes, that the property of self-regulation resides. Here is the machinery for coping with an environment that behaves as though it were eternally hostile and conspiratorially dedicated to life's disruption, fighting and prodding it at every moment of its existence and, inexorably, defeating it and reclaiming its stilled and functionless substance. The power to resist these forces of decay gives its possessor a unique, if temporary, autonomy which manifests itself in a bewildering number of ways.

For example, the living system exposed to cold generates heat in the furnaces of its own metabolism, using for fuel special chemicals stored within its structure. Depletion of stored fuels generates hunger and repletion. Wounds, both to the body of the multicellular organisms and to the subcellular structures of the cell, are repaired by processes of invisible weaving that still far outrun our understanding. Invasion by foreign matter is resisted: bacteria are eaten by blood-borne structures (themselves living systems but also components of larger forms of life) or they are inactivated by antibodies, humors that are produced by life but are not themselves living. Poisons are neutralized by chemical attack; foreign bodies are walled off. External danger is thwarted either by physical movement—voluntary, as in flight, or involuntary in the reflex action of rapid recoil—or by a whole dramaturgy of unbelievable weapons, including eel electricity, serpent poison, thorns, claws, stench, and teeth. All factors, internal and external, tending to disturb the repose of the organism, however subtly or obscurely, are resisted by equally subtle systems that are triggered by the insult via its effect, say on membrane permeability, thermodynamic equilibrium, viscosity, or whatever. The physiological axiom seems reasonable that says every manifestation of life is not an action but a reaction restoring the *status quo*. That is why Homer Smith called the cell "a self-centered comfort machine."

The exquisite precision of life's mechanisms of self-regulation has impressed and inspired biologists for centuries. The ancient symbol of organism was the burning bush—all afire but never consumed. Life's defenses against "time's arrow," the second law of thermodynamics which decrees their need, were called mechanisms of *homeostasis* by Walter Cannon. They are the means whereby stimulus begets reaction to restore equilibrium. Cannon recognized that the homeostatic state, whose existence we can empirically observe, is itself prima facie evidence that certain agencies must be acting to maintain it, whether we can observe them or not. And he pointed out that these controls were largely automatic. To him, this was "the wisdom of the body."

One can fit into the framework of self-regulation every function of the organism. The ingestion of food maintains energy reservoirs for other activities. The wheelworks of metabolism converts assorted nutriments into available energy or building blocks suitable for the manufacture of whatever staples or other concoctions the organism may call forth—from antibodies to offspring, from coconut milk to squid ink. Excretory organs eliminate the unwanted by-products of organismic chemistry and, in addition, do one other thing. As brilliantly demonstrated by Smith, they are important not only for what they eliminate, but for what they keep—a property of immense importance for internal constancy. The *status quo* must be preserved, and especially is this true for the chemical composition of living systems. Homeostatic mechanisms somehow must retain the power of choice over what goes and what stays.

Homeostasis, being an observable reality, can have been actually observed in only a relatively small number of species and in a limited number of spheres. But it is so close to a tautology to say that life is characterized by self-regulation, it seems reasonable to extend the concept to all living forms. It then follows that a failure of self-regulation means death, and it is curious that death is so much easier than life to characterize—and define. In death, the mechanisms of resistance have been overstressed and can respond no longer. Apparently, therefore, death and even senescence are not necessities or inevitable consequences and, thus, attributes of life. It should be remembered that single cells and single-celled organisms like the amoeba do not ordinarily die but divide down the middle to form new offspring, leaving behind no mother, no father, no corpse, and no reality except an amoebic equivalent of the smile of the Cheshire cat. In a sense, this is immortality. Of course, single cells do die when their homeostatic defenses have been crushed, but with good fortune this need not be. Immortality, in another sense, exists in higher forms in the descent of the germ plasm, but in this arrangement there do remain mothers, fathers, and corpses.

Homeostasis is, therefore, one of the great central ideas of biology, for it interlaces every aspect of biological organization. It is homeostasis—the effort of the organismic machine to restore its equilibrium whenever disturbed—that gives the organism an appearance of purposive behavior, since these activities seem directed toward a future steady state. In contrast to the problems of heredity and reproduction, those in this area of biological science are the subject matter of such familiar fields as endocrinology, physiology, immunology, biochemistry, neurophysiology, and so on. Each of these is concerned with the mechanisms of self-regulation at one or another level of organization, and each still harbors great unsolved problems—for example, it is not known how hormones control metabolism or how antibody specificity is achieved. But the inescapable common denominator in all of these problems is the phenomenon of *control.*

Just as with the concept of information, the basic nature of control processes has been examined in recent years under the leadership of Norbert Wiener. What interests us in this body of ideas is the universal pattern of effect acting back upon cause to provide information on the consequence of its previous action, thereby determining its future behavior. The usual illustration is the ordinary room thermostat which turns the heat off when the rising air temperature tells it to. Or the steersman of a boat: when he sees his vessel moving too far to the leeward, he acts by swinging the rudder to the windward. Thus, the controlling function of the steersman (or the thermostat) consists in holding the course (or the temperature) by swinging the rudder (or the heater) in a direction that will offset any deviation from that course. This is called *negative feedback*. In both cases, we will observe that a mechanism or system is essential. It is the whole, the dovetailed integration of co-ordinated processes, that seems greater than the sum of its parts. Control then requires organization.

With this in mind, we may cast another glance at evolution, this time viewing it, not as a means of explaining the origin of snails and chickens, but in more abstract terms—as a process whereby complexity was added to patterns of biological organization. For example, it is interesting to consider how single-celled organisms which reproduce by fission evolved into highly organized many-celled organisms which reproduce sexually, irrespective of the particular species. Reproduction seems tidy and forthright as it is transacted by individual cells. In dividing by mere fission, they give the whole affair an elegant, if deceptive, simplicity. Life did not evolve far, however, before the reproductive process took on a new dimension. It may have taken a long time to emerge, but sexual reproduction, once elaborated, was the basis for rapid upward surges in evolutionary progress. For the first time, substance from *two* living systems joined to create the primordial cell of a third. When one considers the difference in complexity between single cells and multicellular organisms, it is apparent that until some sort of fusion could occur evolution could not move far beyond the single cell.

The first step toward sexuality was fusion or conjugation, the precise opposite of fission. In this curious process, which originated in the larger, more complicated unicellular forms, two cells that normally multiplied by fission joined together, internally exchanged parts of their anatomy, and then fused into one. After a period of rest, multiplication by fission resumed just as before. Biologists have long recognized that, after many generations of multiplication by fission, cells will often show decreasing vigor and increasing somnolence. In time, they may seem near death. If at this point, conjugation can occur between two such cells, the resulting organism has great new vigor and proceeds to subdivide by fission for many generations. Why does conjugation invigorate? The answer is that through mating, an organism, weakened by the prolonged reinforcement of its own weakest "family" genes, now receives a therapeutic transfusion of strengthening new dominant genes. This explains the vigor of hybrids.

The next evolutionary step toward greater complexity of form was the establishment by individual cells of cell colonies. While clearly not multicellular organisms, the colonies were considerably more than casual get-togethers of random cells. Although the first such grouping probably happened by chance, its survival value for the participants quickly gave significance to the arrangement, thus converting a chance distribution into one of meaningful order. The problem was: If a group of cells should discover each other and find that living together is exceedingly beneficial for one and all, how would it be possible to transmit this confidential information to the offspring so long as each member cell continues to multiply by solitary fission. There could be no way except to appoint a keeper of the plan, a specialized cell that could somehow retain within its structure the coded pattern of colony structure.

When the designation was made, the precedent was set for specialization within the community. The cell-elect became a productively active member of the colony and, as was "hoped," gave rise exclusively to cells with an inborn predilection for colony life. It could reasonably be asked in this borderline situation: Which was the individual, the cell or the colony? All such questions, of course, evaporate the instant the associations of cells developed shadings of cellular specialization and interdependence. At that point, the individual cells had cast their lots; thenceforth they could live better lives, but only if they lived with each other. For the community to become a perpetuating entity, however, the process of reproduction would have to yield *new communities*, not merely new gregarious individual cells. Within the community, cells could still divide as individuals but, as individuals, they could not be responsible for perpetuating the whole. And, for the first time, reproduction of cells was to occur within a framework of higher integration.

As a means of accomplishing this, conjugation of whole multicellular organisms was clearly an awkward idea. Reproduction of higher organisms, it turned out, would require an improvement of the device developed in colony life, the designation of certain cells as reproductive specialists. By having the cell-designates of one organism fuse with the equivalent cells of another, species could propagate and retain to itself all the advantages of specialization, interdependence, growth by fission, and reproduction (and continuing invigoration) by fusion. Life divided into animal and plant kingdoms long before the appearance of the more complex single-celled organisms, and it is suggested that both branches of life probably evolved the cell fusion method of reproduction independently. It was, apparently, the only way.

The ultimate importance to the species of designation of the germ cell is illustrated by the following. In the very early course of differentiation and morphogenesis of the embryo a remarkable thing occurs. At perhaps the eight- or sixteen-cell stage, one cell becomes visibly different from the rest, and as the others writhe in metamorphosis, changing and evolving into new shapes and functions, this cell remains unchanged, primitive and mute. It is this cell, still unspecialized and uncommitted, that in the midst of its immensely specialized and otherwise preoccupied siblings, becomes the vault of the germ plasm, the sperm or egg of the future being. The earliest of all differentiations is the one that ensures the continuity of the species.

Evolution has kept these basic devices and elaborated them into a variegated universe of detail and invention. The means and mechanisms that evolved to foster the sexual union of two individuals (only later identifiable as male and female) are almost as varied as life itself. With the sharp differentiation of sex cells into ova and sperm, evolution unveiled a number of basic technics of accomplishing their union. Among primitive sponges, worms, and corals, sexual reproduction depended upon chance collisions between eggs and sperm which had been merely ejected into the water. When a whole population of sea urchins, for example, discharged eggs and sperm over a wide area, the probability of such a collision could be quite high. Advanced forms soon developed special organs with duct systems for the production and delivery of the germ cells, although the union of germ cells took place outside the body until the great evolutionary development of internal fertilization. Reproduction also acquired cyclical patterns in time and rhythmic periodicity. For certain species, sexual development could occur only as a consequence of sexual stimulation, or puberty, or special foods (for example, the famous blood meal of the Diptera). In others, sexual activity was limited to certain times of the year by the seasonal growth and recession of the sexual organs and the oestrous cycle. In all cases, life evolved elaborate inventions to make sexual union a reliably likely occurrence. When the advent of sense organs and nervous systems made co-operation between the sexes a prerequisite for fertilization, there emerged the phenomenon of courtship, a phenomenon we will not enter into here.

Biologists today are deeply involved in investigating

the detailed nature of the mechanisms of control at every level of organization. Yet, interestingly, there are at least two zones of inquiry in the domain of organism in which little has been learned despite their supreme importance. We will speak of them briefly in closing our sketch of the organism.

The first has to do with the process of *differentiation,* a truly astonishing feature of higher organic life. It is the problem posed by the emergence of an organism from its embryo. In differentiating, *single fertilized egg cells,* the progenitors of the adult multicellular organism, not only must undergo division to produce the new cells that growth requires, but somehow must be transfigured in the course of time from the general to the specific. The progeny of this "first cell," though remaining true to species, must nevertheless acquire new forms and function as liver cells, nerve cells, and blood cells appear in the course of embryonic development.

"The process of differentiation," wrote C. H. Waddington, "has always seemed particularly mysterious because there are so few phenomena in the non-living world that might give us clues as to how it takes place. In the inanimate realm we do not often come across a situation in which parts of a single mass of material gradually diverge from one another and become completely distinct in character." Thus, the problem of cellular differentiation is a classic example of the biologist's dilemma, having led him into logical fallacies and methodological dead ends by the dozen.

How can a single, amorphous, nondescript "precursor cell" give rise to innumerable offspring, not only infinite in variety but also rigidly on schedule? Chrysanthemum seeds contain plans for autumn, not spring, blossoms, and a single sperm-fertilized human ovum carries on its schedule one set of teeth that in six years and nine months will be replaced. Since the fourth century B.C., this problem has been debated by the advocates of two theories. One group held that the "precursor cell," the fertilized egg, contained all parts of the future organism in miniature and given time these would grow to adult size. The human egg, in this view, contained a tiny, dwarf-like homunculus in the shape of a man but greatly abridged in size. (This is the little man that Leeuwenhoek thought he saw within the sperm cell.) The other theory, the one held by Aristotle, stated that organs and parts arose by gradual interaction of the simpler constituents of the egg.

In this view, we are confronted with a single cell, a precursor of precursors, containing in addition to its normal inclusions nothing more than the genic blueprints and timetables and perhaps a few bricks and mortar for the big construction job ahead. We can see nothing more in the small space. It is true that newer technics of visual examination—electron microscopes and such—may improve the power of our vision, but, in the words of Weiss, "we are still essentially concerned with tracing 'products' rather than the production processes that lie behind. Once we can detect the 'product,' most of the story of its production is over and we have certainly missed its essential beginnings. It looks as if the analytical methods at hand are of no avail."

What solution there is for this dilemma has come from the experimental embryologist using "behavioral" rather than "analytic" tests upon his material. His premise is that if you watch two systems under identical conditions, cells or organisms, and they behave identically, they *are* identical and if they behave differently, they are and must have been different from the very beginning. Failure to detect differences in the appearance of two seeds, for example, means nothing if, when planted side by side, one yielded marigolds and one poppies. If two cells thus judged to be different can be shown to arise from the same precursor cell, they must then have *become* different (*i.e.*, differentiated), identical external appearances to the contrary notwithstanding. In a sense, it is the test of progeny all over again.

Let us state once more, for the purpose of emphasis, what is meant by differentiation: though we have marveled at the process of reproduction wherein a cell *duplicates* itself in every detail of form, function, and species, cells that are *differentiating* are becoming something quite new in form and function, though they do remain of the species. The problem confronting the biologist wishing to study this phenomenon is quite simple in its hulking, immense way. He cannot get his hands on experimental material. Since differentiation occurs chiefly during embryonic life, studying it means more or less ending it. In grappling with this dilemma, experimental embryologists may have come up with a fascinating solution to their technical problem. First, the simple observation was made that when the gullet end of a single-celled protozoon is cut off with a tiny needle, a complete new one grows back in the course of several hours. It seems reasonable to suppose that this process of regeneration is one of cell differentiation completely analogous or identical to the process occurring in embryonic cells. In acquiring a new gullet, the protozoon cell changed its character before the investigator's eyes, thus providing a whole new experimental object. Among other things, the technic has disclosed intriguing relationships between the regenerative or differentiative process and the internal architecture of the cell. Somewhere geometry must be involved. Why else would the cell grow a new gullet and not a tail?

The second virgin corner in the science of organism needs only to be mentioned, for we alluded to it earlier in remarking that biologists today feel unqualified to discuss life. It is the problem of grappling, once and for all, with the problems of organism and organization. For years, the "purposiveness of life" has been a topic for philosophers and wise men. Now it is time for the scientist to take over. Recent work, such as that by Sommerhoff, shows beyond any question that the total organism —as distinct from isolated physical or chemical systems—

can be treated with a mathematical rigor completely devoid of vagueness, ambiguity, inconclusiveness, and spirits. Goal-directed behavior has nothing mystical about it; it is a property of material systems that is susceptible to analysis. When this begins in earnest, the science of organism will come into its own.

This then—in a word—is the living organism today.

CHAPTER XIV

THE TASTE OF FRUSTRATION: SOME UNSOLVED PROBLEMS

Klüver: What about the relationship between humor and irony?

Bateson: Do you mean irony in the classical sense, such as occurs in Greek tragedy . . . ? Or do you mean irony in the sense of saying the opposite of what is meant?

Teuber: One would be the irony of the situation of Oedipus who does not know what everybody else knows, and the other would be the Socratic irony. Socrates insists he doesn't know what everybody else presumes to know. . . .

Mead: Just a moment. Why are we getting so literary?

Pitts: Well, who started it?

Mead: I'm just raising it as a question. Why this outcrop of literary-historical erudition here?

Gerard: Maybe we haven't anything constructive to say.

—From the *Transactions of the 9th Macy Conference on Cybernetics*

We have now painted a somewhat impressionistic landscape of the great rolling hills and cultivated plains of contemporary biological thought. And we have seen how the flowering of these fields has been aided and enriched by the fertile humus of modern philosophy and physical science. For those who believe and hope that science will again find the basic unity it lost in the avalanches of complexity and specialization—and of segregative rather than integrative writers like Du Noüy, who wrote in *Human Destiny*, ". . . it is *totally impossible* to account scientifically for all phenomena pertaining to Life"—there is much satisfaction in witnessing this trend in biological thinking. At last, it would seem, is the road staked out that will lead us to the future.

Unfortunately, this rosy picture has a less optimistic side, for there is an inescapable implication within our new-found sophistication. It is that the problems we have so far failed to solve must, therefore, be more sophisticated than we are. This is sobering and, hence, worth reflecting upon. There are, of course, many questions that science has not answered because the questions themselves have not yet been discovered. New discoveries raise new questions and we cannot anticipate what these will be. But there are also many questions that have been before us for years and that science, despite a massive attack, has so far failed to answer. There is much to be learned in considering these areas of frustration. For one thing, we may see how the sharp cutting edge of contemporary analytic thought planes away at flimsy constructions, by recognizing no question incapable of answer and no answer incapable of proof. Moreover, we may witness again what frustration can do to its victims. Since many of these problems are in areas affecting human welfare—the nature of cancer, and other diseases—because men *want* these questions answered and scientists want to answer them, an atmosphere of pressure can sometimes build up which may generate exceedingly strange behavior.

It is not difficult to understand why men would want science to lift their burden and relieve their suffering. It is also understandable that the scientist is almost never subjected to external pressure for the solution of abstract problems which have no visible connection with human welfare. However, since no one knows in advance which "useless" scientific inquiry will ultimately benefit mankind, there is some irony in the drum-beating surrounding "cancer research" when it is entirely reasonable to suppose that the cause of malignant growth may some day be found by a seaweed physiologist.

No one is at fault, of course, in failing to solve a scientific problem. But when failure occurs, it is useful to ask why it occurred. In an age when science can "do anything," why are there areas in which it has done nothing? And—perhaps of equal interest—why are men outside of the scientific community often led to believe that the answers are "just around the corner" when, in some cases, the fact is that science hasn't even found the street of this mythical corner?

We have already mentioned a number of basic biological problems that are yet to be solved—the basis of the ordered arrangement of DNA, the explanation of organismic architecture, the nature of differentiation. Somewhere in these puzzles may be the answers to the two biological problems I propose to discuss in this chapter—the nature of cancer and the nature of mind—both enigmas whose solutions now seem far away despite sanguinary popular accounts. It is always interesting to try to locate the dividing line between knowledge and ignorance. But our effort here is also directed at exploring the possible reasons for our ignorance and at arousing a genuine respect for these difficulties. In no case is one justified in assuming such problems to be either "almost solved" or impossible of solution. We can say only that they are difficult problems whose solution will require time and intelligence. For the working scientist who has so far failed, no further excuses are required; for the public to whom he looks for support, no cajolery should be necessary beyond this statement.

The great cancer mystery

The trouble starts with the word "cancer." The biological phenomenon to which we refer in speaking of cancer has a single characteristic by which we recognize its existence. It is a pattern of growth behavior exhibited by certain cells within a larger community of cells. Usually, this behavior is described by an analogy. The cancer cells are outlaws who show contempt for the welfare and orderly life of the community at large—that is, the whole organism—recklessly plundering and aggressively invading in a thoroughly nonaltruistic manner. As of this moment, we are able to recognize cancer cells *only* by this behavior pattern. If a cancer cell has been removed from the organism and successfully grown in a culture plate, we could identify it as a cancer cell only by transplanting it back into the organism and observing its growth pattern.

This problem of *recognizing* a cancer cell is a singularly slippery one. As we remarked in speaking of the definitions of words, a clear understanding of the zone of applicability of a word such as "cancer" is an absolute prerequisite to knowing what one is talking about. The question is really one of taxonomy, that old and honored subdivision of biology which is concerned with the accurate identification of organisms. It is the taxonomist's problem, for example, to decide whether the frog before him is or is not *Rana pipiens*. As we mentioned earlier, biologists have long worried over whether there really exists such a thing as species, for the overlap and variability of many living organisms make it difficult to define the word "species." No matter what the definition, many creatures refuse to be "either" or "or" and at least one taxonomist has defined species as an assemblage of animals recognized as a species by a competent taxonomist. This is not entirely facetious, for it implies that the most important purpose of the species concept is to facilitate thinking and communication. This definition recognizes that when one biologist says "rabbit" to another biologist they will understand each other; the odd cases will remain odd cases despite our concern. Thus, to whatever extent the dilemma has been resolved, its solution has rested on a now familiar proposition: Our definition of species is bound up with the phenomena we see and the operations we go through in seeing them. It is not related to our ideas of what ought to be seen.

These considerations are particularly relevant to the cancer problem. For in trying to establish some agency as the cause of cancer, we are obliged to find it operating in cancer cells and absent or inactive in noncancer cells. In other words, as scientists, our problem is the problem of proof. If there are varieties of "in-between" cells—as there appear to be—the problem of proof is made that much more difficult.

Another hazard in the word "cancer" is the hidden implication that all cells which exhibit this behavior pattern do so for the same reason. A wildly proliferating cell in the human stomach or breast as much deserves to be called a cancer cell as a similar type of growth in a plant. It is perfectly reasonable to use a single word in referring to such growth behavior wherever it may be found. It is fallacious, however, to assume uncritically that one instance has the same cause as the other, even in cases of cancers of the same cell type. In other words, it is true that they *may* but false that they *must* have the same cause. One might reasonably argue that an ordered and controlled growth pattern is quite probably a delicately adjusted mechanism, somewhat like a smiling baby. And as a shrieking infant may have many "causes," any one of a large number of things could disturb a cell's growth-controlling mechanism. In the absence of control, it does the only thing there is left to do (if it is to grow at all): it grows without control. Presumably, if we could demonstrate one reliable instance in which two similar-appearing cancers had clearly different causes, we might then be encouraged to look more closely for the relevant differences in the cancers that must surely be there. In such a case, we would be reminded again of the superficiality of "appearances" as criteria of identity.

A second difficulty, then, is our ignorance of whether cancer has one or many causes. Scientists trying to resolve this question have naturally looked into all types of cancerous growths in search of a common denominator which would simplify the inquiry. The search has been a long and arduous attempt to discover some other property—chemical, physical, or whatever—which is *universally* present and hence will serve both as an aid in its taxonomic recognition or diagnosis and as a clue to the events underlying disordered growth. Scientists are still deeply involved in this search and large volumes can be filled with the data so far accumulated. Here we encounter another great difficulty, for a number of differences *have* been found between normal and cancer cells in addition to their differences in growth behavior. For example, there are certain chemical differences between normal white blood cells and the cells of leukemia; there is a typical pattern of sugar metabolism in almost all cancer cells wherein larger quantities of lactic acid are formed than in the normal cell. These are exciting findings and, in the vernacular of the headline writer, may be "a clue" to the cause of cancer. Unfortunately, no shred of evidence is so far available to tell us whether such abnormalities are *causes* or *consequences* of the cancer with which they are associated.

An extremely thorny problem faces the scientist who would explain the behavior of the cancer cell by some property he has observed *in that cell.* As we agreed in speaking of causality in an earlier chapter, the most that can ever be said in proving that A causes B is that A regularly and necessarily *precedes* B. For the scientist, this means that all chemical or physical abnormalities must not only be unique to the cancer cell, they must be discernible prior to the appearance of abnormal growth if they are to be considered as possible causes or links in the causal chain. In seeking the events that regularly *precede* the malignant state, we are often hard put to find experimental material whose destiny we can be sure is to undergo malignant transformation. To some extent, this obstacle can be circumvented by the use of animal strains with a known high incidence of spontaneous cancer, or of tissues exposed to certain chemical compounds that have been shown to produce malignant growth.

The observation that cancer cells have an abnormally high rate of lactic acid production has an interesting and illuminating place in the history of this search. This discovery was made in the 1920's by Otto Warburg, the great German biochemist whose many other contributions helped make biochemistry what it is today. At the time, this observation was hailed as one of the greatest possible discoveries. Here at last was a deeper point of difference between normal and cancer cells. But its discoverer had no hesitation in declaring that this unique property of cancer cells was the cause of cancer. As the years went by, however, "abnormal" rates of lactic acid production were found in certain rapidly proliferating normal cells, such as the white blood cell, and it began to appear that a high rate of lactic acid production was not the cause of cancer but a consequence of rapid growth (or something else), whether normal or abnormal. Warburg attempted to dismiss these findings by stating that injured tissues may show such a pattern, and it is common knowledge that the white cell is easily injured. However, the only evidence which indicated that his white cells were indeed injured was the observed rate of lactic acid production. In other words, either they had to be injured or else the theory would have been. Warburg, however, stuck to his guns and as recently as 1956 published an article called "On the Origin of Cancer Cells" in the journal *Science*—an article which, as might be expected from its title and distinguished authorship, was widely reported in the press. In it, Warburg said, "What was formerly only qualitative has now become quantitative. What was formerly only probable has now become certain." No one today will deny that Warburg's metabolic pattern *may* be involved in the causation of cancer. Whether it is or not, however, can be ascertained only from airtight evidence. Most biochemists would agree, I feel sure, that such evidence has not yet been produced.

Many stories of this kind could be told. In 1926, the Nobel Prize was awarded to a man named Fibiger for "proving" that cancer was caused by certain small worms. Over the years, scientists have implicated bacteria, molds, viruses, emotions, and in each case a nebulous association evaporated under rigorous examination. Within recent years, however, the frustration has deepened because a body of work has begun to emerge that permits some imaginative speculation within the framework of solid evidence. The result has been a number of tantalizing hypotheses on the origin of cancer cells whose only difficulties are the traditional ones, the problem of proof. Behind this thinking lies a number of well-established experimental facts. It is known, for example, that the incidence of cancer in men and animals can be greatly increased by exposure to radiation, the same agency which is known to cause mutations. In addition, a large number of chemical compounds have been discovered—chiefly in tar—which induce cancer in experimental animals. Some of these compounds have been found in the tars of cigarette smoke. In each case, the cancer-producing compounds can be shown by appropriate methods to be capable of inducing mutations. It would appear, then, that the cancer cell may be a *mutant*, characterized by a deficient ability to mature and grow in an orderly manner. In this view, we might imagine that cancer originates from the chance encounter of a normal cell with some mutagenic agent in its environment—a molecule of coal-tar derivative or a stray bolt of radiation. Surely the chances of such an encounter are as good as the chances of any given cell becoming malignant, for cancer remains an exceedingly rare event when one considers the large number of cells in the body, the duration of human life, the rarity of two separate cancers in a single individual, and the known incidence of cancer in the human race.

There is another exciting view about the origin of cancer. Several recent workers have isolated a filtrable virus-like agent which transmits cancer from one animal to another. In the light of newer developments in our understanding of the virus and the gene, the hypothesis that cancer is caused by a virus may still be reconciled with the view that it results from mutation. In the last chapter, we spoke of the transforming principle, a fragment of genetic material (now known to be DNA) which was capable of transforming another strain of bacteria in a manner which otherwise would have indicated that it had undergone mutation. It is now known that a similar transformation may be caused in bacteria as a result of their invasion by certain bacteriophages. In these cases, the bacterial host does not immediately break open to yield a new generation of phages. Instead, the phage becomes part of the genetic material of the host cell where it remains quietly. When the host bacterium reproduces by division, the passenger phage particle does likewise so that both offspring bacteria carry within their chromosomes a latent bacteriophage. This may be carried down for many generations and, in a sense, the host cell may now be considered not only to be infected but also to have acquired a new gene—and it is interesting that to whatever extent the acquisition of new genic material is the same as infection, fertilization itself of egg by sperm may be termed an infection. In this case, however, the dormant phage particle retains its potential ability to start reproducing itself in the traditional style of viruses, and this can be brought on experimentally by some external insult such as *radiation*. We may readily imagine, however, that such phage particles could lose their ability to exist separately and may continue as part of the host chromosome for the rest of biological time. Conversely, many existing cells may be carrying such passengers, whose ancestors "came aboard" millions of years ago. Some of these may still be capable of activation by radiation; some may not.

Conceivably such a "virus-gene" could convert its host into a cancer cell—or when set free could do the same to neighboring cells. In any case, we begin to see the dim outlines of a theory that will explain the known facts about cancer, particularly its resemblance to mutation, its apparent transmissibility in certain animals, its high incidence following radiation, and its heritability in certain animal strains. In the search for the cause of cancer, this work is clearly the bellwether of the future.

Frustration would reach its zenith, no doubt, if such events were proved to be the cause of cancer. For then we would know all there was to know about cancer except how to prevent it or cure it. Yet these are the aspects of the cancer problem that touch upon human welfare. If cancer should be shown to result from some mutagen, such as radiation, the most we could accomplish toward prevention would be to advise radiologists to be diligent in their safety precautions and to minimize those chemical compounds in our environment—such as cigarette smoke if current evidence is substantiated—which predispose cells to malignant transformation. As for the problem of cure, here would be the greatest irony of all, for knowing the cause would net us nothing in our search for a cure. Despite the great and continuing search for a successful therapeutic agent in cancer, we know of no method to convert a cancer cell into a normal one. The only successful treatment to date depends upon total extermination of the cancer cell by radical excision or massive radiation. Much of the investigation into the metabolism of cancer cells has not only been aimed at revealing the cause of cancer, it has also sought to characterize and describe the metabolic processes of these cells, for their own sake, in hopes of locating points of vulnerability, areas of metabolism upon which the cell's existence depends, particularly if these "lifelines" are different in quantity or quality from those of normal cells.

If such were discovered, we might then have some rational point of attack in planning a drug that will reliably kill the cancer cell while sparing the normal. To date, no such drug has been found. Many have been turned up which will eradicate cancer cells by blocking their metabolism, but in all cases these ultimately affect normal cells too—and this is like trying to starve the criminals out of a community by cutting off the food supply for the whole town. Moreover, even those drugs which seem to affect cancer cells preferentially have failed in their intended purpose, because, in almost every case, one or more of the cancer cells develop resistance to the drug, by a process of mutation. Then when all susceptible cells have been killed off, only the resistant ones remain to produce a whole new generation of drug-resistant offspring.

Because of its transcending importance, a number of laboratories throughout the world are engaged in "screening" chemical compounds of all descriptions in the hope of finding one that will be efficacious in the treatment of cancer. In the rare instance when one seems to be promising in experimental animal tumors, it is given a more detailed examination and, if warranted, is tried in human cancer. There has been much debate over the merits of such an approach. Its defenders, some of whom are quite vociferous, point out that pure luck led to the discovery of penicillin, morphine, digitalis, and quinine, and that a number of useful agents have already come out of these screening programs that are helpful, if not decisive, in the treatment of cancer. Its detractors claim it is a wasteful approach, a mere gathering of data in the fashion of Bacon which is almost foredoomed to failure. Each year a thick publication appears containing the negative data that have accumulated in this search. It is difficult to take sides in this controversy. Everyone agrees that the cure of a disease may be found long before its cause is known. Smallpox vaccination was discovered years before the word virus had been spoken. Surely no stone should be left unturned in our efforts to relieve man of the scourge of cancer. Unfortunately, any search for a drug that is unguided by rational considerations is almost certainly bound to fail. It is argued that similar points were raised concerning the drug treatment of bacterial infection prior to the discovery of antibiotics. This is no defense, since there were then no good reasons for making such a statement, but there are many reasons for making it about cancer. We have evidence now to support our discouragement. No matter what we say, however, and despite our solidly rooted belief in its unsoundness, perhaps it is just as well that this work continues. We may just possibly be wrong. What would be highly desirable, however, would be a period of lessened loquacity from the workers in this field and their spokesmen until they have something to tell us.

And so the problem of cancer stands unsolved. This is the frustrating truth behind the barrage of half-truths to which the public is subjected. It is not wholly true, as was stated in a recent publication, that "steady progress continues in our understanding of the manner in which cancer-producing substances act." It is not true, despite the wide publicity given to its announcement, that a blood test is known that will reveal the presence of cancer. There are many available blood tests but they are not any good. It is not true that early and repeated medical examination can be reliably depended upon to "discover cancer while it is still curable"—though there is obviously a better chance of exterminating it surgically or radiologically while it is small and localized. But a negative medical examination does not rule out the presence of cancer, as much as we would like it to.

The problem of cancer remains a Gargantuan challenge to the science of biology. Some day it may yield, but until it does, biologists have their work cut out for them. Nothing substantial is yet known about normal growth! Why, when a wound heals, do the regenerating skin cells cease growing at the proper moment? How is it that most organisms reach a size limit which they rarely exceed, although limitation in size is not a universal phenomenon? Why do some living systems (trees, certain fishes, etc.) continue to grow as long as they live? The complexity of growth regulation is also evidenced by its periodicity—typified by seasonal growth, whose traces are the growth rings of cut wood, the stripes of feathers, and the markings of seashells—and by the great rarity of freaks, giants, and dwarfs, whose growth has been quantitatively peculiar. It is interesting, too, that abnormal growth is so much rarer in large multicellular organisms than it is among the less complex organisms.

The answers to many of these questions will ultimately come from the new frontiers that are advancing into the problems of gene, virus, and organism. But it is difficult to know whether optimism or pessimism is presently called for. One may look at our present state of knowledge in two lights: we may feel proud at the great accomplishments science has achieved or we may bemoan the fact that we have gone no further than we have, that we wasted a millennium in the Middle Ages, that we have allowed wars and fear to hold us back. We may also lament one other phenomenon in our midst. It is the scientists who evoke optimism or despair with no justifiable reason. A book was published recently which illustrates the point—*The Biology of the Spirit* by Edmund W. Sinnott, Dean of the Graduate School at Yale University. In this puzzling volume, the author presents "scientific" evidence for the existence of the soul and a personal God. His argument is based on his inability to comprehend life's complexity and its apparent pursuit of goals. Caught in a blizzard of uncertainty between science and mysticism, he finally throws his hands up and joins the mystics. As was pointed out by Martin Grant, Professor Sinnott, in one quotation, "begins with a case of reasoning-by-analogy, which is followed by a mixture of three unsupported assumptions and three non-sequiturs." This from within our scientific ranks. This in a discussion of the very subject upon which our ultimate understanding of cancer must depend, the nature of organism.

In this light, I believe we might say that cancer research has a very long road to travel, longer perhaps than it ought to have.

The mind as an object of biological interest

We now enter biology's Grand Guignol. No question in the whole of scientific history has proved more deceptive, exciting, frustrating, and elusive. In considering the mind, biology meets its greatest challenge, for in no other area of inquiry are there richer opportunities for self-delusion and verbal sophistry, and in no other are the implications of success greater. Every facet of human life, every issue of science and philosophy, every question of truth, memory, reality, belief, and ethics rests within the structure of the mind. Repeatedly in these pages, we have noted the peculiar role that man's conception of mind has played in the evolution of his ideas. As we mentioned earlier, Descartes was one of the first to state formally a point of view which had been implicit for centuries in mankind's mythological, animistic, and theological beliefs. It was the "common-sense" view that matter is one thing and mind is another. Matter occupies space; mind does not. They are different existences, different categories of being, and are therefore incapable of interacting. As C. E. M. Joad put it, "A paving-stone can crush an egg because an egg belongs to the same order of being as the stone. But how can the paving-stone crush a wish, or be affected by a thought?"

It has also been held that the principle of complementarity must be invoked to resolve the "psychophysical" dilemma. This is the principle, we will recall, that holds that mind and matter are merely different, though fully autonomous and complete descriptions of the same thing. It is typified, according to D. M. MacKay, by the following two descriptions of the same encounter with a friend. We may say, "'He rises to his feet wreathed in smiles and greets us heartily,' *or* 'A mass of pink protoplasm rises to a height of five feet and begins to pucker and wobble up and down noisily.'" Both descriptions are correct, but in one context one is appropriate, in another the other is.

To the thoughtful scientist, such pronouncements contain little nourishment, even though scientists have originated many of them. To maintain that the mind and brain do or do not "interact" seems to suggest that they are separate entities which impinge upon one another through *physical* interaction. What entity would a brain be impinging upon in these circumstances? This would be like arguing that the Beethoven Violin Concerto "interacts" physically with what William James called the rasping of hairs from a horse's tail on the intestines of a cat. What we can say from the elementary evidence is that so-called mental activity *accompanies* somatic activity—whether its mechanism be dualism, interactionism, parallelism, or whatever. *Causal* interaction may thus be postulated to exist between psychic and somatic activities: as when shame produces blushing and Benzedrine, elation. And yet, even here we encounter difficulty, since we are usually incapable of observing the temporal priority of the mental event over the somatic event or vice versa—and, in looking for temporal sequence, we are in danger of assuming a separateness of mind and body, thus prejudging the issue. Our problem then should presumably be "what do we mean by mental activity?" Can the phenomena of mentality be causally explained by physical and chemical events within the brain and, if so, how?

Unfortunately, we are almost as much in the dark on this question as we were a century ago. To explain the physical causes of mental activity, we need empirical data on both brain and mind from which we have so far been barred by methodological difficulties. Moreover, we have here entered an area that is conceptually hazardous. How, indeed, could a feeling of indignation be one and the same as some observable neurophysiological event? How, in fact, may we convert into a scientific datum an introspective account of what is going on in our own heads, if, indeed, it is possible to introspect the relevant things that go on in our heads? These are as much problems in logic as biology, and logicians have had considerable to say on the subject. The logical positivist H. Feigl has contended that there is an absolute identity between the corresponding introspective, behavioral, and physiological events, and he dismisses the "mind-body problem" as a relic of the Stone Age. For one thing, introspective observations are *private* facts in contrast to the public nature of ordinary scientific data. Thus, there are profound differences between the two in terms of the accessibility of data and the ways in which such facts are known. The only way in which we could establish a correlation between private introspective facts and public neurophysiological facts would be to perform both observations within our own brains.

Because this has not yet been really feasible (notwithstanding Penfield's experiences in interviewing subjects while probing their brains with energized surgical needles), a school of psychological thought was developed in the early part of the twentieth century which is known as *behaviorism*. This view accepts the impossibility of ascertaining private facts in other minds, or in the minds of experimental animals, and instead sticks only to what can be observed, external behavior. Here is a remarkable thesis! In its strict form, behaviorism tells us that what we observe are not mental processes but various bodily actions. To the behaviorist, the act of thinking or perceiving is equated with a certain pattern of bodily behavior. The introduction of this sweeping concept as an alternative to introspective psychology set off one of biology's most intemperate tongue wars. The cry went round that behaviorism seeks to get rid of the mind completely. Writings appeared such as the following by J. W. N. Sullivan:

> We do not think; we make incipient speech movements. We do not perceive anything; we adjust our eyeballs. It would certainly seem to be a waste of time to discuss this theory were it not for the fact that there are a fair number of people who profess to believe it, as well as a large number of people who, for one emotional reason or another, would like to believe it.

We will not presume to enter into this controversy. It is still claimed by more sober critics that strictly interpreted behaviorism leads to trouble. Much of their criticism goes to the point that behaviorists deny introspection and the "inner life." This, of course, is not so. Behaviorism merely affirms that, as a science, psychology cannot make use of the private data of introspection. But even this is not as simple as it sounds. Observations may be open to the public, but *making* the observation is, in one sense, itself a private experience. The behaviorist does not record how far a needle moves, he records how far *it seemed to him* to have moved.

The fact remains, however, that we may have made real progress in turning our backs at last on "the mind" as a separate metaphysical entity. Again we must witness the downfall of such a verbal abstraction. As Sherrington pointed out, the "mind" is utterly dependent upon the detailed architecture and function of the brain. Later workers have preferred to speak of consciousness instead of mind. Here perhaps is an observable state of the organism which is carefully defined by the physiologist Homer Smith as an "awareness of environment and of self, revealed objectively by self-serving, neuromuscular activity which exhibits choice between alternative actions and simultaneously relates past experience to anticipated future." In this view we may have the makings of a new way of visualizing mental activity, for this definition is closely tied to the physiological and anatomical aspects of neural activity, those phenomena to which we must ultimately look for an explanation of conscious experience.

Here, too, we are in deep trouble. Neurophysiology has yet been unable to provide any description of the events taking place in the neural unit during the simplest possible forms of mental activity. It seems clear, however, that all hopes of progress lay in deepening our understanding of the neural organization of the brain itself. Just as our description of the action of muscle depends on knowledge of the structure of muscle, we must eventually comprehend both the individual neural units of the brain and their patterns of higher organization if we are to fathom the connection between brain and consciousness. What, in other words, can we point to in the neuron as a correlate of conscious experience?

While there is no answer to this question at the present time, it is extremely interesting to note how the problem is being attacked by contemporary biology. For one thing, the brain itself has been carefully examined from a number of different angles. Structurally, it is an unbelievably complex knot of nerve cells and fibers, which, though characteristic in their basic arrangement, vary in detail from individual to individual. It was early observed that weak electrical emanations which could be readily picked up and recorded accompanied brain function. The observed patterns of these "brain waves" could soon be correlated empirically with a number of functional states of the brain—such as sleep, active thinking, and certain abnormal conditions such as epilepsy—though again there was no way of knowing whether these electrical patterns were causes or consequences of the functional states in which they appeared.

In time, it became clear that each nerve cell and its fiber, that is, each neural unit, were parts of a complex *network* which transmits (or "intentionally" fails to transmit) electrical impulses throughout the brain. It is now recognized that the patterns of movement of these excitation waves—their rhythm, arrangement, timing, and spatial distribution—are the phenomena which somehow we must learn to correlate with consciousness. Thus, for example, *memory* could conceivably be explained as a property of a circular network. If a number of neurons were arranged in a ring, an impulse introduced into the circle could circulate indefinitely as long as energy remained available to maintain electrical activity. Patterns of impulses could thus be stored in the brain in the form of permanent reverberating circuits.

It also became apparent that the possible number of patterns of electrical behavior is as staggeringly great as the possible dimensions of mental experience. Hence, the attempt to correlate the two is virtually doomed before it starts. We therefore reach the point where evidence fades into speculation. Many speculative theories have been advanced to "help" the neurophysiologist in his dilemma. For example, it is suggested that when we perceive a triangle, a little triangle is projected in the brain in electrical form. This *isomorphic* theory could not be supported, however, nor was it felt that such a neural copying process would gain us very much in terms of understanding. And yet, the neurophysiologist has been unable to eliminate from his thinking the necessity for some sort of *code* in the patterns of neural excitation. From information theory, we would expect that the physical arrangement of neural impulses must in some manner account for the content of mental activity. It was this realization that started the communication engineers trooping to neurophysiology seminars and the "information theorists" off into gleeful calculations of what the brain code "has" to be like, speculative abstractions which many physiologists look upon with jaundiced eye.

Nevertheless, if the brain is an electrical network

whose connections work on an all-or-none basis (that is, they pass an impulse or they don't), then we have before us an elaborate communication system for sending coded messages from one place to another. It is, in fact, a great calculating machine which affords us the most exciting possible opportunity to make progress in this field. The "electronic brains" that have arisen in our midst are, in fact, engineer's copies of the functioning brain. They are also *models* of unprecedented usefulness in advancing our understanding of the brain. As noted by W. Grey Walter, "A model or analogue of this sort is, in fact, a crystallized hypothesis; it should be clear and brittle. When it breaks down, as all working hypotheses must, its failure must be obvious and explicit." The giant computing machines have served this purpose well. In addition to revealing how an unvarnished mechanism can perform all the operations of memory, choice, logic, learning, satiety, "neurosis," recognition, and prediction, it has forcefully set before us a number of difficult verbal issues. How do we now define feeling, perception, and thinking? Perhaps the answer ultimately lies in circuity. Since it is as foolish to argue that machines can think as it is to maintain that they cannot think, we have found our way home again to the quicksand of words.

Warren McCulloch recently put it this way: "To the theoretical question, Can you design a machine to do whatever a brain can do? the answer is this: If you will specify in a finite and unambiguous way what you think a brain does do with information, then we can design a machine to do it. Pitts and I have proved this constructively. But can you say what you think brains do?"

We hope Dr. McCulloch isn't looking at us.

CHAPTER XV

THE BOY ON THE SEASHORE

God has given the earth to the faithful, and the sea to the infidels.

—Proverb

A youngish man has moved to the speaker's rostrum, across whose front are the words *Hotel Statler*. He peers into the gloom and, for a brief moment, examines his audience. Though strewn through the hall in no sensible pattern, they have for some reason left the first three rows vacant. It is a curious miscellany of people, and in the span of faces can be seen many things. Some show expectant interest, others boredom. Some seem lost in thought, others cruelly beset by the penalties of diversion. Over to one side are two well-known investigators in earnest conversation. From their expressions, it is clear that delectable morsels are being exchanged. A small group of wanderers enter through ornate French doors and, to the man, they trip noisily over the skein of wires on the floor leading to a lantern slide projector. In the last row, a pair of glazed eyes has finally closed.

The chairman rises. "Each speaker will have exactly ten minutes. When the alarm clock rings, please have the courtesy to conclude your remarks." And the first paper begins. All that can now be seen in the dimly reflected light of the lantern slides is a sea of inscrutable faces. The speaker reads on, the bell rings, and as the chairman menacingly comes to his feet, a concluding paragraph is hurriedly launched. "Thank you," says the chairman. "There will be five minutes for discussion."

The audience stirs itself in momentary hesitation. Several tentative arms go up. One of the elders rises. "I just want to congratulate the speaker on a piece of work well done." Suddenly the room comes alive, engulfing the elder, who makes for his seat. Questions crackle forth, counter-evidence is unsheathed. The speaker handles himself well, though he acknowledges that much work remains to be done. "Have you tried this experiment in chickens?" someone calls out. "No," replies the speaker, "I haven't tried this experiment in chickens." An ancient enemy comes to his feet to fulfill a fancied obligation: under no circumstances must a traditional vendetta be allowed to "just end." Among the younger members of the audience, few can summon the courage to speak. Of the two who do, one is brash, the other is brilliant.

The audience, this time, has been deeply stimulated and there are murmurs of protest when the chairman terminates the discussion. "I'm sure the speaker will be glad to continue this privately. We must get on to the next paper." The audience looks at its programs, and in the babble of voices is heard the sound of intellectual peristalsis. Several individuals shuffle out; newcomers arrive, each tripping over the wires. Over on one side, the well-known investigators are deep in the same conversation. The fact of the matter is it had never really stopped.

Though it was a brief quarter of an hour, in it we have seen re-enacted a drama as old as human intelligence. If there be any sacred rite in science, this must surely be it.

The pursuit of science

The meeting—local, national, international—is an indispensable institution in the pursuit of science. It is here that each man is given his hearing, his opportunity to communicate to his scientific peers the results of his own observations of nature. It is his opportunity to hear the criticism of his fellows and their leavening suggestions, as his ideas are given their intense moment of cool imaginative attention. It is, moreover, his hour of glory, the recognition from his colleagues for which the scientist works, and which, in many ways, is his only tangible reward.

Science today is a very large enterprise. It has proliferated throughout the world into an almost unmanageable giant. The number of scientific journals is constantly increasing, while each journal's backlog of papers, awaiting publication, is increasing too. Great new problems have arisen around the mere matter of recording and communicating new scientific information as it appears. To avoid duplication of work, scientists must be aware of what other scientists are doing, but in today's rising mountain of scientific literature, a real crisis confronts the documentation experts who must make the contents of the archives conveniently accessible to its users.

Only recently has science grown so large, particularly in the United States. Modern science was developed chiefly in England, France, and Germany, and, except for a limited number of active centers, large-scale scientific development did not begin in America until both World Wars had introduced new military scientific requirements and a variety of annoying shortages. Dramatic scientific developments, such as the atomic bomb and the "wonder drugs," abruptly brought science to the public's attention, and, to the average man, it began to appear that science was an inexhaustible national resource that could produce pretty much anything from fertilizer to television, while, at the same time, guaranteeing the nation's military security.

One direct result of this belief was an unfamiliar torrent of funds in support of scientific research. The government began providing enormous quantities of money for pure and applied research through numerous channels: the military services, the Atomic Energy Commission, the Public Health Service, the Veterans Administration, the Department of Agriculture, and many others. Many private agencies began collecting and distributing funds for specific projects such as research "against" cancer, heart disease, poliomyelitis, muscular dystrophy. Likewise, industry entered the field of basic research, and giant corporations such as Du Pont and Bell Telephone developed laboratories whose atmospheres were unmistakably academic. This outpouring of money is still accelerating at the present time, new spurts usually following close upon the illness of a public figure or reports of technological progress in the enemy camp.

In view of this sudden influx of monetary support into areas so recently impoverished, it seems the best part of prudence to keep a careful watch over this situation, for scientific progress will be hindered by financial indigestion. But even more serious is the threat of public disenchantment if it learns, without understanding, some things that scientists already know: that money alone will not solve problems, that the problems we face are increasingly difficult, that the great advances in science such as the works of Newton, Darwin, and Einstein, did not stem from highly organized "crash programs" and "teamwork" but from genius and imagination, that science can flourish only in an atmosphere of freedom, mutual respect, and understanding, and that the university is not quite what many people think it is, according to Robert Hutchins—a large football field next to which strange people can be found inexplicably splitting atoms!

It is gratifying to see scientists being showered with

support, even though many of them feel individually neglected. One wishes, however, that generous support would be given for the right reasons. Scientists are not an occult priesthood, science is not wisdom, it is not for the few, it is not the road to certainty. It is rather a way of looking at the world which permits us to extract knowledge from our experience. Furthermore, scientists, as this book has tried to make clear, are people who bleed when they are pricked. Despite the impersonal objectivity of scientific knowledge, the pursuit of science is a fabric of passion and feeling. We have spoken of the frustration that accompanies failure and the elation of discovery, whose typical image is that of Archimedes jumping out of his bath to rush through the streets of Syracuse shouting "Eureka!" Science is exciting. It is fun! It is a romantic and compelling call to adventure. What could more dependably fire the imagination than an expedition into the unknown by man armed only with curiosity and ingenuity? It is the passion of scientists that alone leads them from problem to discovery, and from discovery to persuasion and sometimes to controversy.

In view of these things, it is difficult to understand the temper of current opinion, one of whose manifestations is the so-called "scientist shortage." There will, of course, always be a shortage of scientists in comparison to the number of unsolved problems. Furthermore, a whole generation of scientists ten times over would constitute a shortage if the problem requires an Einstein and there is none among them. But, forgetting for the moment the difference between ordinary scientists and great scientists, we are undeniably faced today with a growing shortage of technically and scientifically trained young people. In plain words, there is a shortage of "brains." This fact, it would seem, is a prima-facie indictment of our educational system. Too many of our talented young people fail to obtain a real education, too much mediocrity has invaded the teaching profession and no one seems to care enough to do anything about it. The nation can afford no longer to stand with the newspaper columnist who began an article with the sentence, "We Americans have been confronted with an arrogant proposition that persons presuming to call themselves intellectuals, and particularly those who claim the title of scientist, are a superior cult entitled to deference or even homage from the common man."

If such a viewpoint were widely held, dreadful damage would be done to the future prospects of science. When a young man chooses a profession, he is almost always selecting from among the popular stereotyped images which the different professions have acquired. A generation ago, science was *Arrowsmith* and *Tom Swift*, its symbols were freedom and intellectual adventure. Today, unfortunately, it is more like the quotation above. It is also a picture of regimentation and security restrictions. Somehow, we must find a way to communicate the true essence of today's science to our young people. Somehow, thinking must again be made popular, and great thinking synonymous with high adventure. In biology, for example, the contemporary scene is exciting and dramatic, swift-paced and paradoxical. Every innovation both converges toward and diverges from new insights. Traditional interdisciplinary barriers are all but gone: all science is now biology. Regardless of our own scientific latitudes, we are each interested in the same thing—the living organism. And yet new barriers keep arising. The field of learning is deeply scored and broken into fragments of specialism, pieces and corners each the size of a man's mind. Fortunately or unfortunately, no one knows where the next advance will take place. The new biology is being spoken everywhere and by everyone—by intellectual giants and bunglers, by physicists and cosmologists on sabbaticals, in the laboratories of Cambridge and Iowa State, in the journals of microbiology, at the summer seminars in physical chemistry at Woods Hole, in the third-class cabins of Fulbright scholars, at the International Congresses of Biochemistry, in the wards and corridors of great medical schools, at the Cold Spring Harbor symposia on "the gene" or on "nerve function," next to the lead-shielded monsters of the United States Atomic Energy Commission, on the docks of the Oceanographic Institute. The living organism today has as many profiles as viewers, as many dimensions as measuring rods. Its image should be an image of adventure.

Perhaps, youth's alienation from science is a problem for science itself. Surely some explanation may be found in the socio-psychological area for the recent discovery that no one likes mathematics any more, for the fear that seems to pervade our high schools that science is "hard." Perhaps some of the antagonism arises from the feeling that modern science is too materialistic and opposed to humanism. If so, we have returned to home base, for we are back to the problem with which we started this book. Can this gap be bridged between science and humanism? Can science, and particularly biology, make a meaningful contribution to culture? To a large extent, these are questions for the future. Let us look then at our science of biology and see if we can divine where it is destined to lead us. What will be biology's contribution to the future community of men?

To the future, where science and mankind must meet

In attempting to speculate on the future course of biological thought, one is suddenly struck with the almost incredible fact that modern biology has been a going concern for only about a hundred years. And what we have called "the new biology," the vigorous and dynamic science of today, has actually come into being only since World War II. In this brief decade, we have witnessed: the demonstration of genetic recombination in viruses; the first synthesis of a hormone; the discovery of coenzyme A, the key to the processes by which biological compounds are synthesized; the synthesis of artificial RNA; the demonstration that virus nucleic acid by itself is infective; the production of the giant electronic computers; the development of modern information and communication theory—all of this in the last ten or twelve years. What then, in the name of Miserere, may we expect in the next ten years, in the next century and millennium? For the world has this and much more to look forward to. Our new biology is an infant with a future unimaginable.

We will only mention in passing the more obvious inevitabilities of biological progress: birth control, food production, medical progress, domestication of animals (it has already been suggested that we train monkeys to pick crops). These will be the by-products of increasing knowledge and must surely lie ahead.

One of the great concerns of the biology of the future will be with the problem of aging. As we gradually prolong human life, we must simultaneously make old age more than mere dilapidated despair. In time, human life may go on indefinitely, for I can see no reason why death, in the nature of things, need be inevitable. The great complexity of living systems numerically increases their areas of vulnerability, increasing also the probability that time and circumstance will eventually overthrow the balance at one point or another. In multicellular organisms, where all cells live by a measure of mutual dependence, the smallest break in the dike upsets the community equilibrium, causing death or a state of senescence, that unraveling which is ultimately destined to exceed the tolerable limits within which life can exist. Could this probability be lowered, life would be lengthened, persisting on until it ended on the shoals of the next probability metric. Medicine has done just this for man. Free of the diseases of childhood, he now lives to die of something else. Freed of today's diseases of old age, man might live as long as the giant sequoias. Were all disease and want eliminated, life expectancy would depend almost entirely on the accident (or suicide) rate. In principle, the probability of fatal adversity could be almost zero (that is, if we restrict the scope of the future to our own neighborhood in the time scale—say, the next 10^{12} years). In reality, it could never be exactly zero. Among other things, there is a limit in the supply of food and the materials which conceivably could be turned into food. This would, at least, prevent immortality from being widely practiced.

As might be anticipated, scientific thought about senescence has been so laden down with metaphysical and verbal confusion, the area will serve as yet another illustration of how intellectual slums develop. Despite the theoretical and practical importance of understanding senescence, almost no work has been done in the field for twenty years. Alex Comfort lamented this situation in a recent review and commented on the close connection of aging with human fears and aspirations, all of which is reflected in theories that attempt to invoke a "general principle of senescence" for all living organisms and use phrases like "aging is the price of multicellular existence" and "it results from the exhaustion induced by reproduction." Such views are all mixed in with philosophical meditations on the necessity and meaning of decline and death.

Most of the conceptual smog results from the elementary error of reasoning by inappropriate analogy. The word "aging" immediately suggests analogous behavior in inanimate systems. We hear talk of "old" red blood cells and "old" tissue colloids, presumably meaning cells and colloids produced by an "old" organism and implying that they are as deteriorated as "old" machines. The error is apparent. As Comfort explains:

> The difference between an old cart and an old horse are self-evident: the cart consists of its original material and has never possessed the potentiality of being self-maintaining against wear; the horse

contains few or none of its original materials and has for some twenty years been substantially self-repairing, but is losing that power.

"Senescence," in fact, is a generic term for those processes in certain organisms which lead to a decreasing power of homeostasis with increasing chronological age. Decreasing homeostasis with increasing age may have different causes in different phyla. There appears to be no single or "inherent" process to explain all types of senescence. Though a certain life span is a characteristic of each species, we do not yet know what this means. Conceivably, each species is transmitting from generation to generation an adverse trait which waits to act until the Biblical span is done and the young have been born. This would determine the life span. Obviously, extinction would occur if it acted before a new generation could appear.

The death of organism, of course, ends only one life, not living—life goes on in surviving individuals. Should the environment be altered importantly, *all* individuals could perish at once, or one by one. In a species or society, mass senescence could occur and total death follow. This is extinction. To date, the voids left by the departed millions of extinct forms have been filled by other species and life has gone on. But I see no reason why a major event could not end all life. Unless we have managed to escape into space, the ultimate denouement that is so lugubriously predicted for the earth by sacred and profane alike will be preceded by millions of years of biological senescence. And it is abundantly clear that this process will be greatly accelerated if the background radiation is even slightly increased by the atmospheric pollutions of men who are not primarily interested in the welfare of future generations. Modern war would, at least, bring a livelier finale.

Will the biologist someday synthesize a living organism? I dearly hope so, if only to bring peace of mind and eternal rest to those writers of science fiction, from the author of Frankenstein on down, who seem morbidly preoccupied with this possibility. In view of what we have said about "life," the synthesis of a living organism may or may not make a fundamental contribution to our understanding. But it surely will not have metaphysical significance except to those who prefer to see it that way. In this sense, it will be rather like aviation's "breaking the sound barrier." Once it happened, it became a routine matter. That this, too, will one day happen, I have no doubt. I do doubt, however, that it will become the preferred method of creating life.

In thinking of the future, one comes to realize that biology is destined to have its greatest impact in another realm. This prediction is strengthened by the striking parallels which may be drawn between the history of physics and that of biology. Both sciences had first to find their elementary units—in physics, the atom, in biology, the cell. In Darwin, biology had its Newton, for both gave their science great unifying theories. And, in modern genetics, in whose methodology mutation plays such a large part, we have an analogy to the nuclear physicist's approach to the particles of the atom. For he sees them only as an indirect result of having blasted them with other particles of radiation. What we seek now is that something in biology which will parallel the impact of modern physics upon philosophy. True, Darwinism has already swept into the arena of culture; but for the purposes of our argument, we will set this opposite the philosophy of mechanism that emerged from seventeenth-century physics. No, the new biology has not yet reached out to touch the philosophical balance. I believe, however, that it is now about to—and the questions it will influence will be those concerned with human behavior and ethical values.

The fragments which together make a possible basis for this belief can be seen in several places. Philosophers have long tussled with the problem of human values, and it is widely believed by analytical thinkers that it is not possible for science to tell us what is right and good, how we *ought* to behave. Science is considered to be ethically neutral: it can tell you how to get what you want but not what you ought to want. This view, I believe, is open to challenge, both on philosophical grounds and on the grounds of what I feel to be a reasonable appraisal of biology's future prospects. I will not presume to discuss the philosophical aspects of ethical theory, except to record my respect for the writings of men like Charles Stevenson and Paul Edwards, who have not been intimidated by the more intractable varieties of logical empiricism. Stevenson, for example, developed the so-called emotive theory of ethics which, in a superficial word, holds that moral behavior is related to one's own psychological and emotional attitudes and patterns, and that ethical words, therefore, serve both emotional and descriptive purposes. And when experience shows that such and such a property is regularly associated with a "value attitude," this property comes to serve as a sign of value. While this is not a declaration that ethics is a branch of psychology, it does place ethical decisions within the purview of emotional phenomena.

Next, we note a recent discussion by Priscilla Robertson in which reference is made to three new scientific studies by distinguished biologists who have attempted —apparently successfully—a direct *empirical* attack on the problems of value. Thus, she quotes the work of the psychopathologist Kurt Goldstein, who believes that the soundly functioning human brain involves biological behavior patterns which have always been termed "moral values" from other points of view; the British psychologist Money-Kyrle similarly has shown that soundly functioning perceptions lead to reparative consciences, and thus to kindness as well as creativity; and the anthropologist LaBarre, who finds in family love a steady support for human society.

And, finally, we have the unmatched studies of

Charles Morris, who, by ingeniously designed questionnaires, empirically examined the life-orientations and preferred value conceptions of many individuals from widely differing cultural backgrounds. Among other things, Morris presents impressive evidence that some of the value dimensions are readily recognizable at the level of organism. Using Sheldon's somatotypes as a biological variable, he shows definite relationships between ectomorphy (fragility and "linearity" in body build) and detachment, between mesomorphy (predominance of muscle and bone) and dominance through action, and between endomorphy (roundness and softness throughout the body) and receptivity—all of which showed a striking congruence with value ideas.

With this sort of beginning in the biological approach to the problems of ethics, it seems not a very large jump to a future in which neurophysiology will have finally achieved a deeper understanding of the physical basis of mental activity. It is this development to which we may reasonably look for explanations of altruism, goodness, and love in terms of bioelectric circuits! When these things have happened, we will no longer need to concern ourselves with the gap between biology and human culture. For they will then be the same thing.

Who should have imagined that all of this could have come from an ancient sea?

Second prologue

And thus we have made the great circle. In human values, we find the product of human needs and desires. In short, we find the essence of humanity, whose embodiment is culture.

We have seen also that neither culture nor science is omnipotent. And if one of these is to be our "father," it is the task of maturity to reduce him to human dimensions. For human dimensions are not small. Neither are they Promethean except in our wishes.

What we must conclude, then, is that nowhere will we find the Answer. It is not science rampant on a field of analytical philosophers, since science ultimately must rest upon faith—faith in causality or induction or the accessibility of the universe to understanding. But this is not the same as religious faith, for the faith of the scientist consists in what he or anyone else *has to believe* if he wishes to predict or control the course of experience.

Moreover, we must never forget in our enlightenment what lies just beneath the clean surface of enlightenment. There are our feelings, passions, drives, and vulnerabilities, those things which make human existence eternally precarious and potentially tragic—and which continue to keep alive the human search for certainty despite our knowledge that the search must fail.

The human problem, thus, would seem to be the art of avoiding the inevitable consequence of a paternal creed: the surrender of intelligence in the purchase of emotional security—or, in a word, infantilism. For no human institution, not culture, science, history, or the holy hegemony, is going to take care of man. Man, I'm afraid, is going to have to take care of himself.

Realizing this should not strike us rudderless. It should make us band together in strength, in wholeness, in manly purpose. Ambiguity will be our shibboleth and responsibility our creed. Man is capable of these things. As he stands on the seashore, at the edge of a new tomorrow, in control of the energy of the atom, in possession of the exciting knowledge that he is part of wonderful nature, he must realize that it is now time to stick out the chin. Man has already done much, but it is dawn, not midnight, and, in the gathering light, he looks magnificent.

LIST OF BOOKS, ARTICLES, AND MEMOIRS QUOTED OR CITED IN THE TEXT

ARBER, A. *The Mind and the Eye.* Cambridge, London, 1954.

BACON, F. *Advancement of Learning.* London, 1605.

BAHM, A. "Teleological Arguments." *Scientific Monthly.* Vol. 58, 1944.

BELLO, F. "The Young Scientists." *Fortune.* Vol. 10, 1954.

BERGSON, H. *Matter and Memory.* Allen & Unwin, London, 1919.

BERNAL, J. D. "The Origin of Life." *New Biology.* Vol. 16, 1954.

BEUTNER, R. *Life's Beginning on Earth.* Williams & Wilkins, Baltimore, 1938.

BLANSHARD, B. "The New Philosophy of Analysis." *Proceedings of the American Philosophical Society.* Vol. 96, 1952.

BLUM, H. *Time's Arrow and Evolution.* Princeton, 1951.

BORING, E. "Psychological Factors in the Scientific Process." *American Scientist.* Vol. 42, 1954.

BOYLE, R. *The Sceptical Chymist.* Oxford, London, 1680.

BRIDGMAN, P. W. *The Logic of Modern Physics.* Macmillan, N. Y., 1927.

BRINTON, C. *Ideas and Men.* Prentice-Hall, N. Y., 1950.

BROAD, C. D. *Scientific Thought.* Harcourt, Brace, N. Y., 1923.

BRONOWSKI, J. "The Educated Man in 1984." *Science.* Vol. 123, 1956.

CAJORI, F. *Sir Isaac Newton's Mathematical Principles of Natural Philosophy and His System of the World* (A. Motte trans.). California, Berkeley, 1954.

CALVIN, M. "Chemical Evolution and the Origin of Life." *American Scientist.* Vol. 44, 1956.

CAMERON, G. R. *The Pathology of the Cell.* Thomas, Springfield, 1951.

CANNON, W. *The Wisdom of the Body.* Norton, N. Y., 1932.

CASTIGLIONE, A. *A History of Medicine*. Knopf, N. Y., 1941.

COHEN, M. *Studies in Philosophy and Science*. Holt, N. Y., 1949.

COMFORT, A. "Biological Aspects of Senescence." *Biological Reviews*. Vol. 29, 1954.

CONKLIN, E. "Predecessors of Schleiden and Schwann." *Biological Symposia*. Vol. 1, 1940.

DAMPIER, W. C. *A History of Science and Its Relations with Philosophy and Religion*. 4th ed. Cambridge, London, 1949.

DANTZIG, T. *Number, the Language of Science*. 4th ed. Macmillan, N. Y., 1954.

DARWIN, C. *The Origin of Species*. Random House ed. N. Y., 1936.

DARWIN, C. G. *The Next Million Years*. Doubleday, N. Y., 1953.

DE KRUIF, P. *Microbe Hunters*. Harcourt, Brace, N. Y., 1926.

DESCARTES, R. *Philosophical Works*. Cambridge ed. London, 1911.

DEWAR, D., and SHELTON, H. *Is Evolution Proved?* Hollis & Carter, London, 1947.

DOBZHANSKY, T. "A Comment on the Discussion of Genetics by His Holiness, Pius XII." *Science*. Vol. 118, 1953.

DRIESCH, H. *History and Theory of Vitalism*. Macmillan, N. Y., 1914.

DUBOS, R. *Louis Pasteur, Free-Lance of Science*. Little, Brown, Boston, 1950.

DU NOÜY, L. *Human Destiny*. Longmans, Toronto, 1947.

EDITORIAL. "Some Limits to Popular Science." *Endeavour*. Vol. 59, 1956.

EDWARDS, P. *The Logic of Moral Discourse*. Free Press, Glencoe, Ill., 1955.

EINSTEIN, A. "On the Method of Theoretical Physics." *Philosophy of Science*. Vol. 1, 1934.

EINSTEIN, A. *The Meaning of Relativity*. 5th ed. Princeton, 1955.

EISELEY, L. C. "Fossil Man." *Scientific American*. Vol. 189, 1953.

EVANS, E. J. *Biochemical Studies of Bacterial Viruses*. Chicago, 1952.

FEIGL, H. "Logical Empiricism." From *Twentieth Century Philosophy,* D. D. Runes, ed. Philosophical Library, N. Y., 1943.

FEIGL, H. "The Mind-Body Problem in the Development of Logical Empiricism." *Revue International de Philosophie.* Vol. 4, 1950.

FRAZER, J. G. *The Golden Bough.* 3rd ed. Macmillan, London, 1911–26.

GAMOW, G. *Biography of the Earth.* Viking, N. Y., 1941.

GERARD, R. "The Biological Roots of Psychiatry." *American Journal of Psychiatry.* Vol. 112, 1955.

GERR, S. "Language and Science." *Philosophy of Science.* Vol. 9, 1942.

GHISELIN, B. *The Creative Process.* California, Los Angeles, 1952.

GLASS, B. "The Long Neglect of a Scientific Discovery: Mendel's Laws of Inheritance." In *Studies in Intellectual History.* Hopkins, Baltimore, 1953.

GOLDSCHMIDT, R. "Evolution as Viewed by One Geneticist." *American Scientist.* Vol. 40, 1952.

GOLDSCHMIDT, R. *Understanding Heredity.* Wiley, N. Y., 1952.

GRANT, M. "'Proof' Again." *The Humanist.* Vol. 16, 1956.

GRÜNBAUM, A. "Modern Science and Refutation of the Paradoxes of Zeno." *Scientific Monthly.* Vol. 81, 1955.

HALDANE, J. B. S. *A Banned Broadcast and Other Essays.* Chatto & Windus, London, 1946.

HALDANE, J. B. S. *Science and Human Life.* Harper, N. Y., 1933.

HALDANE, J. S. *The Sciences and Philosophy.* Doubleday, N. Y., 1929.

HARROD, R. F. *Foundations of Inductive Logic.* Harcourt, Brace, N. Y., 1957.

HARVEY, W. *On the Motion of the Heart and Blood in Animals.* London ed. 1908.

HEMPEL, C. "A Logical Appraisal of Operationism." *Scientific Monthly.* Vol. 79, 1954.

HERTWIG, O. *The Cell and the Tissue.* (Campbell trans.) London, 1895.

HOGBEN, L. *The Nature of Living Matter.* Knopf, N. Y., 1931.

HOOKE, R. *The Micrographia.* London, 1665.

HOOTON, E. *Up from the Ape.* Macmillan, N. Y., 1946.
HOROWITZ, N. "On the Evolution of Biochemical Syntheses." *Proceedings of the National Academy of Sciences.* Vol. 31, 1945.
HUXLEY, J. *Heredity East and West.* Schuman, N. Y., 1949.
HUXLEY, J. *Evolution: The Modern Synthesis.* Harper, N. Y., 1943.
HUXLEY, J. *Man Stands Alone.* Harper, N. Y., 1940.
HUXLEY, T. "Biogenesis and Abiogenesis" and "Yeast." In *Discourses Biological and Geological.* Appleton, N. Y., 1898.
HUXLEY, T. *Man's Place in Nature.* Appleton ed., N. Y., 1896.
JEANS, J. *The Mysterious Universe.* Cambridge, N. Y., 1937.
JEFFREYS, H. *Theory of Probability.* Oxford, London, 1939.
JOAD, C. E. M. *Guide to Philosophy.* Gollancz, London, 1946.
KARLING, J. S. "Schleiden's Contribution to the Cell Theory." *Biological Symposia.* Vol. 1, 1940.
KILLIAN, J. R., JR. "The Shortage Re-examined." *American Scientist.* Vol. 44, 1956.
KUBIE, L. "Some Unsolved Problems of the Scientific Career." *American Scientist.* Vol. 41, 1953.
LEWIS, C. I. "Experience and Meaning." *Philosophical Review.* Vol. 43, 1934.
LOCKE, J. *An Essay Concerning Human Understanding.* London, 1690.
LURIA, S. "Bacteriophage: An Essay on Virus Reproduction." *Science.* Vol. 111, 1950.
LURIA, S. *General Virology.* Wiley, N. Y., 1953.
MCCULLOCH, W. S. "Mysterium Iniquitatis of Sinful Man Aspiring into the Place of God." *Scientific Monthly.* Vol. 80, 1955.
MCDOUGALL, W. *The Riddle of Life.* Methuen, London, 1938.
MACH, E. *Science of Mechanics.* (T. McCormack trans.) Open Court, Chicago, 1942.
MACKAY, D. M. "Mentality in Machines." *Aristotelian Society, Supplementary Volumes.* Vol. 26, 1952.
MASSERMAN, J. H. "Faith and Delusion in Psychotherapy." *American Journal of Psychiatry.* Vol. 110, 1953.

MEDAWAR, P. B. "Problems of Adaptation." *New Biology.* Vol. 11, 1951.

MONTAGU, M. F. A. "Vesalius and the Galenists." *Scientific Monthly.* Vol. 80, 1955.

MORRIS, C. *Varieties of Human Value.* Chicago, 1956.

MULLER, H. J. *The Uses of the Past.* Oxford, N. Y., 1954.

MULLER, H. J. "Science in Bondage." *Science.* Vol. 111, 1951.

MUMFORD, L. *The Condition of Man.* Harcourt, Brace, N. Y., 1944.

NAGEL, E. "Mechanistic Explanation and Organismic Biology." *Philosophy & Phenomenological Research.* Vol. 11, 1951.

NAGEL, E. *Sovereign Reason.* Free Press, Glencoe, Ill., 1954.

NEEDHAM, J. *Science, Religion, and Reality.* Braziller, N. Y., 1955.

NEEDHAM, J. *Order and Life.* Yale, New Haven, 1938.

NEWTON, I. *Opticks, or a Treatise on the Reflections, Refractions, Inflections and Colours of Light.* Dover ed. N. Y., 1952.

O'MALLEY, C. D., and SAUNDERS, J. B. "Andreas Vesalius, Imperial Physician." In *Science, Medicine, and History.* E. Underwood ed. Oxford, N. Y., 1953.

OPPENHEIMER, J. R. *The Open Mind.* Simon & Schuster, N. Y., 1955.

PAGEL, W. "The Reaction to Aristotle in Seventeenth Century Biological Thought." In *Science, Medicine, and History.* E. Underwood ed. Oxford, N. Y., 1953.

PEATTIE, D. *Green Laurels.* Simon & Schuster, N. Y., 1936.

PIRIE, N. W. "The Meaninglessness of the Terms 'Life' and 'Living.'" In *Perspectives in Biochemistry.* J. Needham and D. Green ed. Cambridge, London, 1937.

PIRIE, N. W. "The Origin of Life." *Discovery.* Vol. 114, 1953.

PIRIE, N. W. "Vital Blarney." *New Biology.* Vol. 12, 1953.

RAFFERTY, J. A. "Mathematical Models in Biological Theory." *American Scientist.* Vol. 38, 1950.

REICHENBACH, H. *The Rise of Scientific Philosophy.* California, Los Angeles, 1950.

ROBERTSON, P. "On Getting Values Out of Science." *The Humanist.* Vol. 16, 1956.

ROSENBLEUTH, A., WIENER, N., and BIGELOW, J. "Behavior, Purpose, and Teleology." *Philosophy of Science.* Vol. 10, 1943.

ROYAL SOCIETY OF LONDON *Newton Tercentenary Celebration.* Cambridge, London, 1947.

RUSSELL, B. *Human Knowledge: Its Scope and Limits.* Simon & Schuster, N. Y., 1948.

RUSSELL, E. S. *Form and Function.* Dutton, N. Y., 1917.

SARTON, G. *Galen of Pergamon.* Kansas, Lawrence, 1954.

SCHLICK, M. "Meaning and Verification." *Philosophical Review.* Vol. 45, 1936.

SELYE, H. "On the Nature of Disease." *Texas Reports on Biology & Medicine.* Vol. 12, 1954.

SHAW, G. B. *Back to Methusaleh.* Dodd, Mead, N. Y., 1949.

SHERRINGTON, C. S. *Man on His Nature.* Cambridge, London, 1951.

SHERRINGTON, C. S. *The Endeavour of Jean Fernel.* Cambridge, London, 1946.

SHULL, A. F. *Evolution.* 2nd ed. McGraw-Hill, N. Y., 1951.

SIMPSON, G. G. "Evolutionary Determinism and the Fossil Record." *Scientific Monthly.* Vol. 71, 1950.

SIMPSON, G. G. *The Major Features of Evolution.* Columbia, N. Y., 1953.

SIMPSON, G. G. *The Meaning of Evolution.* Yale, New Haven, 1949.

SINGER, C. *A History of Biology.* Schuman, N. Y., 1950.

SINNOTT, E. W. *The Biology of the Spirit.* Viking, N. Y., 1955.

SMITH, H. W. *From Fish to Philosopher.* Little, Brown, Boston, 1953.

SMITH, H. W. *Man and His Gods.* Little, Brown, Boston, 1952.

SMITH, J. L. B. "The Second Coelacanth." *Nature.* Vol. 171, 1953.

SMITH, W. A. *Ancient Education.* Philosophical Library, N. Y., 1955.

SMUTS, J. C. *Holism and Evolution.* Macmillan, London, 1926.

SOMMERHOFF, G. *Analytical Biology.* Oxford, London, 1950.

STEVENSON, C. L. *Ethics and Language.* Yale, New Haven, 1943.

STRAUS, W., JR. "The Great Piltdown Hoax." *Science.* Vol. 119, 1954.

STUNKARD, H. W. "Freedom, Bondage, and the Welfare State." *Science.* Vol. 121, 1955.

SULLIVAN, J. W. N. *The Limitations of Science.* Viking, N. Y., 1933.

TARSKI, A. "The Semantic Conception of Truth and the Foundations of Semantics." *Philosophy & Phenomenological Research.* Vol. 4, 1944.

TOYNBEE, A. "Poetical Truth and Scientific Truth in the Light of History." *International Journal of Psychoanalysis.* Vol. 30, 1949.

UREY, H. C. "On the Early Chemical History of the Earth and the Origin of Life." *Proceedings of the National Academy of Sciences.* Vol. 38, 1952.

VAN HOUWENSVELT, S. *Darwinism Has Deceived Humanity.* Routledge, London, 1931.

VESALIUS, A. *De Humani Corporis Fabrica.* Basel, 1543.

WADDINGTON, C. H. "How Do Cells Differentiate?" *Scientific American.* Vol. 189, 1953.

WALD, G. "The Origin of Life." *Scientific American.* Vol. 191, 1954.

WALTER, W. G. "The Imitation of Mentality." *Nature.* Vol. 177, 1956.

WEINER, J., OAKLEY, K., and CLARK, W. *Bull. Brit. Mus. (Nat. Hist.), Geol.* Vol. 2, 1953.

WEISS, P. "Differential Growth." In *The Chemistry and Physiology of Growth.* A. Parpart ed. Princeton, 1949.

WELLS, H. G., HUXLEY, J., and WELLS, G. P. *The Science of Life.* Doubleday, N. Y., 1935.

WESTERMARCK, E. *The Origin and Development of Moral Ideas.* Macmillan, London, 1908.

WHITEHEAD, A. N. *Science and the Modern World.* Macmillan, N. Y., 1947.

WIENER, N. *Cybernetics.* Wiley, N. Y., 1948.

WIGHTMAN, W. P. D. *The Growth of Scientific Ideas.* Yale, New Haven, 1953.

WILLIAMS, R. C. "The Shapes and Sizes of Purified Viruses as Determined by Electron Microscopy." *Cold Spring Harbor Symposia on Quantitative Biology.* Vol. 18, 1953.

WOODGER, J. H. *Biological Principles: A Critical Study.* Harcourt, Brace, N. Y., 1929.

WOODGER, J. H. *Biology and Language.* Cambridge, London, 1952.

WOODRUFF, L. "Microscopy before the 19th Century." *Biological Symposia.* Vol. 1, 1940.

ZIRKLE, C. "Citation of Fraudulent Data." *Science.* Vol. 120, 1954.

ZIRKLE, C. "The Knowledge of Heredity before 1900." In *Genetics in the 20th Century.* L. C. Dunn ed. Macmillan, N. Y., 1951.

INDEX